3-5 ~~SPAC~~ ED
4-6 spacing

AIRCRAFT **Structural Technician**

DALE HURST

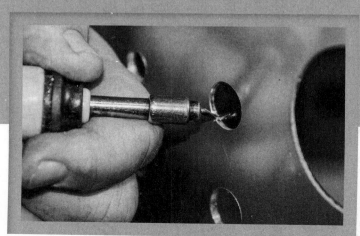

AVOTEK®
INFORMATION RESOURCES

Edgar Rodriguez

Production Staff

Designer Amy Siever
Designer Dustin Blyer
Senior Designer Roberta Byerly
Production Manager Holly Bonos

International Standard Book Number 1-9708109-0-3
ISBN 13: 978-0-9708109-0-8
Order # T-AST-0101

For Sale by: Avotek
A Select Aerospace Industries, Inc. company

Mail to:
P.O. Box 219
Weyers Cave, Virginia 24486
USA

Ship to:
200 Packaging Drive
Weyers Cave, Virginia 24486
USA

Toll Free: 1-800-828-6835
Telephone: 1-540-234-9090
Fax: 1-540-234-9399

First Edition
Fourth Printing
Printed in the USA

www.avotek.com

Preface

While serving on an advisory subcommittee for the proposed FAA AMTT project, the basis for this text arose. Over five years of meetings, the subject matter of current training materials were discussed at length.

That is the reason for the *Aircraft Structural Technician* textbook. It covers aircraft structural repair with more detail and allows for a more complete course of study. It is also designed for a stand alone course in sheet metal structural repair. Some of the coverage, heat treating rivets as an example, is not really used in general aviation. However, the airline training departments wanted it included. They still use the process. Besides, understanding the process puts emphasis on correct hardware choices.

As with any textbook, only the processes can be taught. The most important part of aircraft maintenance and repair, *thinking,* can not be taught. We can, however, try to present enough information so that the student can understand how all things are related.

This textbook is obviously for training purposes. All information on repairing any aircraft structure can only come from the aircraft manufacturer. They are always the first and last word on the materials and processes. Many times a manufacturers repair instructions will even include the tools to be used for fabrication. It is our hope that we have helped you learn how to use them.

There are two thoughts I would like to leave you, as a student, with.

Number one is to always think a job through all the way to it's completion. It will save you a lot of effort throughout your career.

Secondly, having thought the job through to its completion, go back and figure out how to do it without hurting yourself or someone else. ➤

SAFETY FIRST!

Dale Hurst

Email us at comments@avotek.com for comments or suggestions.

Avotek® Aircraft Maintenance Series
Introduction to Aircraft Maintenance
Aircraft Structural Maintenance
Aircraft System Maintenance
Aircraft Powerplant Maintenance

Avotek® Aircraft Avionics Series
Avionics: Fundamentals of Aircraft Electronics
Avionics: Beyond the AET
Avionics: Systems and Troubleshooting

Other Books by Avotek®
Aircraft Corrosion Control Guide
Aircraft Structural Technician
Aircraft Turbine Engines
Aircraft Wiring & Electrical Installation
AMT Reference Handbook
Avotek Aeronautical Dictionary
Fundamentals of Modern Aviation
Light Sport Aircraft Inspection Procedures
Structural Composites: Advanced Composites in Aviation

Contents

1

Aircraft Structures

Fixed-wing aircraft are sorted out in many different categories such as the number of wings and whether they are braced or not. The number of wings which an aircraft can have is classified as monoplane, biplane, and tri-plane. These wings are in turn divided into cantilever and semi-cantilever wings. The location of the wing in reference to the fuselage is another important aspect of wing design. Wings are located at the top, mid, and lower section of a fuselage.

A biplane is an aircraft which has two wings, and upper and a lower set. Usually the flight controls are attached to the lower set of wings. On some high performance aerobatic aircraft, both sets of wings will have control surfaces attached. The wings of biplanes are fixed in place using "N" struts and sets of flying and landing wires. The wires are external, therefore, they create a certain amount of drag which needs to be minimized by using streamlined wires.

A tri-wing aircraft is one which has three tiers of wings stacked one over another. The tri-wing aircraft was popular during the first World War. The reason for using three wings was to increase the square foot area of the wings to produce more lift without increasing the length or width of the airplane.

The type of metal used for the construction of wings, fuselage and control surfaces must be of a quality which can withstand the stresses and strains imposed on them during the time the aircraft is statically and dynamically loaded. The aircraft speed and design weight control what types of alloys and fasteners can be used.

An airframe of a fixed-wing aircraft consists of five principal units: the fuselage, wings,

Left. An understanding of the various types of structures found in aircraft is a key part of repairing them properly.

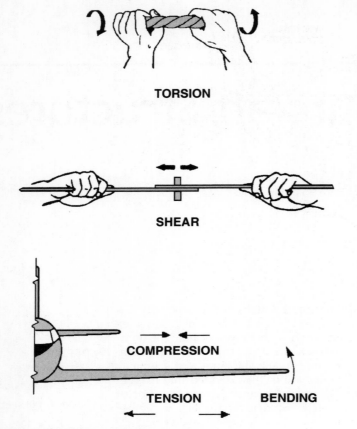

Figure 1-1-1. Five stresses acting on an aircraft

Section 1
Major Structural Stresses

In designing an aircraft, every square inch of wing and fuselage, every rib, spar, and even each metal fitting must be considered in relation to the physical characteristics of the metal of which it is made. Every part of the aircraft must be planned to carry the load to be imposed upon it. The determination of such loads is called stress analysis. Although planning the design is not the function of the aviation technician, it is, nevertheless, important that he/she understand and appreciate the stresses involved in order to avoid changes in the original design through improper repairs.

There are five major stresses to which all aircraft are subjected (Figure 1-1-1):

1. Tension
2. Compression
3. Torsion
4. Shear
5. Bending

Stress is defined as an applied force or system of forces that tends to strain or deform a body. Whereas strain is the resistance to pulling, drawing, or stretching of an aircraft part. An aircraft part becomes stressed when an external force is applied to a part causing it to stretch. Strain is energy imposed on an aircraft joint or part during static or dynamic operations.

Tension (Figure 1-1-1) is the ability of the metal to withstand being pulled apart. For example, when the wing of a large jet transport flexes downward the upper wing skin becomes loaded in tension as it stretches. The stretch in the upper skin is under tension. The tensile strength of a material is measured in p.s.i. and is calculated by dividing the load (required to pull the material apart) in pounds by its cross-sectional area, in square inches.

Compression (Figure 1-1-1) is strength that resists the stress of a crushing force. For example, the opposite side of an aircraft wing in tension can be used to explain a part in compression. As the outside of a skin panel is bent, it stretches while the other side compresses. The compressive strength of a material is measured in p.s.i. Compression is stress that tends to bunch the grain of the metal together. If maximum compression of a sheet of metal is exceeded, the metal on the stretched side will crack.

stabilizers, flight control surfaces, and landing gear.

Airframe parts are manufactured from a variety of metals and are joined by rivets, bolts, screws, welding, or adhesives. These parts and components consist of structural members such as stringers, longerons, ribs, bulkheads, etc.

Aircraft structural members are designed to carry static and dynamic loads and to resist stress. An aircraft structural design may be such that the initial load is taken up by one member and then shared with several others to absorb shock an resist permanent deformation. Certain members, like longerons and stringers, primarily carry end loads, while skins carry bending and twisting loads. However, when the skins covering the wings or fuselage are carrying twisting and bending loads the resulting effects are transmitted on to the stringer, longerons, and etc.

Strength is always the principal requirement in structures, even with parts which are not necessarily considered primary structures such as, cowling, fairing, and similar parts. These parts, just like the primary ones, must have such properties as neat appearance and streamlined shapes to reduce drag.

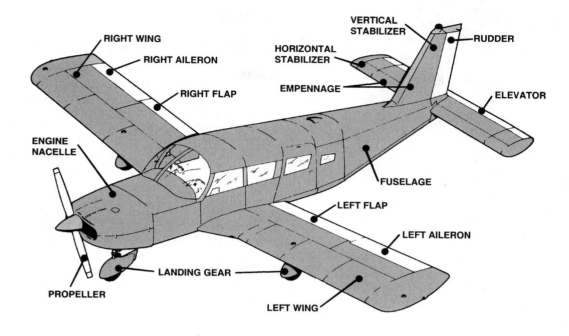

Figure 1-1-2. Aircraft structural components

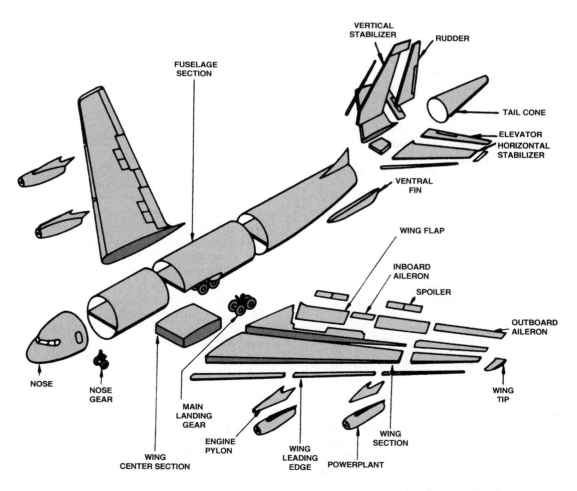

Figure 1-1-3. Typical structural components of a turbine powered airplane

Shear is an applied force, or system of forces, that tends to produce a shearing strain, called shear stress. For example, when two sheets of metal are riveted together, the rivets will try to prevent the two sheets from sliding past each other (Figure 1-1-1) under load. Most shear loads obtained by tensile testing are determined by placing the joint under double shear load. Usually, the shearing strength of a metal fastener is equal to or less than the joints tension or compression strengths. Aircraft hardware, especially screws, bolts, and rivets, are subjected primarily to shear loading.

Bending stress is a combination of compression and tension. The wing in Figure 1-1-1 has been shortened (compressed) on the one side and stretches on the other side of the bend.

The principal components of a single-engine, propeller-driven aircraft are shown in Figure 1-1-2.

Figure 1-1-3 illustrates the structural components of a typical turbine powered aircraft. Wings, fuselage and the empennage assemblies are shown in an exploded view. Specific details of other external controls and parts are also shown.

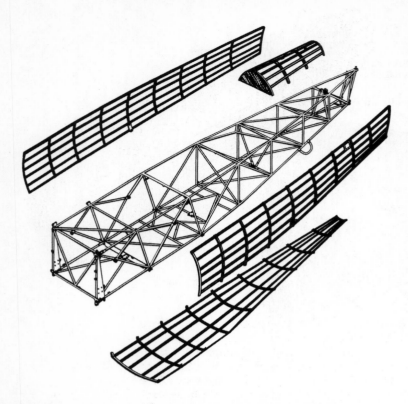

Figure 1-2-1. Welded steel truss fuselage with sheet metal formers

Torsion is a twisting motion caused when one end of an object is twisted one way and the other end is twisted the opposite way. The energy applied to an object being twisted is called torsion (Figure 1-1-1). For example, while the aircraft is moving forward, the engine will twist to one side. In this case, the twisting action is absorbed by the engine mount and the aircraft frame. The torsional strength of a material is its resistance to twisting or torque.

Section 2

Fuselage

The fuselage of an aircraft houses all of the parts necessary to make the aircraft fly. All structural components are connected directly to the fuselage superstructure. It provides space for pilot, crew, passengers, fuel and cargo. For single-engine aircraft, it provides the structural housing for the powerplant. In tri-jet multi-engine aircraft, one engine is housed on the aft fuselage while the other two are connected to the wings.

Truss Type

The truss-type fuselage frame (Figure 1-2-1) is made from chrome-molybedenum steel tubing welded together so that all members of the truss carry both tension and compression loads. The truss fuselage design is divided into Pratt and Warren constructions. The Pratt construction (Figure 1-2-1) consists of longerons with vertical bay member which are supported by diagonal members. The Warren truss type of construction does not have vertical members at each bay. The truss fuselage is normally covered with fabric.

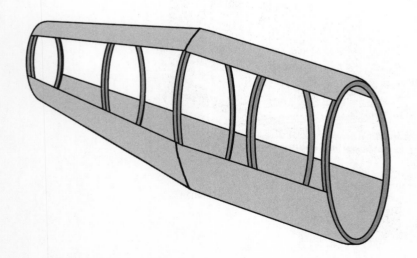

Figure 1-2-2. Monocoque construction

Monocoque Type

The monocoque fuselage relies largely on the strength of its skin to carry the primary stresses. The design may be divided into two types: monocoque and hybrid. A full monocoque fuselage construction (Figure 1-2-2) consists of former rings, bulkheads, and skins to give strength shape to the fuselage. The skin carries the primary structural load of the fuselage. Since no internal bracing members are used, the skin must assume the loads normally carried by the longerons and stringers. All repairs to the skin of a monocoque fuselage is classified as major repairs.

In an effort to overcome the weight problem associated with using the full monocoque or semi-monocoque fuselage for light aircraft, a hybrid monocoque fuselage has emerged. The hybrid monocoque fuselage consists of bending a flanged seam at the edge of the joint where two skin lap over on another. Bending the edge of the skin forms a stringer which is part of the skin thus eliminating any addition weight while at the same time adding strength to the joint.

Semi-Monocoque Type

To compensate for the additional weight (due to thick and heavier skins) which a full monocoque fuselage would require of a larger aircraft, a modification called semi-monocoque construction (Figure 1-2-3) was developed. With the building of large aircraft, heavier internal parts were needed to carry the load. By using thinner skins and lighter internal supports (stringers and former rings), a reduction in total weight without sacrificing strength was successfully made using the semi-monocoque type of construction.

The semi-monocoque fuselage has, in addition to formers and bulkheads, additional members such as longerons, stringers, former rings, gussets, keel beams and center section. The skins of a semi-monocoque fuselage are not as heavy as those needed for the full monocque construction.

The semi-monocoque fuselage (Figure 1-2-4) is constructed primarily from heat-treated aluminum alloys. Other metals used for the construction of modern fuselage assemblies are stainless steel and titanium. These two alloys are used as fasteners in high structural load and high temperatures areas. Primary loads in the fuselage are absorbed by the longerons which run along the horizontal axis and bulkheads which are placed vertical to the longerons. Longerons, like stringers, are one piece

Figure 1-2-3. Semi-monocoque construction

parts made from heat-treated aluminum alloys which are extruded or formed. The bulkheads and former rings, which give shape to the fuselage, are tied together with stringers. Stringers are smaller and lighter than longerons. They have some rigidity and serve to fill in as stiffeners between longerons when riveted to the skins. Stringers are usually of a one-piece aluminum alloy construction and are manufactured in a variety of shapes by casting, extrusion, or forming.

The structural members used for the construction of a fuselage are cold joined, which means the previously mentioned parts are held together by fasteners such as rivets, nuts and bolts, metal screws, or adhesives. A gusset is a

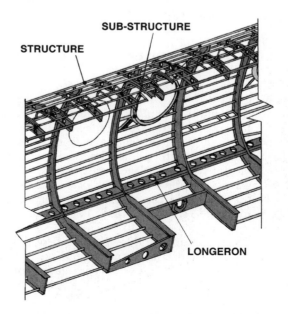

Figure 1-2-4. Fuselage structural members

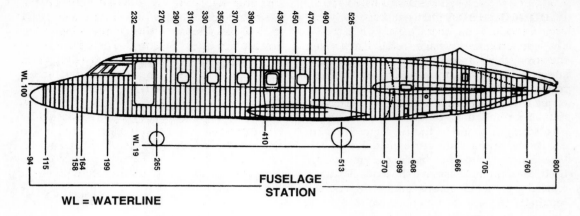

WL = WATERLINE

Figure 1-2-5. Fuselage stations

type of connecting bracket used to hold stringers to former rings.

The fuselage of a large jet transport is made in as many as six mating sections at different locations in the aircraft factory. It is not until final assembly that all the fuselage sections are joined together. The joint made where the fuselage sections join together is called the manufacturer's break or splice joint. On light aircraft, the fuselage is made in one or two simple section and later joined in final assembly.

Along the sides and in the belly of the fuselage, there are a distribution of access plates or inspection covers to gain access to accessories and other types of equipment. Landing gear wheel assemblies are located in the fuselage of some aircraft. Servicing diagrams showing the arrangement of equipment and location of access doors are supplied by the manufacturer in the aircraft maintenance manual.

Location Numbering Systems

All aircraft locations are broken down into inches away from a fixed or imaginary line. However, in the case of most large aircraft the tip of the nose is station zero. From station zero moving along the horizontal axis from left to right each one inch, is a station. Thus, when a blueprint reads, fuselage frame station 137, that particular frame station is located 137 in behind the nose of the aircraft. A typical station diagram is shown in Figure 1-2-5.

To locate structures to the right or left of the center line of an aircraft, many manufacturers consider the center line as a zero station for structural member location to its right or left. With such a system, the stabilizer frames can be designated as being so many inches right or left of the aircraft center line.

The applicable manufacturer's numbering system and abbreviated designations or symbols should always be reviewed before attempting to locate a structural member. The following list includes location designations typical of those used by many manufacturers.

- Fuselage stations (Fus. Sta. or F.S.) are numbered in inches from a reference or zero point known as the reference datum. The reference datum is an imaginary vertical plane at or near the nose of the aircraft from which all horizontal distances are measured. The distance to a given point is measured in inches parallel to a center line extending through the aircraft from the nose through the center of the tail cone. Some manufacturers may call the fuselage station a body station, abbreviated B.S.

- Buttock line or butt line (B.L.) is a width measurement left or right of, and parallel to, the vertical center line.

- Water line (W.L.) is the measurement of height in inches perpendicular from a horizontal plane located a fixed number of inches below the bottom of the aircraft fuselage.

- Aileron station (A.S.) is measured outboard from, and parallel to, the inboard edge of the aileron, perpendicular to the rear beam of the wing.

- Flap station (F.S.) is measured perpendicular to the rear beam of the wing and parallel to, and outboard from, the inboard edge of the flap.

- Nacelle station (N.C. or Nac. Sta.) is measured either forward of or behind the front spar of the wing and perpendicular to a designated water line.

In addition to the location stations listed above, other measurements are used, especially on large aircraft. Thus, there may be horizontal stabilizer stations (H.S.S.), vertical stabilizer stations (V.S.S.) or powerplant stations (P.P.S.). In every case, the manufacturer's terminology and station location system should be consulted before locating a point on a particular aircraft.

Section 3

Wing Structure

Two types of wing design used for modern aircraft are semi-cantilever and full cantilever. Another name used for semi-cantilever is a braced wing. The wings of an aircraft provides the surfaces used to produce lift when it is moving through the air. The particular design for any given aircraft depends on several factors such as, size, weight, use, speed, rate of climb and the type of wing. The location of the wings of an aircraft are designated as left and right. The left wing is located on the left side of the pilot when seated in the cockpit.

Semi-Cantilever or Braced Wings

A semi-cantilever wing obtains its strength from internal structures as well as from wing struts and/or flying and landing wires. The wing struts are made from chrome-molybdenum steel and the wires are made from hardened steel. The length of the wing strut is determined by the length of the wing it supports. If a wing span is very wide, a long strut with a jury strut is required. The purpose of a jury strut (Figure 1-3-1) is to prevent vibrations which often occur with long struts during flight. The vibration occurs because the long strut wants to lift up and down during flight, thus setting up a vibration which will eventually cause strut failure. If the wings are short, no jury strut is needed.

For many years, light aircraft have been using a semi-cantilever-type wing. The early models had long struts while the new models use shorter wing struts. The internal parts of a braced wing consist of compression ribs, former ribs, spars and skin coverings.

For the most part, these lightweight aircraft wings have very little internal bracing. The most effective internal bracing used for light aircraft wings are trammeling wires which are also called drag and anti-drag wires. Drag and anti-drag wires are crisscrossed between the spars and compression ribs to form a squared truss to resist forces acting on the wing in the direction of the wing chord. The wire used to resist the backward forces is called a drag wire, while the wire used to resist forward forces is called the anti-drag wire. The trammeling wires are used to square and give rigidity to each wing bay. Each wing bay is separated by a compression rib. Most modern aircraft use aluminum alloy for this type of wing construction. Early aircraft used wings with internal parts made from wood and covered with fabric or plywood.

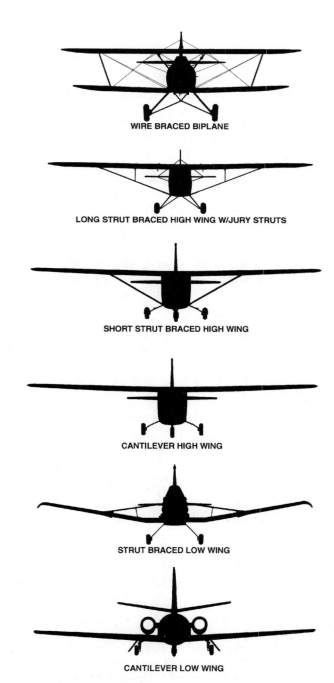

Figure 1-3-1. Common wing forms

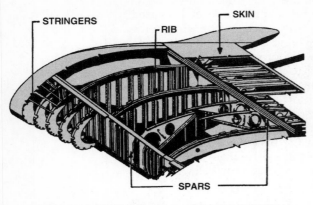

LARGE AIRCRAFT TWO SPAR WING CONSTRUCTION

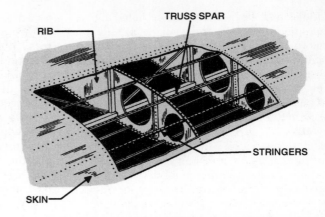

LIGHT AIRCRAFT STRESSED SKIN CONSTRUCTION

Figure 1-3-2. Internal wing construction

Full Cantilever Wings

The wings of some aircraft are of cantilever design; that is, they are built so that no external bracing is needed. The skin is part of the wing structure and carries part of the wing stresses. The internal strength of a wing is carried primarily by the spar and compression ribs. The spars and stringers run spanwise, and compression and former ribs run chordwise (leading edge to trailing edge). The skin attached to the internal members carry part of the loads stressing the wing. During flight, the skins are constantly flexing therefore they carry much of the external loads. All loads are transmitted to the internal structural parts, no aircraft structural part ever stands alone. The spars absorbs all the distributed wing loads as well as the weights of landing gears, fuel, and engines (Figure 1-3-2).

The wing of a large jet transport is constructed in sections. Inspection openings and access doors are provided, usually on the lower surfaces of a wing. Drain holes are also placed in the lower surface to provide for drainage of accumulated moisture or fluids. On some aircraft, built-in walkways are provided on the areas where it is safe to walk or step. On some aircraft, jacking points are provided on the underside of each wing.

Various points on the wing are located by station number. Wing station 0 (zero) is located at the center line of the fuselage, and all wing stations are measured outboard from that point, in inches.

In general, wing construction is based on one of three fundamental designs:

- Monospar

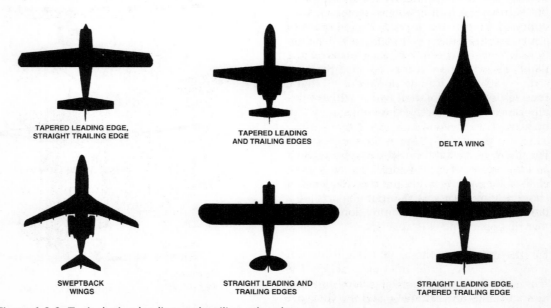

TAPERED LEADING EDGE, STRAIGHT TRAILING EDGE

TAPERED LEADING AND TRAILING EDGES

DELTA WING

SWEPTBACK WINGS

STRAIGHT LEADING AND TRAILING EDGES

STRAIGHT LEADING EDGE, TAPERED TRAILING EDGE

Figure 1-3-3. Typical wing leading and trailing edge shapes

- Multi-spar
- Box beam

Modifications of these basic designs may be adopted by various manufacturers.

The monospar wing incorporates only one main longitudinal member in its construction. Ribs or bulkheads supply the necessary contour or shape to the airfoil. Although the strict monospar wing is not common, this type of design, modified by the addition of false spars or light shear webs along the trailing edge as support for the control surfaces, is sometimes used.

The multi-spar wing incorporates more than one main longitudinal member in its construction. To give the wing contour, ribs or bulkheads are often included.

The box beam type of wing construction uses two main longitudinal members with connecting bulkheads to furnish additional strength and to give contour to the wing. A corrugated sheet may be placed between the bulkheads and the smooth outer skin. This allows the wing to better carry tension and compression loads. In some cases, heavy longitudinal stiffeners are substituted for the corrugated sheets. A combination of corrugated sheets on the upper surface of the wing and stiffeners on the lower surface is frequently used.

Wing Configurations

Depending on the desired flight characteristics, wings are built in many shapes and sizes. Figure 1-3-3 shows a number of typical wing leading and trailing edge shapes.

In addition to the particular configuration of the leading and trailing edges, wings are also designed to provide certain desirable flight characteristics, such as greater lift, balance, or stability. Figure 1-3-3 shows some common wing forms.

Features of the wing will cause other variations in its design. The wing tip may be square, rounded, or even pointed. Both the leading edge and the trailing edge of the wing may be straight or curved, or one edge may be straight and the other curved. In addition, one or both edges may be tapered so that the wing is narrower at the tip than at the root where it joins the fuselage.

Wing Spars

The main structural parts of a wing are the spars, the ribs or bulkheads, and the stringers or stiffeners, as shown in Figure 1-3-2. The spar

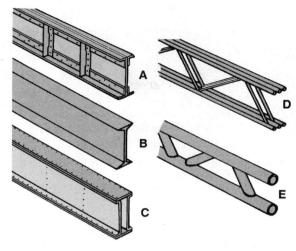

Figure 1-3-4. Metal spar shapes

is the primary load carrying member running parallel to the lateral axis (from butt to tip) in each wing of an aircraft. The number of spars used in a wing construction ranges from one to as many as three members. The spar is similar to the longeron in a fuselage construction though their purposes are different.

Figure 1-3-4 shows the basic configuration of some typical metal spars. Most metal spars are built up from extruded aluminum alloy sections, with riveted aluminum alloy web sections to provide extra strength.

Although the spar shapes of Figure 1-3-4 are typical of most basic shapes, the actual spar configuration may assume many forms. For example, a spar may have either a plate- or truss-type web. The plate web (Figure 1-3-5) consists of a solid plate with vertical stiffeners which increase the strength of the web. Some spar plate webs are constructed differently.

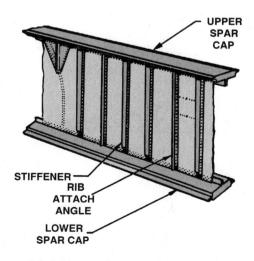

Figure 1-3-5. Plate web wing spar

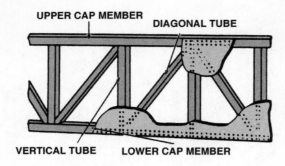

Figure 1-3-6. Truss wing spar

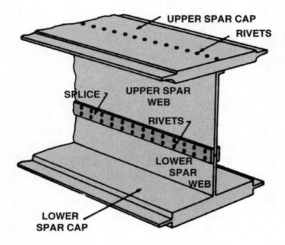

Figure 1-3-7. Wing spar with "fail-safe" construction

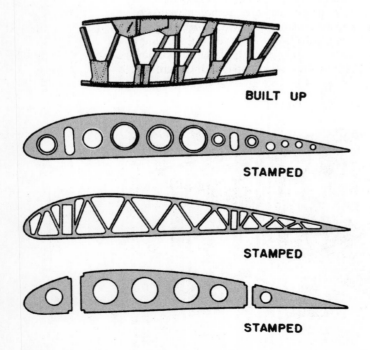

Figure 1-3-8. Basic rib structure

Some have no stiffeners; others contain flanged holes for reducing weight. Figure 1-3-6 shows a truss spar built up of an upper cap, a lower cap, and connecting vertical and diagonal tubes.

A structure may be designed so as to be considered fail-safe. In other words, should one member of a complex structure fail, some other member would assume the load of the failed member.

A spar with fail-safe construction is shown in Figure 1-3-7. This spar is made in two sections. The top section consists of a cap riveted to the upper web plate. The lower section is a single extrusion, consisting of the lower cap and web plate. These two sections are spliced together to form the spar. If either section of this type of spar breaks, the other section can still carry the load, which is the fail-safe feature.

Most wing structures incorporate two spars. One of these spars is located near the front of the wing while the other is located near the rear. Because of the wing design, when one spar is placed under a load, the ribs and bulkheads distribute the load to the other spar. This enables the two spars to absorb most of the load placed on the wing.

Wing Ribs

Two types of ribs, former and compression, are used for the construction of either a full or semi-cantilever wing. Former ribs are not considered primary structure while compression ribs are main structural wing parts. The wing bays on light aircraft are divided using compression ribs to separate the front and rear spars.

The ribs of a modern aircraft are made from heat-treated aluminum alloy. Ribs are structural crosspieces which begin at the leading edge of the wing shaping the contour of the wing to its trailing edge. Former ribs give the wing its cambered shape and transmit aerodynamic loads from the skin to the stringers and spar. Ribs are used throughout all the wing-like surfaces of an aircraft including the flight controls.

Two types of ribs called compression and former ribs are illustrated in Figure 1-3-8. Wing ribs, sometimes called nose ribs, middle or main ribs, and trailing or end ribs. A nose rib gives shape to the leading edge of the wing. It extends from the wing leading edge back to the front spar. The main or middle rib extends from the front spar to the rear spar and in some cases to the trailing edge of the wing. The wing butt rib is a heavy compression rib stressed to carry the loads imposed by being connected to the fuselage. The butt rib in conjunction with the spars provides the attachment points to the fuselage. A butt rib may also be called a wing bulkhead.

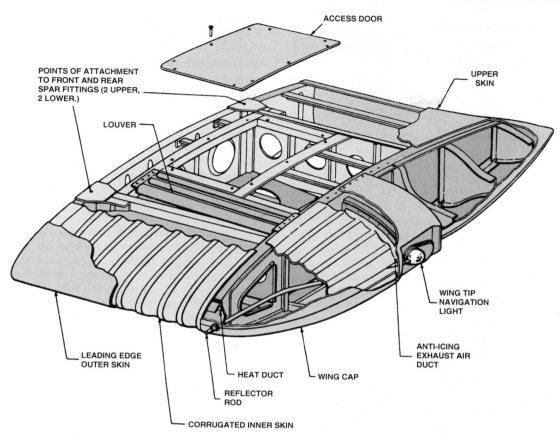

Figure 1-3-9. Removable wing tip

Most non-fabric covered light aircraft wings have removable tips. The wing on some modern aircraft have winglets which are used to reduce wing tip vortices. Some wing tips are removable which make them easy to change when damaged and provides internal access to the outer wing. Figure 1-3-9 shows a removable wing tip for a large aircraft wing. Removable wing tips for small aircraft are typically made from one piece fiberglass construction.

Wings tips assemblies are made from heat-treated aluminum alloys and on modern, light, aircraft they are made from high pressure plastics. The wing tip (flange) cap is secured to the wing tip butt rib with the appropriate types of fasteners. The tip leading edge has provisions for a heating duct, anti-icing duct, and wing tip light.

Figure 1-3-10 shows an isometric view of an all-metal full cantilever wing core section which

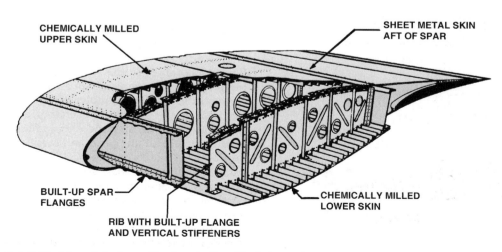

Figure 1-3-10. All-metal wing with chemically milled channels

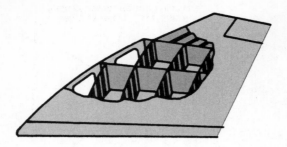

Figure 1-3-11. Box beam milled wing

contains spars, ribs, leading edge, and both skin panels. All full cantilever wing of this type are designed with stressed skins. Stressed skin means that part of the wing structural load is absorbed by the skins. The aerodynamic loads are initially picked up by the flexing of the skins then transmitted to the ribs and spars. To increase strength, keeping weight to a minimum and to support the weight of a bladder type fuel cell, a corrugated stiffener section is attached to the primary skin; see lower skin in Figure 1-3-10. A wing that stores fuel without the use of a conventional fuel tank is called a wet wing. A wet wing which holds fuel in the wing has a cell made up of front and rear spars, compression ribs on each side, baffles to prevent fuel agitation, and upper and lower wing skins.

The box-beam design shown in Figure 1-3-11 is a good example of how a honeycomb wing is made. The core structure in the wing is covered with a thin skin that is held on by a thermo adhesive. This type of construction increases strength and reduces weight.

Both aluminum and fiber glass honeycomb material are used for the construction of wings, stabilizers, and flight controls. Aluminum honeycomb material is made of aluminum foil honeycomb core bonded by adhesive between sheets of core and aluminum alloy skins. Fiberglass honeycomb material consists of fiberglass honeycomb core bonded between layers of fiberglass cloth.

Many of the modern jet transports as well as corporate jet aircraft are built with honeycomb parts. Lightweight honeycomb panels sandwiched between two thin skins of aluminum alloy or fiberglass face plates have done much to improve the useful load of these large and intermediate size jet transports.

Aircraft honeycomb parts are manufactured in various shapes. The shapes vary from flat to those that are tapered to meet the configurations of a flight control. An example of each is shown in Figure 1-3-12.

A top view of a modern jet transport with honeycomb control surfaces is shown in Figure 1-3-13. Large surfaces such as spoilers and the trailing edges of wing surfaces are made from honeycomb panels. A leading edge sandwich construction is illustrated in Figure 1-3-14. In this case, the sandwich leading edge of the wing is bonded to the metal spar.

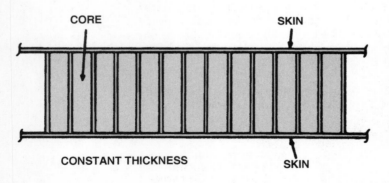

CORE   SKIN

CONSTANT THICKNESS   SKIN

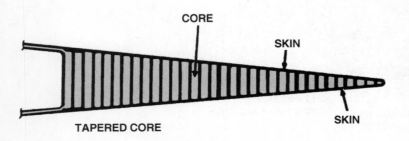

CORE

SKIN

TAPERED CORE   SKIN

Figure 1-3-12. Constant-thickness and tapered core honeycomb section

Section 4

Nacelles or Pods

Nacelles or pods are streamlined enclosures used on multi-engine aircraft primarily to house engines and landing gears. On multi-engine aircraft, the nacelle is contoured so it flows smoothly into the wing. The nacelle is located in the butt end third of a wing. Passing through the nacelle are the spars which carry the load of the engine and landing gear. To reduce drag on an airplane during flight, the landing gear of high speed and large aircraft are retracted into a location called the wheel well. Retracting the gear streamlines the airflow and reduces drag and increase aircraft performance. On some aircraft, the landing gear retracts into the fuselage.

An engine nacelle or pod consists of skin, cowling, structural members, firewall, and engine

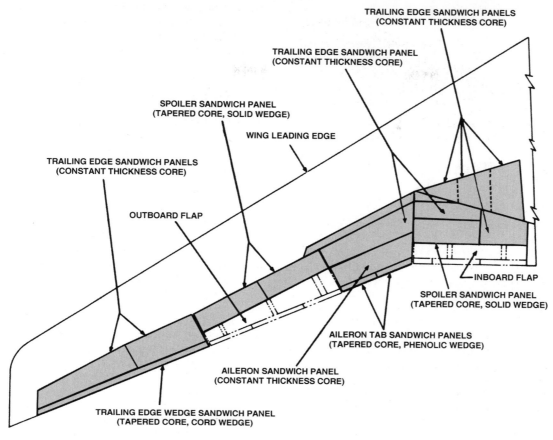

TRAILING EDGE SANDWICH PANELS
(CONSTANT THICKNESS CORE)

TRAILING EDGE SANDWICH PANEL
(CONSTANT THICKNESS CORE)

SPOILER SANDWICH PANEL
(TAPERED CORE, SOLID WEDGE)

WING LEADING EDGE

TRAILING EDGE SANDWICH PANELS
(CONSTANT THICKNESS CORE)

OUTBOARD FLAP

INBOARD FLAP

SPOILER SANDWICH PANEL
(TAPERED CORE, SOLID WEDGE)

AILERON TAB SANDWICH PANELS
(TAPERED CORE, PHENOLIC WEDGE)

AILERON SANDWICH PANEL
(CONSTANT THICKNESS CORE)

TRAILING EDGE WEDGE SANDWICH PANEL
(TAPERED CORE, CORD WEDGE)

Figure 1-3-13. Honeycomb wing construction on a large jet transport aircraft

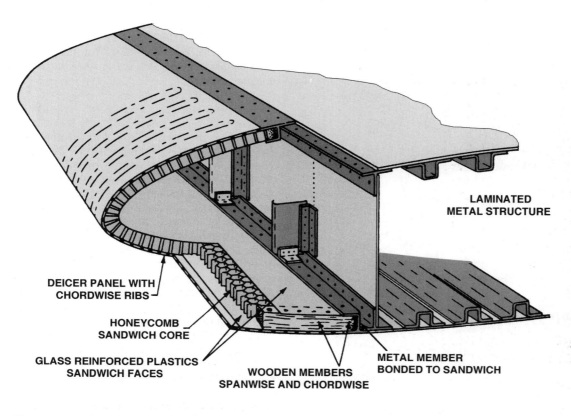

LAMINATED
METAL STRUCTURE

DEICER PANEL WITH
CHORDWISE RIBS

HONEYCOMB
SANDWICH CORE

GLASS REINFORCED PLASTICS
SANDWICH FACES

WOODEN MEMBERS
SPANWISE AND CHORDWISE

METAL MEMBER
BONDED TO SANDWICH

Figure 1-3-14. Leading edge sandwich material bonded to metal wing member

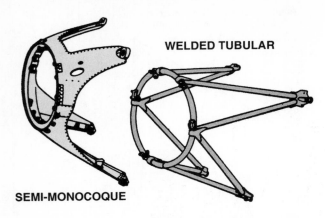

WELDED TUBULAR

SEMI-MONOCOQUE

Figure 1-4-1. Semi-monocoque and welded tubular steel engine mounts

mount. Skin and cowling cover the outside of the nacelle. Both are made of sheet aluminum alloy, stainless steel, or titanium which is attached to the skins with rivets or special fasteners.

Nacelle internal structures are very similar to those of a semi-monocoque fuselage. A nacelle contains a firewall which separates the engine compartment from the area aft of the engine. This firewall bulkhead is made of stainless steel, terneplate, and/or titanium.

Attached to the nacelle is the engine cowling. Enclosed in the cowling and attached structurally to the firewall attachments is an engine mount. The engine mount attachment points are connected with through bolts into vibration-absorbing rubber cushions. Figure 1-4-1 shows examples of a semi-monocoque and a tubular steel engine mount for a reciprocating engine.

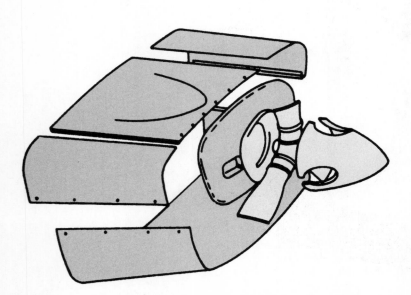

Figure 1-4-2. Cowling for horizontally opposed engine

Engine mounts are designed to carry torque and thrust load imposed on them during engine operation. The size of the engine, the amount of heat that has to pass by the engine for cooling, and the torque determines the design characteristics of an engine mount. Most engine mounts are constructed in one piece and can be removed quickly and simply from the attachment points. Welded engine mounts are made from chrome-molybdenum steel tubing.

Cowling

Engine cowling is a set of detachable permanently formed skins which are designed to fit over an engine to streamline the airflow and aid in cooling the engine. Figure 1-4-2 shows an exploded view of a typical light aircraft cowling used by an opposed engine. Some large radial engines are enclosed by banana-peel cowling panels. The cowl panels are attached to the firewall by hinges mounted to a structural ring which is connected to the nacelle as shown in Figure 1-4-3.

Cowl flaps are located aft of the cowling at the trailing end. Cowl flaps are operated manually, hydraulically and electrically. Most modern aircraft use electrical cowl flaps which open and close automatically by heat sensors. The operating range of automatic cowl flaps are from full closed to full open. For cruise conditions, the cowl flaps are in the trail position. For cold weather engine run-up, the cowl flaps are full closed. When the engine runs hot, the cowl flaps are in the open position. Automatic cowl flaps can also be operated using a manual override.

The cowling used on large jet transports is designed, in most cases, for high by-pass of air between the outer engine and the cowling. Just as with other components which protrude from an airframe, a jet engine produces drag. Wing pylons hold the jet engine in place and as much as possible the cowling streamlines the airflow around the outside in an attempt to reduce drag. Figure 1-4-4 shows a jet engine which is side mounted.

Section 5

Empennage

The tail section of fixed wing aircraft is called the empennage section. The empennage section consists of a horizontal stabilizer, elevators, vertical stabilizer, rudder, and necessary

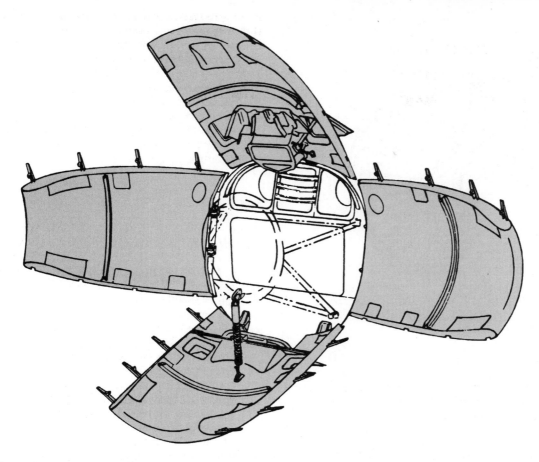

Figure 1-4-3. "Orange peel" cowling opened

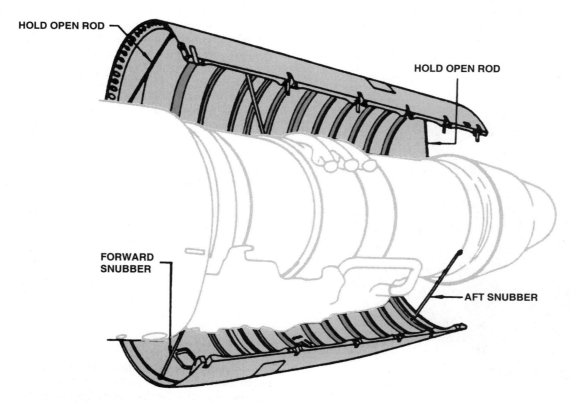

Figure 1-4-4. Side mounted turbojet engine cowling

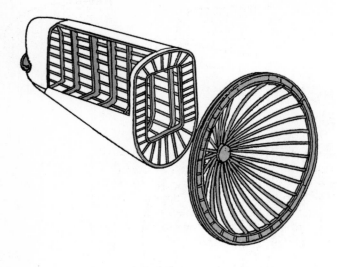

Figure 1-5-1. The fuselage terminates in a tail cone

tabs. Some aircraft vertical stabilizers are streamlined by a dorsal fin. The internal parts of the empennage section are assembled and joined similar to those of a full cantilever wing. On some airplanes, the horizontal stabilizer moves instead of an elevator to raise and lower the nose of the aircraft. These are called stabilators.

The aft section of the fuselage varies with each different type of aircraft design. Typically, the tail cone (Figure 1-5-1) used on large aircraft is constructed like the forward section, but often times are made from lighter materials. The purpose of the tail cone is to close the aft end of the fuselage by providing a finished look and to smooth the air flow under and around the empennage section.

The construction of the vertical stabilizer and the rudder are shown in Figure 1-5-2. It is built up the same way as the internal parts of a full cantilever wing. Until the jet age, many large air transports used fabric coverings on their flight controls to reduce tail weight.

Section 6

Flight Control Surfaces

A flight control is used to move an aircraft about a major axis. The three axes of an aircraft are vertical, longitudinal, and lateral. The lateral is sometimes called the horizontal axis. The rudder moves the aircraft about the vertical axis. The ailerons move the aircraft about the longitudinal axis. The elevators move the aircraft about the lateral or horizontal axis. Flight controls are divided into primary and secondary, or auxiliary. Primary flight controls are ailerons, elevators, and rudder. Auxiliary or secondary flight controls are cockpit adjustable trim tabs, ground adjustable tabs, and leading edge slots or slats. Auxiliary controls are spoilers, dive brakes, and high lift devices.

Control surfaces are made of an aluminum alloy or advanced composites. Special manufacturing techniques have been tried in order to reduce the weight of control surfaces. Most control surfaces are statically balanced to improve their flight characteristics. If a flight control is unbalanced, it will flutter in flight and set up an unstable flying condition. All moveable control surfaces have a re-balancing procedure that must be followed after repairs.

The control surfaces described above are considered to be the conventional type. However, on some aircraft, control surfaces serve a dual purpose. For example, a V-tail aircraft uses ruddervators, which combine to do the job of both rudder and elevators. Yet, on another type of aircraft design, elevons are used, and they combine the operation of ailerons and elevators. On many large jet transports, the horizontal stabilizer is moved up or down by adjusting the trim in the cockpit to change its angle of attack in flight.

The purposes of secondary controls are to assist the pilot when trimming the aircraft to be flown with the least amount of effort. A

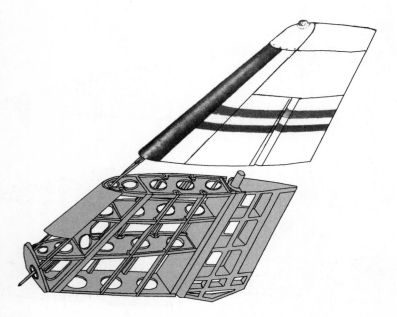

Figure 1-5-2. Construction features of rudder and vertical stabilizer

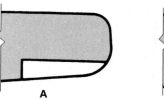 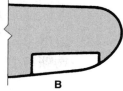 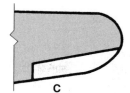 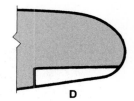

Figure 1-6-1. Aileron location on various wing tip designs

trimmed aircraft can be flown hands off while flying straight-and-level.

Ailerons

The total wing area of an aircraft also includes the area of the ailerons, flaps and auxiliary controls. Ailerons are attached on the outer third of the wing and outboard of the flaps. Ailerons are connected to the wheel on the control column in the cockpit. They are moved by turning the wheel, controller, or control stick from right to left. The ailerons move opposite from the left to right side. For example, if the left aileron was moved down, the right aileron would move up. The result of this action is the left wing moves up. Examples of conventional ailerons are shown in Figure 1-6-1.

Ailerons are connected in the control system to move the aircraft about the longitudinal axis. This is accomplished when one aileron is moved down and there is an increase in lift while the aileron on the other wing is moved upward and lift decreases. The increasing of lift on one side and the decrease of lift on the other side is what causes the aircraft to roll about the horizontal axis.

An end view of a typical metal rib in an aileron is shown in Figure 1-6-2. The hinge point of this type of aileron is behind the leading edge of the aileron to provide a more sensitive response to control movements. The horns attached to the aileron spar are levers to which the aileron control cables or push rods are secured. Figure 1-6-3 shows several examples of aileron installation.

The control surfaces of a large turbojet aircraft are shown in Figure 1-6-4. Certain large jet transports use a standard aileron for low speed and another inboard aileron for high speed. At high speeds, flaps are retracted and the outboard ailerons are locked out of the aileron control system. This greatly reduces the bending stresses on the wing structure.

A major portion of the skin of the inboard ailerons is made from aluminum honeycomb panels. Exposed honeycomb edges are covered

with sealant and protective finish. The aileron nose tapers and extends forward of the aileron hinge line. Each inboard aileron is positioned between the inboard and outboard flaps at the trailing edge of the wing. The aileron hinge supports extend aft and are attached to aileron hinge bearings to support the aileron.

The outboard ailerons are made up of a nose spar and ribs covered with aluminum honeycomb panels. A continuous hinge attached to the forward edge of the nose is grooved to mate with the hem of a fabric seal.

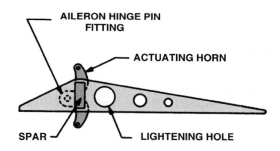

Figure 1-6-2. End view of aileron rib

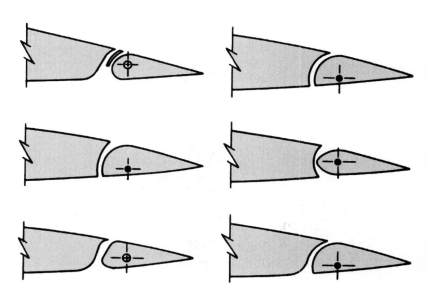

Figure 1-6-3. Aileron hinge locations

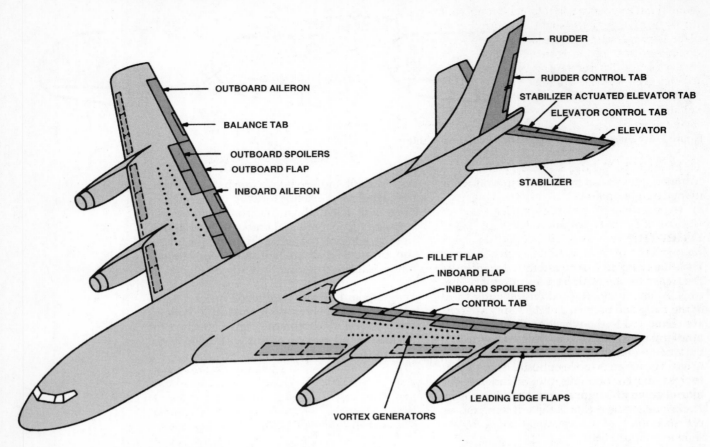

Figure 1-6-4. Control surfaces of a large turbojet aircraft

The outboard ailerons are located in the trailing edge of each outboard wing section. Hinge supports extend aft from the wing and are attached to the aileron hinge bearing to support the aileron. The nose of the aileron extends into a balance chamber in the wing and is attached to balance panels.

Aileron balance panels (Figure 1-6-5) reduce the force necessary to position and hold the ailerons. The balance panels may be made of aluminum honeycomb skin bonded to an aluminum frame, or of aluminum skin-covered assemblies with hat-section stiffen-

ers. Clearance between the aileron nose and wing structure provides a controlled airflow area necessary for balance panel action. Seals attached to the panels control air leakage.

Air loads on the balance panels (Figure 1-6-5) depend on aileron position. When the ailerons are moved during flight to either side of the streamline position, differential pressure is created across the balance panels. This differential pressure acts on the balance panels in a direction that assists aileron movement. Full balance panel force is not required for small angles of aileron displacement because the

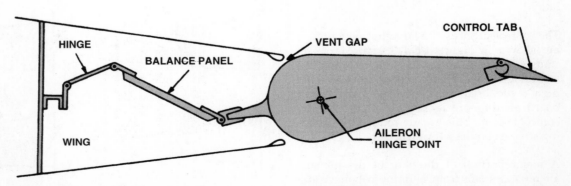

Figure 1-6-5. Aileron balance panel

manual force necessary to rotate the control tab through small angles is slight. A controlled air bleed is progressively decreased as the aileron displacement angle is increased. This action increases the differential air pressure on the balance panels as the ailerons rotate from the streamline position. The increasing load on the balance panel counteracts the increasing load on the ailerons.

Auxiliary Wing Flight Surfaces

The ailerons are part of the primary wing flight surfaces. Auxiliary wing flight surfaces include trailing edge flaps, leading edge flaps, speed brakes, spoilers, and leading edge slats. The number and type of auxiliary wing flap surfaces on an aircraft vary widely, depending on the type and size of aircraft.

Wing flaps are used to give the aircraft extra lift. They reduce the landing speed, thereby shortening the length of the landing rollout to facilitate landing in small or obstructed areas by permitting the gliding angle to be increased without greatly increasing the approach speed. In addition, the use of flaps during takeoff reduces the length of the take-off run.

Most flaps are hinged to the lower trailing edges of the wings, inboard of the ailerons. Leading edge flaps are also used, principally on large high-speed aircraft. When they are in the up (or retracted) position, they fair in with the wings and serve as part of the wing leading edge. When in the down (or extended) position, the flaps pivot on the hinge points and drop to about a 45° or 50° angle with the wing chord line. This increases the wing camber and changes the airflow, providing greater lift.

Some common types of flaps are shown in Figure 1-6-6. The plain flap forms the trailing edge of the wing when the flap is in the up (or retracted) position. It contains both the upper and lower surface of the wing trailing edge.

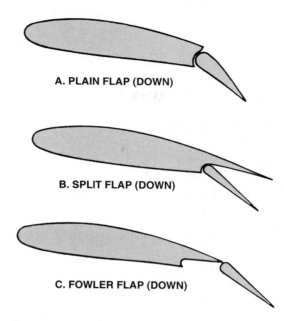

Figure 1-6-6. Wing flaps

The plain split flap is normally housed flush with the undersurface of the wing. It is similar to a plain flap except that the upper surface of the wing extends to the flap trailing edge and does not droop with the flap. This flap is also called the split-edge flap. It is usually just a braced, flat metal plate hinged at several points along its leading edge.

Aircraft requiring extra wing area to aid lift often use Fowler flaps. This system houses the flaps flush under the wings much as the plain split flap system. But, instead of the flaps hinging straight down from a stationary hinge line, worm-gear drives move the flaps leading edge rearward as the flaps droop. This action provides normal flap effect, and at the same time, wing area is increased when the flaps are extended.

An example of a triple-slotted segmented flap used on some large turbine aircraft is shown in Figure 1-6-4. This type of trailing edge flap system provides high lift for both takeoff and

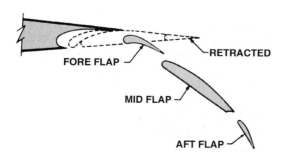

Figure 1-6-7. Triple-slotted trailing edge flaps

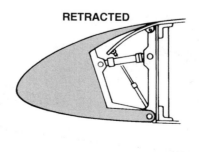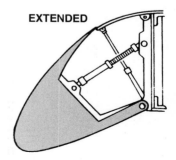

Figure 1-6-8. Cross section of a leading edge flap

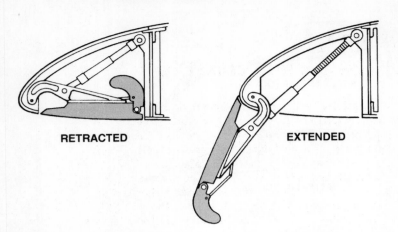

RETRACTED

EXTENDED

Figure 1-6-9. Leading edge flap

landing. Each flap consists of a fore flap, a mid-flap, and an aft-flap. The chord length of each flap expands as the flap is extended, providing greatly increased flap area. The resulting slots between flaps prevents separation of the airflow over the flap area.

The leading edge flap (Figure 1-6-8) is similar in operation to the plain flap; that is, it is hinged on the bottom side, and, when actuated, the leading edge of the wing extends in a downward direction to increase the camber of the wing. Leading edge flaps are used in conjunction with other types of flaps.

Kruger-type flaps can be installed on each wing leading edge. The flaps are machined magnesium castings with integral ribs and stiffeners. The magnesium casting of each flap is the principal structural component and consists of a straight section with a hollow core called the torque tube extending from the straight section at the forward end.

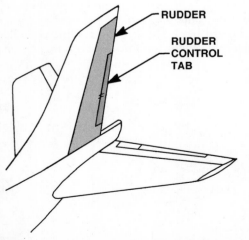

RUDDER

RUDDER CONTROL TAB

Figure 1-6-10. Typical location of rudder control tab

Each leading edge flap has three gooseneck hinges attached to fittings in the fixed wing leading edge, and a hinged fairing is installed on the trailing edge of each flap. Figure 1-6-9 shows a typical Kruger-type flap in a retracted and an extended position.

Speed brakes, sometimes called dive brakes, serve to slow an aircraft in flight. These brakes are used when descending at a steep angle or when approaching the runway for a landing. The brakes themselves are manufactured in many shapes, and their location depends on the design of the aircraft and the purpose of the brakes.

The brake panels may be located on certain parts of the fuselage or on the wing surfaces. Brakes on the fuselage are small panels that can be extended into the smooth airflow to create turbulence and drag. Wing-type brakes may be multiple-finger channels extending above and below the wing surfaces to break up smooth airflow. Usually, speed brakes are controlled by electrical switches and actuated by hydraulic pressure.

Another type of air brake is a combination of spoilers and speed brakes. A typical combination consists of spoiler flaps located in the upper wing surfaces ahead of the ailerons. When the operator wishes to use both air brakes and spoilers, he can slow the flight speed and maintain lateral control as well.

Spoilers are auxiliary wing flight control surfaces, mounted on the upper surface of each wing, which operate in conjunction with the ailerons to provide lateral control.

Most spoiler systems can also be extended symmetrically to serve a secondary function as speed brakes. Other systems are equipped with separate ground and flight spoilers. Most spoiler panels are bonded honeycomb structures with aluminum skin. They are attached to the wing structure by machined hinge fittings which are bonded into the spoiler panel.

Tabs

Most aircraft have trim tabs located on the flight control surfaces. These tabs may be either permanently set or they may be adjustable from the cockpit. The trim tabs provide for easier movement of the control surfaces. They allow the pilot to "trim" the flight controls to require a very little amount of force to move the flight controls (Figure 1-6-10). They also balance the pressure required to hold the aircraft level. The aircraft can then fly "hands off."

Section 7

Skin and Fairing

The smooth outer cover of the aircraft is referred to as skin. The skin covers the fuselage, wings, empennage, nacelles, and pods. The material used for the skin covering is usually sheet aluminum alloy, treated so that it will not corrode. Stainless steel and titanium are also be used on large jet transports. The thickness of the skins covering a structural unit may differ depending on the load and stresses imposed internally and externally on a structure.

Wing fairings are used to smooth out the airflow over the angles formed by the junction of the wing with the fuselage. Fairings are sometimes referred to as fillets. Some fairings are removable to provide access to aircraft components, while other fairings can be riveted to the aircraft structure.

Section 8

Access and Inspection Doors

Access doors can permit a normal or emergency entrance or exit from an aircraft. They also provide access to servicing points and manually operated drains. Inspection covers or doors provide access to a particular part of an aircraft during inspection and/or maintenance. Access or inspection doors can be either hinged or removable. They are fastened to the closed position with catch and locking mechanisms, machine screws, quick-release devices, or cowling type fasteners. Access plates for servicing fuel and oil tanks have stenciled on them the type of fuel or oil used for the aircraft.

2

Metals

Section 1

Metal Terminology

Knowledge and understanding of the uses, strengths, limitations, and other characteristics of structural metals are vital to properly construct and maintain any equipment, especially airframes. In aircraft maintenance and repair, even a slight deviation from design specification, or the substitution of inferior materials, may result in the loss of both lives and equipment. The use of unsuitable materials can readily erase the finest craftsmanship. The selection of the correct material for a specific repair job demands familiarity with the most common physical properties of various metals.

Properties of metals are of primary concern in aircraft maintenance. Of specific importance are such general properties of metals and their alloys as strength, hardness, malleability, ductility, brittleness, conductivity, thermal expansion, elasticity, toughness, fusibility, and density. These terms are explained within this section to establish a basis for further discussion of structural metals.

Explanation of Terms

Ferrous Metals

The term ferrous applies to the group of metals having iron as their principal constituent.

Strength

The ability of a material to withstand forces which tend to deform it in any direction, and

Left. Aircraft sheet metal structures, while primarily aluminum, may contain a number of other metals.

the ability of that material to resist stress without breaking is known as strength. There are four primary types of strength which are of importance when working with metals: tensile, yield, shear, and bearing strengths.

The tensile strength of a material is its resistance to a force which tends to pull it apart. Tensile strength is measured in pounds per square inch (p.s.i.), and is calculated by dividing the load, in pounds, required to pull the material apart by its cross-sectional area, in square inches.

Yield strength is that point at which a load would cause an initial indication of a permanent distortion. It is measured in p.s.i.

Shear strength is that point at which a material would fail under a shear force. The shear strength, measured in p.s.i., is found by dividing the shear force or load by the shear area.

Bearing strength is the ability of a material to resist the forces that tend to damage it at the point of an applied load. As an example, if a bolt were installed in a hole that was too big, when torque was applied to that bolt, the head could be pulled through the material if the bearing strength of the material were insufficient.

The relationship between the strength of a material and its weight per cubic inch, expressed as a ratio, is known as the strength-to-weight ratio. This ratio forms the basis for comparing the desirability of various materials for use in airframe construction and repair. Neither strength nor weight alone can be used as a means of true comparison.

Hardness

The ability of a metal to resist abrasion, penetration, cutting action, or permanent distortion is referred to as hardness. Hardness may be increased by cold-working the metal, and in the case of steel and certain aluminum alloys, by heat treatment. Structural parts are often formed from metals in their soft state, and are then heat-treated to harden them so that the finished shape will be retained. Hardness and strength are closely associated properties of metals.

Malleability

A metal which can be hammered, rolled, or pressed into various shapes without cracking, breaking, or having some other detrimental effect, is said to be malleable. This property is necessary in sheet metal that is worked into curved shapes such as cowlings, fairings, or wingtips. Copper is an example of a malleable metal.

Ductility

Similar to malleability, ductility is the property of a metal which permits it to be permanently drawn, bent, or twisted into various shapes without breaking. This property is essential for metals used in making wire and tubing. Ductile metals are greatly preferred for aircraft use because of their forming ease and resistance to failure under shock loads. For this reason, aluminum alloys are used for cowl rings, fuselage and wing skin, and formed or extruded parts, such as ribs, spars, or bulkheads. Chromium molybdenum steel is also easily formed into desired shapes.

Brittleness

The property of a metal which allows little bending or deformation without shattering is brittleness. A brittle metal is apt to break or crack without change of shape. Because structural metals are often subjected to shock loads, brittleness is not a very desirable property. Cast iron, cast aluminum, and very hard steel are examples of brittle metals.

Conductivity

The ability of a metal to transmit heat or electricity is known as conductivity.

Thermal conductivity is the ability of a metal to transmit heat. The thermal conductivity of a metal must be carefully considered if the metal is to be used in applications where the metal will be welded or where expansion and contraction are critical.

Electrical conductivity is the ability of a metal to freely accept and release electrons when an electrical current is applied. To eliminate radio interference in aircraft, electrical conductivity and bonding of metal parts must be considered.

Elasticity

The property which enables a metal to return to its original shape, when the force which causes the change of shape is removed, is elasticity. This property is extremely valuable because it would be highly undesirable to have a part permanently distorted after an applied load was removed. Each metal has a point known as the elastic limit beyond which it cannot be loaded without causing permanent distortion. In aircraft construction, parts and components are designed so that the maximum loads to which they are subjected will not stress them beyond their elastic limits. This desirable property is present in spring steel.

PERCENT OF ALLOYING ELEMENTS - ALUMINUM AND NORMAL IMPURITIES CONSTITUTE REMAINDER									
Alloy	Copper	Silicon	Manganese	Magnesium	Zinc	Nickel	Chromium	Lead	Bismuth
1100	-	-	-	-	-	-	-	-	-
3003	-	-	1.2	-	-	-	-	-	-
2011	5.5	-	-	-	-	-	-	0.5	0.5
2014	4.4	0.8	0.8	0.4	-	-	-	-	-
2017	4.0	-	0.5	0.5	-	-	-	-	-
2117	2.5	-	-	0.3	-	-	-	-	-
2018	4.0	-	-	0.5	-	2.0	-	-	-
2024	4.5	-	0.6	1.5	-	-	-	-	-
2025	4.5	0.8	0.8	-	-	-	-	-	-
4032	0.9	12.5	-	1.0	-	0.9	-	-	-
6151	-	1.0	-	0.6	-	-	0.25	-	-
5052	-	-	-	2.5	-	-	0.25	-	-
6053	-	0.7	-	1.3	-	-	0.25	-	-
6061	0.25	0.6	-	1.0	-	-	0.25	-	-
7075	1.6	-	-	2.5	5.6	-	0.3	-	-

Table 2-2-1. Nominal composition of wrought aluminum alloys

Toughness

A material which possesses toughness will withstand tearing or shearing, and may be stretched or otherwise deformed without breaking. Toughness is a desirable property in aircraft metals.

Fusibility

Fusibility is the ability of a metal to become liquid by the application of heat. Metals are fused in welding. Steels fuse around 2,600°F, and aluminum alloys will fuse at approximately 1,250°F.

Density

The mass of a unit volume of a material is density. In aircraft work, the specified mass of a material per cubic inch is preferred, since this figure can be used in determining the weight of a part before it is actually manufactured. Density is critical when choosing a material to be used in the design of a part, so that the proper weight and balance of the aircraft can be maintained.

Section 2

Nonferrous Metals

The term nonferrous refers to all metals which have elements other than iron as their base or principal constituent. This group includes such metals as aluminum, titanium, copper, and magnesium, as well as alloyed metals such as Monel.

Aluminum and Aluminum Alloys

One of the most widely used metals in modern aircraft construction, aluminum is vital to the aviation industry because of its high strength-to-weight ratio, and its comparative ease of fabrication. Aluminum melts at the comparatively low temperature of 1,250°F, is nonmagnetic, and is an excellent conductor.

Commercially pure aluminum has a tensile strength of about 13,000 p.s.i. By alloying with other metals, or by using heat-treating processes, the tensile strength may be raised to as high as 65,000 p.s.i., or to within the strength range of structural steel.

Aluminum alloys, although strong, are easily worked because they are malleable and ductile. They may be rolled into sheets as thin as 0.0017″ or drawn into wire 0.004″ in diameter. Most aluminum alloy sheet stock used in aircraft construction ranges from 0.016″ to 0.096″ in thickness. However, some of the larger aircraft use sheet stock which may be as thick as 0.356″.

Aluminum Alloy Designations

Wrought aluminum and wrought aluminum alloys are designated by a four-digit index system as seen in Table 2-2-1. The system is broken into series as follows:

- **1000 series** — 99 percent or higher purity, 1000 series aluminum offers excellent corrosion resistance, high thermal and electrical conductivity, low mechanical properties, and excellent workability. Iron and silicon are its major impurities. The alloy normally encountered is 1100.

- **2000 series** — Copper is the principal alloying element of this series. Using solution heat treatment, its optimum properties are about equal to mild steel. Having poor corrosion resistance in its unclad form, it is usually clad with 1000 series aluminum alloy, or high-purity alloy. The best known variation of this alloy is 2024.

- **3000 series** — Manganese is the principal alloying element of this series, which is generally non-heat-treatable. The percentage of manganese which will be alloy effective is 1.5 percent. The most popular variation is 3003, which offers moderate strength, but has good working characteristics.

- **4000 series** — Silicon is the principal alloying element used with this series, which lowers its melting temperature. Its primary use is in welding and brazing. When used in welding heat-treatable alloys, the alloys of this series will respond to a limited amount of heat treatment.

- **5000 series** — With magnesium as the principal alloying element, this series of aluminum alloy has good welding and corrosion-resistant characteristics. High temperatures (over 150°F), or excessive cold-working will increase its susceptibility to corrosion. 5052 is the normally encountered alloy.

- **6000 series** — Silicon and magnesium are combined to form magnesium silicide, which makes 6000 series alloys heat-treatable. It is a medium strength alloy, with good forming and corrosion-resistant characteristics. 6061 is the normally encountered alloy.

- **7000 series** — Zinc is the principal alloying element of 7000 series aluminum alloys. When coupled with magnesium, the result is a heat-treatable alloy of very high strength. Copper and chromium are often added to 7000 series alloys, of which the principal alloy is 7075.

The second digit indicates specific alloy modifications in the same way that the first digit of a designation identifies the alloy type. Should the second number be zero, it would indicate no special control over individual impurities. Digits one through nine, however, when assigned consecutively as needed for the second number in this group, indicate the number of controls over individual impurities in the metal.

For structural wrought aluminum alloys, the last two digits identify the aluminum alloy. For example, Alclad 2024-T3, the 24 indicates the type of aluminum alloy. For 99 percent pure aluminum, the code numbers 1100 are used.

The first digit in the 2xxx through 7xxx series indicates the major alloying element used in the formation of the alloy as follows:

- 2xxx — copper
- 3xxx — manganese
- 4xxx — silicon
- 5xxx — magnesium
- 6xxx — magnesium and silicon
- 7xxx — zinc

Alloy	SOLUTION HEAT TREATMENT			PRECIPITATION HEAT TREATMENT		
	Temperature (F°)	Quench	Temper Designation	Temperature (F°)	Time of Aging	Temper Designation
2017	930-950	Cold Water	T4	-	-	T
2117	930-950	Cold Water	T4	-	-	T
2024	910-930	Cold Water	T4	-	-	T
6053	960-980	Water	T4	445-455	1-2 hours	T5
				345-355	8 hours	T6
6061	960-980	Water	T4	315-325	18 hours	T6
				345-355	8 hours	T6
7075	870	Water	-	250	24 hours	T6

Table 2-4-1. Conditions for heat treatment of aluminum alloys

The second digit in the 2xxx through 7xxx alloy groups indicates alloy modifications. If the second digit is zero, it indicates the original alloy, while digits one through nine indicate alloy modifications.

Aircraft are manufactured using heat-treated aluminum alloyed with copper and/or zinc as the major alloying ingredients. Aluminum alloys that use copper as the major alloying ingredient are classified as being in the 2000 series. Alloys made using zinc as the major alloying ingredient are classified as being from the 7000 series.

Those alloys using copper, as in the 2000 series, are given a natural heat treatment. For example, an alloy from the 2000 (copper) series, when heat-treated, will have a code 2024-T4. The T4 means solution heat-treated. An alloy in the 7000 (zinc) category, such as 7075-T6, is first given a natural heat treatment, and soon after the metal is heated and quenched it is given a precipitation heat treatment, or an artificial aging process.

The result of the controlled aging process is a stronger, more corrosion free piece of metal. Thus the T6 in 7075-T6 means solution heat-treated, and then artificially aged. Artificial aging is called precipitation heat treatment. Heat treatments will be discussed in detail later in this section.

Section 3

Thermal Treatment of Nonferrous Metals

Annealing

The annealing procedure for aluminum alloys consists of heating the metal to a given temperature, holding or soaking them at this temperature for a length of time, depending upon the mass of the metal, and then cooling it in still air.

Annealing leaves the metal in the best condition for cold-working. However, when prolonged forming operations are involved, the metal will take on a condition known as mechanical hardness, and will resist further working.

It may be necessary to anneal a part several times during the forming process to avoid cracking. Aluminum alloys should not be used in the annealed state for parts or fittings.

Section 4

Conditions for Heat Treatment of Aluminum Alloys

Temperature

The temperatures for solution heat treatment vary according to the type of metal being treated. Table 2-4-1 shows the heating temperature, quenching medium, and aging time of various types of aluminum alloys. Quenching and aging will be discussed later in this section.

To prevent certain metal elements within the alloy mixture from melting, the temperatures used for solution heat treatment must be closely followed. If those elements were allowed to melt, the ultimate strength of the metal would be questionable.

Time At Temperature

Referred to as soaking time, the time that a metal is held at the specified temperature is measured from the time the coldest part of the metal reaches the minimum limit of the desired temperature range. The soaking time varies, depending on the alloy and thickness, from 10 minutes for thin sheets, to approximately 12 hours for heavy forgings. For heavy sections, the nominal soaking time is approximately 1 hour for each inch of cross-sectional thickness (Table 2-4-2).

A soaking time is chosen that will be the minimum necessary to develop the required physical properties. The effect of an abbreviated soaking time is obvious. An excessive soaking period aggravates high temperature oxidation. With clad material, prolonged heating results in excessive diffusion of copper and other soluble constituents into the protective cladding and may defeat the purpose of cladding.

THICKNESS (INCHES)	TIME (MINUTES)
Up to 0.032	30
0.032 to 0.125	30
0.125 to 0.25	40
Over 0.25	60
NOTE: Soaking time starts when the metal (or the molten bath) reaches a temperature within the range specified above.	

Table 2-4-2. Typical soaking times for heat treatment

Quenching

After the soluble constituents are in solid solution, the material is quenched to prevent or retard immediate re-precipitation. Three distinct quenching methods are employed. The one to be used in any particular instance depends on the part, the alloy, and the properties desired.

Cold Water Quenching

Parts produced from sheet, extrusions, tubing, small forgings, and similar type material are generally quenched in a cold water bath. The temperature of the water before quenching should not exceed 85°F. A sufficient quantity of water should be used to keep the temperature rise of the water under 20°F. Such drastic quenching ensures maximum resistance to corrosion, which is particularly important when working with such alloys as 2017, 2024, and 7075. It is this corrosion resistance which is the reason that a drastic quench is preferred, even though a slower quench may produce the required mechanical properties.

Hot Water Quenching

Large forgings and heavy sections can be quenched in hot or boiling water. This type of quench minimizes distortion, and alleviates cracking which may be produced by the unequal temperatures obtained during the quench. The use of a hot water quench is permitted with these large and heavy parts because the temperature of the quench water does not critically affect the resistance to corrosion of these forging alloys. In addition, the resistance to corrosion of heavy sections is not as critical a factor as for thin sections.

Spray Quenching

High-velocity water sprays are useful for parts formed from clad sheet and for large sections of almost all alloys. This type of quench also minimizes distortion and alleviates quench cracking. However, many specifications forbid the use of spray quenching for bare 2017 and 2024 sheet materials because of the effect on their resistance to corrosion.

Lag Between Soaking and Quenching

The time interval between the removal of the material from the furnace and quenching is critical for some alloys, and should be held to a minimum. When solution heat treating 2017 or 2024 sheet material, the elapsed time must not exceed 10 seconds. The allowable time for heavy sections may be slightly greater.

Allowing the metal to cool slightly before quenching promotes re-precipitation from the solid solution. The precipitation occurs along grain boundaries and in certain slip planes causing poor formability. In the case of 2017, 2024, and 7075 alloys, their resistance to intergranular corrosion is adversely affected.

Reheat Treatment

The treatment of material which has been previously heat-treated is considered a reheat treatment. The unclad heat-treatable alloys can be solution heat-treated repeatedly without harmful effects.

The number of solution heat-treatments allowed for clad sheet is limited due to increased diffusion of core and cladding with each reheating. Existing specifications allow one to three reheat treatments of clad sheet depending on cladding thickness.

Some warping occurs during solution heat treatment producing kinks, buckles, waves, or twists. These imperfections are generally removed by straightening and flattening operations.

Section 5

Straightening After Solution Heat Treatment

When the straightening operations produce an appreciable increase in the tensile and yield strengths, and a slight decrease in the percent of elongation, the material is designated T3 temper. When the above values are not materially affected, the material is designated T4 temper.

The solution heat treatment process which results in the metal becoming age-hardened, goes through three events; heating, quenching, and aging. The heating range is usually about 940°F. The quenching medium is cold water. During this step, the operator wants to get the metal cooled down as soon as possible to prevent early corrosion from starting. The aging period varies for each thickness of metal but usually levels out to about 12 to 16 hours. After the metal has age-hardened, it is suitable for aircraft structural work.

Section 6

Precipitation Heat Treatment

When aluminum is alloyed with other metallic elements such as copper, and in some cases even zinc, the heat treatment process must be more rigidly controlled to prevent internal grain growth from starting. This early internal grain breakdown is the direct cause of intergranular corrosion, which is described in detail in another chapter. To prevent, or greatly reduce, the possibility of corrosion a process called precipitation heat treatment is used. Artificial aging, which causes the alloys internal grains to precipitate, is far superior to the natural aging process. Natural aging is the end result of the regular solution heat treatment process.

Artificial aging following solution heat treatment is required of certain aluminum alloys. This treatment usually involves reheating the material to temperatures ranging from 245°F to 375°F, and soaking the material for a minimum of 1 hour to a maximum of 20 hours. Other alloys age at room temperature for periods of up to 96 hours and do not require precipitation heat treatment.

Precipitation heat treatment makes the metal corrosion resistant by locking its grain structure linkage together, forming very strong internal grain boundaries, or layers. The natural age hardening process does not do this. By using the precipitation heat treatment method, thicker and larger aluminum alloy parts can be produced without the danger of setting up an intergranular corrosion condition.

Section 7

Strain Hardening

Mechanically working metals at temperatures below their critical range (that temperature at which crystals begin to form) results in strain hardening of the metal. The mechanical working may consist of rolling, drawing, stamping, or pressing.

During strain hardening, the metal becomes so hard that it becomes difficult to continue the forming process without softening the metal by annealing.

Strength, hardness, and elasticity are increased by strain hardening, but ductility decreases.

Since this makes the metal more brittle, it must be heated from time to time during certain operations to remove the undesirable effects of the working.

Section 8

Hardness Identification

Where used, the temper designation follows the alloy designation and is separated from it by a dash (e.g., 7075-T6, 2024-T4, etc.).

The temper designations of aluminum alloys in general consist of a letter indicating the basic temper which may be more specifically defined by the addition of one or more digits. These designations are as follows:

- F - As fabricated.
- O - Annealed, recrystallized (wrought products only).
- H - Strain hardened.
- H1 - (plus one or more digits) strain hardened only.
- H2 - (plus one or more digits) strain hardened and partially annealed.
- H3 - (plus one or more digits) strain hardened and stabilized.

The digit following the designations H1, H2, and H3 indicates the degree of strain hardening, with number eight representing the ultimate tensile strength, equal to that achieved by a cold reduction of approximately 75 percent following a full anneal, zero representing the annealed state.

The most widely used alloys in aircraft construction are hardened by heat treatment rather than by cold-work. These alloys are designated by a somewhat different set of symbols: T4 and W indicate solution heat-treated and quenched but not aged, and T6 indicates an alloy in the heat-treated hardened condition.

- W - Solution heat-treated, unstable temper.
- T - Treated to produce stable tempers other than F, O, or H.
- T2 - Annealed (cast products only).
- T3 - Solution heat-treated and then cold worked.
- T4 - Solution heat-treated.
- T5 - Artificially aged only.

- T6 - Solution heat-treated and then artificially aged.

- T7 - Solution heat-treated and then stabilized.

- T8 - Solution heat-treated, cold-worked, and then artificially aged.

- T9 - Solution heat-treated, artificially aged, and then cold-worked.

- T10 - Artificially aged and then cold worked.

Additional digits may be added to T1 through T10 to indicate a variation in treatment which significantly alters the characteristics of the product.

Section 9

Cladding

Pure aluminum has such a very high resistance to corrosion that under normal conditions it rarely ever corrodes. Due to this excellent corrosion-resistant characteristic, sheet metal manufacturers apply, or clad, pure aluminum to the surface of most all aluminum alloy flat stock in a process known as cladding.

In the cladding process, this pure aluminum is applied to each side of an aluminum alloy sheet to a thickness of approximately 5 percent of each side. For example, if the thickness of the clad aluminum alloy sheet was .040, the thickness of the cladding is computed this way:

$$T = 0.040 \times 0.10 = 0.004$$

That means each side would have approximately 0.002-inch thick pure aluminum on each side. This means the total aluminum alloy thickness is only 0.036-inch thick.

Cladding is usually restricted to flat stock only. Other shapes use other forms of surface protections.

Section 10

Substitution of Aircraft Metals

In selecting substitute metals for the repair and maintenance of aircraft, it is very important to check the appropriate structural repair manual. Most manufacturers will have a skin plating chart or diagram listed. As a general rule 2024-T3 can be substituted for 7075-T6 if the next heavier gauge is used. There are exceptions so consult the manual first.

Aircraft manufacturers design structural members to meet a specific load requirement for a particular aircraft. The methods of repairing these members, apparently similar in construction, will thus vary with different aircraft.

Four requirements must be kept in mind when selecting substitute metals. The first and most important of these is maintaining the original strength of the structure. The other three are:

1. Maintaining contour or aerodynamic smoothness

2. Maintaining original weight, if possible, or keeping added weight to a minimum

3. Maintaining the original corrosion-resistant properties of the metal.

If no heat treating facilities are available, and the part was formed from annealed material and then heat treated, substition will have to be made.

Section 11

Magnesium and Its Alloys

Magnesium, the world's lightest structural metal, is a silvery-white material weighing only two-thirds as much as aluminum. Magnesium does not possess sufficient strength in its pure state for structural uses, but when alloyed with zinc, aluminum, and manganese, it produces an alloy having the highest strength-to-weight ratio of any of the commonly used metals.

Among the aircraft parts that have been made from magnesium with a substantial savings in weight are nosewheel doors, flap cover skin, aileron cover skin, oil tanks, floorings, fuselage parts, wingtips, engine nacelles, instrument panels, radio masts, hydraulic fluid tanks, oxygen bottle cases, ducts, and seats.

Possessing good casting characteristics, the properties of magnesium and its alloys compare favorably with those of cast aluminum. In forging, hydraulic presses are ordinarily used.

Magnesium Alloys

Magnesium alloys produced in the United States consist of magnesium alloyed with varying proportions of aluminum, manganese, and zinc. These alloys are designated by a letter of the alphabet, with the number 1 indicating high purity and maximum corrosion resistance.

Magnesium alloys are subject to such treatments as annealing, quenching, solution heat treatment, aging, and stabilizing. Sheet and plate magnesium are annealed at the rolling mill. The solution heat treatment is used to put as much of the alloying ingredients as possible into solid solution, which results in high tensile strength and maximum ductility. Aging is applied to castings following heat treatment where maximum hardness and yield strength are desired.

Magnesium embodies fire hazards of an unpredictable nature. When in large sections, its high thermal conductivity makes it difficult to ignite and prevents it from burning. It will not burn until the melting point is reached, which is 1,204°F. However, magnesium dust and fine chips are ignited easily. Extreme caution must be taken to prevent this from occurring. Should a fire occur, it can be extinguished with an extinguishing powder, such as powdered soapstone or graphite powder. Water or any standard liquid or foam fire extinguisher will cause magnesium to burn more rapidly, and can even cause the magnesium to explode.

Section 12

Titanium and Titanium Alloys

Weighing 0.63 pounds per cubic inch, titanium has a very high strength, particularly in an alloyed form. In addition, it has excellent corrosion-resistant characteristics. Certain forms of titanium alloys are used extensively in many aerospace applications.

Sensitive to both nitrogen and oxygen, titanium has to be converted to titanium dioxide with chlorine gas and a reducing agent, usually carbon, to be used effectively as a strong metal. Not as lustrous as chromium or stainless steel, pure titanium is soft and ductile, and its weight is between that of aluminum and iron.

Titanium alloys are classified as Alpha, Alpha-Beta, and Beta alloys. These classifications are based on the specific chemical bonding within the alloy itself (Table 2-12-1). While the specifics of the chemical composition is not critical to the aircraft technician, the following should be known about each alloy.

ALLOY	COMPOSITION	TENSILE STRENGTH	ELONGATION
ALPHA	5% Al - 2.5% Sn	130 k.s.i.	15%
ALPHA-BETA	6% Al - 4% V	140 k.s.i.	15%
ALPHA-BETA (HEAT TREATED)	6% Al - 4% V	180 k.s.i.	7%
BETA	13% V - 11% Cr - 3% Al	150 k.s.i.	15%
BETA (HEAT TREATED)	180 ksi	200 k.s.i.	6%
Definition of letters are: Al - Aluminum, Cr - Chromium, V - Vanadium, Sn - Tin			

Table 2-12-1. Titanium table

Alpha Titanium Alloy

Alpha alloys have medium strength, and good elevated-temperature strength. They can be welded, and are used mostly for forgings.

Alpha-Beta Titanium Alloy

Alpha-Beta alloys are the most versatile of the titanium alloys. In the annealed condition they have medium strength, but when heat treated their strength greatly increases. This form of titanium is generally not weldable, but it has good forming characteristics.

Beta Titanium Alloy

Beta alloys have medium strength, and excellent forming characteristics. Beta titanium can be heat treated to a very high strength.

Section 13

Nickel Alloys

Monel

Combining the properties of high strength and excellent corrosion resistance, Monel is the leading high-nickel alloy, This metal consists of 68 percent nickel, 29 percent copper, 0.2 percent iron, 1 percent manganese, and 1.8 percent of other elements. It cannot be hardened by heat treatment.

Monel is adaptable to casting and either hot- or cold-working, and it can be successfully welded. It has working properties similar to those of steel, and when forged and annealed, has a tensile strength of 80,000 p.s.i. This can be increased by cold-working to 125,000 p.s.i., which is sufficient for it to be classified among the tough alloys.

Monel has been successfully used for gears and chains to operate retractable landing gears, and for structural parts subject to corrosion. In aircraft, Monel is used for parts demanding both strength and high resistance to corrosion (such as exhaust manifolds and carburetor needle valves and sleeves).

Inconel

Closely resembling stainless steel in appearance, Inconel is a nickel-chromium-iron alloy.

The tensile strength of inconel is 100,000 p.s.i. annealed, and 125,000 p.s.i. when hard rolled. It is highly resistant to salt water and is able to withstand temperatures as high as 1,600°F. Inconel welds readily and has working qualities quite similar to those of corrosion-resistant steels.

Because Inconel and stainless steel look very much alike, a distinguishing test is often necessary. One method of identification is to use a solution of 10 grams of cupric chloride in 100 cubic centimeters of hydrochloric acid.

1. Using a medicine dropper, place one drop of the solution on a sample of each metal to be tested and allow it to remain for two minutes.

2. At the end of the two-minute period, slowly add three or four drops of water to the solution on the metal samples, one drop at a time; then wash the samples in clear water and dry them.

3. If the metal is stainless steel, the copper in the cupric chloride solution will be deposited on the metal leaving a copper-colored spot. If the sample is Inconel, a shiny spot will be seen.

Section 14

Ferrous Aircraft Metals

Many different metals are required in the repair of aircraft. This is a result of the varying needs with respect to strength, weight, durability, and resistance to deterioration of specific structures of parts. In addition, the particular shape or form of the material plays an important role. In selecting materials for aircraft repair, these and many other factors are considered in relation to the mechanical and physical properties. Among the common materials used are ferrous metals. The term ferrous applies to the group of metals having iron as their principal constituent.

Iron

One of the basic chemical elements, iron is extracted from iron ore. When combined with limestone and melted down, iron ore can be converted into what is commercially known as pig iron. Depending on how the iron ore is melted and what its intended use is, the pig iron is then used for castings, wrought iron, or in the manufacture of steel.

Steel

If carbon is added to iron, in percentages ranging up to approximately 1 percent, the product is vastly superior to iron alone, and is classified as carbon steel. Just as with the previously discussed nonferrous metals, a base metal (such as iron) to which small quantities of other metals have been added is called an alloy. The addition of other metals changes, or improves, the chemical or physical properties of the base metal for a particular use. Steel alloys are produced by combining carbon steel with elements which are known to improve the properties of steel. Carbon steel forms the base of those steel alloys.

Alloying Agents in Steel
Carbon

Steel containing carbon in percentages ranging from 0.10 percent to 0.30 percent is classed as low-carbon steel. The equivalent SAE numbers range from 1010 to 1030. (SAE numbers will be discussed in a later paragraph.) Steels of this grade are used for making such items as safety wire, certain nuts, cable bushings, or threaded rod ends. This steel, in sheet form, is used for secondary structural parts, clamps, and in tubular form for moderately stressed structural parts.

Steel containing carbon in percentages ranging from 0.30 percent to 0.50 percent is classed as medium-carbon steel. This steel is especially adaptable for machining or forging, and where surface hardness is desirable. Certain rod ends and light forgings are made from SAE 1035 steel.

Steel containing carbon in percentages ranging from 0.50 percent to 1.05 percent is classed as high-carbon steel. The addition of other elements in varying quantities adds to the hardness of this steel. In the fully heat-treated condition, it is very hard, will withstand high shear and wear, and will have little deformation. It has limited use in aircraft. SAE 1095 in sheet form is used for making flat springs and in wire form for making coil springs.

Sulfur

During the refining process, as much sulfur as possible is removed from the steel, because it causes steel to be brittle during some forming processes. The effect of any sulfur that cannot be removed is counteracted by adding manganese. The manganese will draw the sulfur to it, creating manganese sulfides which have no appreciable detrimental effects in the later forming processes.

Manganese

As carbon steel is processed, if manganese is added, the steel becomes very brittle. As the quantity of manganese is increased, the brittleness increases (up to a point). At a manganese content of about 5.5 percent, the brittleness begins to decrease, with the steel becoming more ductile, and very hard. Manganese steel reaches its maximum hardness and ductility at a manganese content of about 12 percent.

Silicon

When this nonmetallic chemical is added to steel (often manganese steel) it aids in the hardening and ductility qualities of the steel. Silicon is usually added to steel in amounts of fractions of one percent.

Phosphorus

Used to increase the resistance of low-carbon steel to corrosion, phosphorus is added in minute quantities of 0.05 percent or less. Quantities of phosphorus greater than 0.05 percent will cause the steel to become brittle.

Nickel

The various nickel steels are produced by combining nickel with carbon steel. Steels containing from 3 percent to 3.75 percent nickel are commonly used. Nickel increases the hardness, tensile strength, and elastic limit of steel without appreciably decreasing the ductility. It also intensifies the hardening effect of heat treatment. SAE 2330 steel is used extensively for aircraft parts, such as bolts, terminals, keys, clevises, and pins (SAE numbers will be described in detail later in this section).

Chromium

High in hardness, strength, and corrosion-resistant properties, chromium steel is particularly adaptable for heat-treated forgings which require greater toughness and strength than may be obtained in plain carbon steel. It can be used for such articles as the balls and rollers of anti-friction bearings. The amount of chromium used in chromium steels varies greatly, dependent upon the desired usage of the final product.

Molybdenum

In combination with chromium, small percentages of molybdenum are used to form chromium-molybdenum steel, which has various uses in aircraft. Molybdenum is a strong alloying element, which raises the ultimate strength of steel without affecting ductility or workability.

Molybdenum steels are tough and wear resistant, and they harden throughout when heat treated. Because they are especially adaptable for welding, molybdenum steels are used principally for welded structural parts and assemblies. This type of steel has practically replaced carbon steel in the fabrication of fuselage tubing, engine mounts, landing gears, and other structural parts. For example, a heat-treated SAE 4130 chromium-molybdenum steel tube is approximately four times as strong as a carbon steel tube of the same weight and size (4130 is commonly called chrome-moly steel).

Vanadium

When used to alloy steel, vanadium will increase the strength, toughness, and resistance to wear and fatigue. Vanadium steel normally consists of between 0.16 percent and 0.25 percent vanadium, and is often alloyed with chromium. A special grade of this steel in sheet form can be cold-formed into intricate shapes. It can be folded and flattened without signs of breaking or failure. Vanadium steel is used for making springs, gears subjected to severe service conditions, and for all parts which must withstand constant vibrations, varying, loads, and repeated stresses.

Titanium

When alloyed with stainless steel, a small amount of titanium will keep the steel from becoming brittle under high-temperature conditions. This is quite useful for, and is therefore used extensively, in tail pipe and exhaust stack applications.

SERIES DESIGNATION	TYPES
10xx	Nonsulphurized carbon steels
11xx	Resulphurized carbon steels (free machining)
12xx	Rephosphorized and resulphurized carbon steels (free machining)
13xx	Manganese 1.75%
*23xx	Nickel 3.50%
*25xx	Nickel 5.00%
31xx	Nickel 1.25%, Chromium 0.65%
33xx	Nickel 3.50%, Chromium 1.55%
40xx	Molybdenum 0.20% or 0.25%
41xx	Chromium 0.50% or 0.95%, Molybdenum 0.12% or 0.20%
43xx	Nickel 1.80%, Chromium 0.50% or 0.80%, Molybdenum 0.25%
44xx	Molybdenum 0.40%
45xx	Molybdenum 0.52%
46xx	Nickel 1.80%, Molybdenum 0.25%
47xx	Nickel 1.05%, Chromium 0.45%, Molybdenum 0.20% or 0.35%
48xx	Nickel 3.50%, Molybdenum 0.25%
50xx	Chromium 0.25%, 0.40%, or 0.50%
50xxx	Carbon 1.00%, Chromium 0.50%
51xx	Chromium 0.80%, 0.90%, 0.95% or 1.00%
51xxx	Carbon 1.00%, Chromium 1.05%
52xxx	Carbon 1.00%, Chromium 1.45%
61xx	Chromium 0.60%, 0.80%, or 0.95%; Vanadium 0.12%, 0.10%, or 0.15%
81xx	Nickel 0.30%, Chromium 0.40%, Molybdenum 0.12%
86xx	Nickel 0.55%, Chromium 0.50%, Molybdenum 0.20%
87xx	Nickel 0.55%, Chromium 0.05%, Molybdenum 0.25%
88xx	Nickel 0.55%, Chromium 0.05%, Molybdenum 0.35%
92xx	Manganese 0.85%, Silicon 2.00%, Chromium 0% or 0.35%
93xx	Nickel 3.25%, Chromium 1.20%, Molybdenum 0.12%
94xx	Nickel 0.45%, Chromium 0.40%, Molybdenum 0.12%
98xx	Nickel 1.00%, Chromium 0.80%, Molybdenum 0.25%

*Not included in the current list of standard steels.

Table 2-14-1. SAE numerical index

Tungsten

Able to withstand high temperatures without losing strength, tungsten is used extensively in high-speed, metal-cutting tools and metals to be used for magnets. Tungsten steels normally contain between 5 percent and 15 percent tungsten, although as much as 24 percent is not unusual.

In order to facilitate the discussion of steels, some familiarity with their nomenclature is desirable. A numerical index, sponsored by the Society of Automotive Engineers (SAE) and the American Iron and Steel Institute (AISI), is used to identify the chemical compositions of the structural steels. Refer to Table 2-14-1.

Section 15

SAE Classification of Steels

In the SAE numerical index system, a four-numeral series is used to designate the plain carbon and alloy steels; five numerals are used to designate certain types of alloy steels. The first two digits indicate the type of steel, the second digit also generally (but not always) gives the approximate amount of the major alloying element and the last two (or three) digits are intended to indicate the approximate middle of the carbon range. However, a deviation from the rule of indicating the carbon range is sometimes necessary.

Small quantities of certain elements are present in alloy steels that are not specified as required. These elements are considered as incidental and may be present to the maximum amounts as follows: 0.35 percent copper, 0.25 percent nickel, 0.20 percent chromium, and 0.06 percent molybdenum.

The list of standard steels is altered from time to time to accommodate steels of proven merit and to provide for changes in the metallurgical and engineering requirements of industry.

Carbon Steel

The element which provides the greatest influence on steel is carbon. The greater the amount of carbon in the steel, the harder the steel will be. However, the harder the steel, the more difficult it is to weld. Carbon steels vary from soft (low carbon) steels, with between 0.06 percent and 0.60 percent carbon content, to high-grade razor steel at about 1.25 percent carbon content.

Section 16

Alloy Steels

Chromium-Molybdenum Steel

The series of chromium-molybdenum steels most widely used in aircraft construction contains between 0.25 percent and 0.55 percent carbon, 0.15 percent and 0.025 percent molybdenum, and 0.50 percent to 1.10 percent chromium. These steels, when suitably heat treated, are deep hardening, easily machined, readily welded by either gas or electric methods, and are especially adapted to high-temperature service.

Nickel Steel

Sensitive to heat treatment, nickel steels are primarily used in aviation for hardware, such as rod ends, nuts, bolts, and screws.

Chromium-nickel steels are corrosion-resistant metals. The anti-corrosive degree of this steel is determined by the surface condition of the metal as well as by the composition, temperature, and concentration of the corrosive agent.

Stainless Steel

The principal alloy of stainless steel is chromium. The corrosion-resistant steel most often used in aircraft construction is known as 18-8 steel because of its content of 18 percent chromium and 8 percent nickel. One of the distinctive features of 18-8 steel is that its strength may be increased by cold-working.

Stainless steel may be formed to any shape. Because these steels expand about 50 percent more than carbon steel, and conduct heat only about 40 percent as rapidly, they are more difficult to weld. Stainless steel can be used for almost any part of an aircraft.

Section 17

Heat Treatment of Steel

Heat treatment is a series of operations involving the heating and cooling of metals in the solid state. Its purpose is to change a mechanical property or combination of mechanical properties so that the metal will be more useful, serviceable, and safe for a definite purpose. By heat treating, a metal can be made harder, stronger, and more resistant to impact. Heat treating can also make a metal softer and more ductile. However, no one heat-treating operation can produce all of these characteristics. In fact, often one property is improved at the expense of another. For example, in the process of being hardened, a metal may be made brittle.

The various heat-treating processes are similar in that they all involve the heating and cooling of metals. They differ, however, in the temperatures to which the metal is heated, the rate at which it is cooled, and in the final result.

The most common forms of heat treatment for ferrous metals are annealing, normalizing, hardening, tempering, and casehardening. An advantage of ferrous metals over nonferrous metals is that most nonferrous metals can be annealed, and many of them can be hardened by heat treatment, but, there is only one nonferrous metal, titanium, that can be casehardened, and none can be tempered or normalized.

Knowing the chemical composition is the first important consideration in the heat treatment of a steel part. This, in turn, determines its upper critical point. When the upper critical point is known, the next consideration is the rate of heating and cooling to be used. Carrying out these operations involves the use of uniform heating furnaces, proper temperature controls, and suitable quenching mediums.

Annealing

Metals are annealed to relieve internal stresses, soften the metal, make it more ductile, and refine the grain structure. In the annealed state, steel has its lowest strength. In general, annealing is the opposite of hardening.

Annealing of steel is accomplished by heating the metal to just above the upper critical point, soaking at that temperature, and cooling very slowly in the furnace (see Table 2-17-1 for recommended temperatures). Soaking time is approximately one hour per inch of thickness of the material.

To produce maximum softness in steel, the metal must be cooled very slowly. Slow cooling is obtained by shutting off the heat and allowing the furnace and metal to cool together to 900°F or lower, then removing the metal from the furnace and cooling in still air. Another method is to bury the heated steel in ashes, sand, or other substance that does not conduct heat readily.

Normalizing

The process of normalizing steel removes the internal stresses set up by welding, machining, forming, or any type of handling. These stresses, if not reduced or eliminated, will eventually cause extreme brittleness, which in turn will lead to cracking. The application of the normalizing process does exactly what the name implies. It brings the metal back to a normal, shock-resistant state.

Applying to ferrous metals only, normalizing is accomplished by heating the steel above the upper critical point and cooling in still air. The more rapid quenching obtained by air cooling, as compared to furnace cooling, results in a harder and stronger material than that obtained by annealing. Recommended normalizing temperatures for the various types of aircraft steels are listed in Table 2-17-1.

One of the most important uses of normalizing in aircraft work is in welded parts. Welding causes strains to be set up in the adjacent material. Additionally, the weld itself is a cast structure, as opposed to the wrought structure of the rest of the material. These two types of structures have different grain sizes. To refine the grain as well as to relieve the internal stresses, all welded parts should be normalized after fabrication.

Hardening

Pure iron, wrought iron, and extremely low-carbon steels cannot be appreciably hardened by heat treatment, since they contain little or no hardening element. Since the maximum hardness depends almost entirely on the carbon content of the steel, as the carbon content increases, the ability of the steel to be hardened increases, to a point. When the carbon content is increased beyond that point (which is about 0.85 percent) there is no appreciable increase in hardness.

For most steels, the hardening treatment consists of heating the steel to a temperature just above the upper critical point, soaking or holding at that temperature for the required length of time, and then cooling it rapidly by plunging the hot steel into oil, water, or brine. Hardening increases the strength of the steel but makes it less ductile.

When hardening carbon steel, it must be cooled to below 1,000°F in less than one second. Should the time required for the temperature to drop to 1,000°F exceed one second, the hardness will vary and will not reach the maximum hardness possible. After the 1,000°F temperature is reached, the rapid cooling must continue if the final structure is to reach the maximum hardness.

When alloys are added to steel, the time limit for the temperature drop to 1,000°F increases above the one second limit for carbon steels. Therefore, a slower quenching medium will produce hardness in alloy steels.

Because of the high internal stresses in the as quenched condition, steel must be tempered just before it becomes cold. The part should be removed from the quenching bath at a temperature of approximately 200°F, since the temperature range from 200°F down to room temperature is the cracking range. Hardening temperatures and quenching mediums for the various types of steel are listed in Table 2-17-1.

Tempering

Tempering reduces the brittleness imparted by hardening and produces definite physical properties within the steel. Tempering always follows, never precedes, the hardening operation. In addition to reducing brittleness, tempering softens the steel.

Tempering Temperature

Tempering is always conducted at temperatures below the low critical point of the steel.

When hardened steel is reheated, tempering begins at 212°F and continues as the temperature increases toward the low critical point. By selecting a definite tempering temperature, the resulting hardness and strength can be predetermined. Approximate temperatures for various tensile strengths are listed in Table 2-17-1.

The minimum time at the tempering temperature should be one hour. If the part is over one inch in thickness, the time should be increased by 1 hour for each additional inch of thickness. Tempered steels used in aircraft work have from 125,000 to 200,000 p.s.i. ultimate tensile strength.

The rate of cooling from the tempering temperature generally has no effect on the resulting structure; therefore, the steel is usually cooled in still air after being removed from the furnace.

Determining the Temperature of Steel

If temperature-measuring equipment is not available, it becomes necessary to estimate temperatures by some other means. An inexpensive, yet fairly accurate method involves the use of commercial crayons, pellets, or paints that melt at various temperatures within the range of 125°F to 1,600°F. The least accurate method of temperature estimation is by observation of the color of the work.

The heat colors observed are affected by many factors, such as the conditions of artificial or natural light, the character of the scale on the work, etc.

Steel Number	TEMPERATURE				TEMPERING (DRAWING) TEMPERATURE FOR TENSILE STRENGTH (P.S.I.)				
	Normalizing Air Cool (°F)	Annealing (°F)	Hardening (°F)	Quenching Medium (n)	100,000 (°F)	125,000 (°F)	150,000 (°F)	180,000 (°F)	200,000 (°F)
1020	1,650 - 1,750	1,600 - 1,700	1,575 - 1,675	Water	-	-	-	-	-
1022 (x1020)	1,650 - 1,750	1,600 - 1,700	1,575 - 1,675	Water	-	-	-	-	-
1025	1,600 - 1,700	1,575 - 1,650	1,575 - 1,675	Water	(a)	-	-	-	-
1035	1,575 - 1,650	1,575 - 1,625	1,525 - 1,625	Water	875	-	-	-	-
1045	1,550 - 1,600	1,550 - 1,600	1,475 - 1,550	Oil or Water	1,150	-	-	(n)	-
1095	1,475 - 1,550	1,450 - 1,500	1,425 - 1,500	Oil	(b)	-	1,100	850	750
2330	1,475 - 1,525	1,425 - 1,475	1,450 - 1,500	Oil or Water	1,100	950	800	-	-
3135	1,600 - 1,650	1,500 - 1,550	1,475 - 1,525	Oil	1,250	1,050	900	750	650
3140	1,600 - 1,650	1,500 - 1,550	1,475 - 1,525	Oil	1,325	1,075	925	775	700
4037	1,600	1,525 - 1,575	1,525 - 1,575	Oil or Water	1,225	1,100	975	-	-
4130 (x4130)	1,600 - 1,700	1,525 - 1,575	1,575 - 1,625	Oil (c)	(d)	1,050	900	700	575
4140	1,600 - 1,650	1,525 - 1,575	1,525 - 1,575	Oil	1,350	1,100	1,025	825	675
4150	1,550 - 1,660	1,475 - 1,525	1,500 - 1,550	Oil	-	1,275	1,175	1,050	950
4340 (x4340)	1,550 - 1,625	1,525 - 1,575	1,475 - 1,550	Oil	-	1,200	1,050	950	850
4640	1,675 - 1,700	1,525 - 1,575	1,500 - 1,550	Oil	-	1,200	1,050	750	625
6135	1,600 - 1,700	1,550 - 1,600	1,575 - 1,625	Oil	1,300	1,075	950	800	750
6150	1,600 - 1,650	1,525 - 1,575	1,550 - 1,625	Oil	(d)(e)	1,200	1,000	900	800
6195	1,600 - 1,650	1,525 - 1,575	1,500 - 1,550	Oil	(f)	-	-	-	-
NE8620	-	-	1,525 - 1,575	Oil	-	1,000	-	-	-
NE8630	1,650	1,525 - 1,575	1,525 - 1,575	Oil	-	1,125	975	775	675
NE8735	1,650	1,525 - 1,575	1,525 - 1,575	Oil	-	1,175	1,025	875	775
Ne8735	1,625	1,500 - 1,550	1,500 - 1,550	Oil	-	1,200	1,075	925	850
30905	-	(g)(h)	(i)	-	-	-	-	-	-
51210	1,525 - 1,575	1,525 - 1,575	1,775 - 1,850 (j)	Oil	1,200	1,100	(k)	750	-
51335	-	1,525 - 1,575	1,775 - 1,850	Oil	-	-	-	-	-
52100	1,625 - 1,700	1,400 - 1,450	1,525 - 1,550	Oil	(f)	-	-	-	-
Corrosion Resisting (16-2) (l)	-	-	-	-	(m)	-	-	-	-
Silicon Chromium (For Springs)	-	-	1,700 - 1,725	Oil	-	-	-	-	-

NOTES:
a. Draw at 1,150°F for tensile strength of 70,000 p.s.i.
b. For spring temper, draw at 800°F to 900°F; Rockwell hardness C-40-45.
c. Bars and forgings may be quenched in water from 1,500 to 1,600°F.
d. Air cooling from the normalizing temperature will produce a tensile strength of approximately 90,000 p.s.i.
e. For spring temper, draw at 858°F to 950°F; Rockwell hardness C-40-45.
f. Draw at 350°F to 450°F to remove quenching strains; Rockwell hardness C-60-65.
g. Anneal at 1,600°F to 1,700°F to remove residual stresses due to welding or cold work. May be applied to steel containing titanium or columbium.
h. Anneal at 1,900°F to 2,100°F to produce maximum softness and corrosion resistance. Cool in air or quench in water.
i. Harden by cold work only.
j. Lower side of range for sheet 0.06 inches and under. Middle of range for sheet and wire 0.125 inches. Upper side of range for forgings.
k. Not recommended for intermediate strengths because of low impact.
l. AN-QQ-S-770; It is recommended, prior to tempeing, that corrosion-resisting (16 Cr - 2 Ni) steel be quenched in oil from a temperature of 1,875°F to 1,900°F, after a soaking period of 1/2 hour at this temperature. To obtain a tensile strength of 115,000 p.s.i., the tempering temperature should be approximately 525°F. A holding time at these temperatures between 2 hours is recommended. Tempering temperatures between 700°F and 1,100°F will not be approved.
m. Draw at approximately 800°F and cool in air for Rockwell hardness of C-50.
n. Water used for quenching shall not exceed 65°F. Oil used for quenching shall be within a range of 80 to 150°F.

Table 2-17-1. Heat treatment procedures for steel

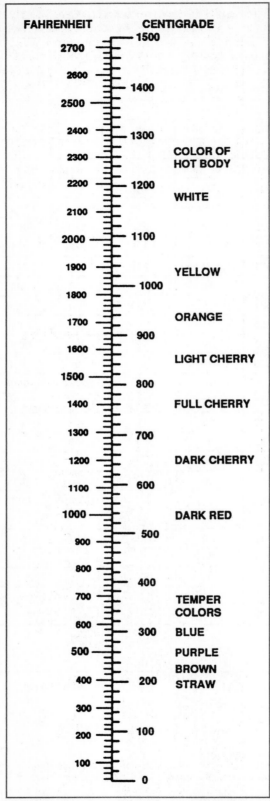

Figure 2-17-1. Temperature vs. color conversion chart

A rough approximation of the correspondence between color and temperature is indicated in Figure 2-17-1.

It is also possible to obtain some idea of the temperature of a piece of carbon or low-alloy steel, in the low-temperature range used for tempering, from the color of the thin oxide film that forms on the cleaned surface of the steel when heated in this range. The approximate temperature/color relationship for a given time at temperature is indicated in Figure 2-17-1.

> **AUTHORS NOTE:** *Judging temperature from color is a holdover from our blacksmithing and ironworker heritage's. It is an outdated process that simply will not go away. Modern steels and alloys require more precise process controls than temperature by color will allow. However, because the FAA still includes the 'smithy' process in training and testing, we cover it here.*

Section 18

Casehardening

Producing a hard wear-resistant surface, or case, over a strong, tough core, casehardening is ideal for parts which require a wear-resistant surface and, at the same time, must be tough enough internally to withstand the applied loads. The steels best suited to casehardening are the low-carbon and low-alloy steels. If high-carbon steel is casehardened, the hardness penetrates the core and causes brittleness.

Carburizing

Carburizing is a casehardening process in which carbon is added to the surface of low-carbon steel. Thus, a carburized steel has a high-carbon surface and a low-carbon interior. When the carburized steel is heat-treated, the case is hardened while the core remains soft and tough.

A common method of carburizing is called pack carburizing. When carburizing is performed using this method, the steel parts are packed in a container with charcoal, or some other material rich in carbon. The container is then sealed with fire clay, placed in a furnace, heated to approximately 1,700°F, and soaked at that temperature for several hours. As the temperature increases, carbon monoxide gas forms inside the container and, being unable to escape, combines with the gamma iron on the surface of the steel. The depth to which the carbon penetrates depends on the length of

Steel begins to appear dull red at about 1,000°F, and as the temperature increases the color changes gradually through various shades of red, to orange, to yellow, and finally, to white.

the soaking period. For example, when carbon steel is soaked for eight hours, the carbon penetrates of about 0.062 inches.

Another method of carburizing is called gas carburizing, in which a rich carbon atmosphere is introduced into the furnace. The carburizing atmosphere is produced by the use of various gases, or by the burning of oil, wood, or other materials. When the steel parts are heated in this atmosphere, carbon monoxide combines with the gamma iron to produce practically the same results as those described under the pack-carburizing process.

A third method of carburizing is called liquid carburizing. In this method the steel is placed in a molten salt bath that contains the carbon based chemicals required to produce a case comparable with one resulting from pack or gas carburizing.

Alloy steels with low-carbon content, as well as low-carbon steels, may be carburized by any one of the three processes. However, some alloys, such as nickel, tend to retard the absorption of carbon. As a result, the time required to produce a given thickness of case varies with the composition of the metal.

Nitriding

Nitriding is unlike other casehardening processes in that, before nitriding, the part is heat-treated to produce definite physical properties. Thus, parts are hardened and tempered before being nitrided. Most steels can be nitrided, but special alloys are required for best results. These special alloys contain aluminum as one of the alloying elements, and are called nitralloys.

In the nitriding process, the part is placed in a special nitriding furnace and heated to a temperature of approximately 1,000°F. With the part at this temperature, ammonia gas is circulated within the specially constructed furnace chamber. The high temperature cracks the ammonia gas into nitrogen and hydrogen. The nitrogen reacts with the iron to form iron nitride. The iron nitride is dispersed as minute particles at the surface and works inward. The ammonia which does not break down is caught in a water trap below the regions of the other two gases. The depth of penetration depends on the length of the treatment. In nitriding, soaking periods as long as 72 hours are frequently required to produce the desired thickness of case.

Nitriding can be accomplished with a minimum of distortion because of the low temperature and because no quenching is required after exposure to the ammonia gas.

The results of heat treatment, as well as the state of a metal prior to heat treatment can be determined by hardness testing. Since hardness values can be tied in with tensile strength values, and in part with wear resistance, hardness tests are a valuable check of heat-treat control and of material properties.

Most hardness-testing equipment uses the resistance to penetration as a measure of hardness. Included among the better known hardness testers are the Brinell and Rockwell testers, both of which are described in this section.

Section 19

Hardness Testing

The Brinell Hardness Testing System

The Brinell tester (Figure 2-19-1) uses a hardened spherical ball, which is forced into the surface of the metal. This ball is 10 millimeters (0.3937″) in

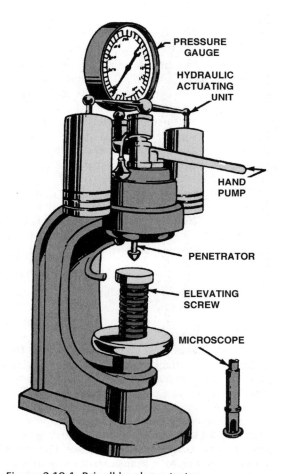

Figure 2-19-1. Brinell hardness tester

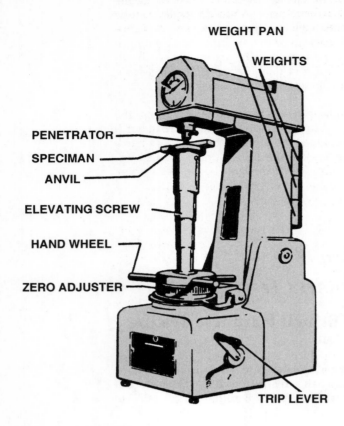

WEIGHT PAN

WEIGHTS

PENETRATOR

SPECIMAN

ANVIL

ELEVATING SCREW

HAND WHEEL

ZERO ADJUSTER

TRIP LEVER

Figure 2-19-2. Rockwell hardness tester

The Rockwell Hardness Testing System

The Rockwell hardness tester (Figure 2-19-2) measures the resistance to penetration, as does the Brinell tester. But instead of measuring the diameter of the impression, the Rockwell tester measures the depth. The hardness is indicated directly on a dial attached to the machine. The dial numbers in the outer circle are black, and the inner numbers are red. Rockwell hardness numbers are based on the difference between the depth of penetration at major and minor loads. The greater this difference, the less the hardness number and the softer the material.

Two types of penetrators are used with the Rockwell tester, a diamond cone (used on materials known to be hard and on materials of unknown hardness) and a hardened steel ball (used to test soft materials). The load which forces the penetrator into the metal is called the major load and is measured in kilograms. The results of each penetrator and load combination are reported on the separate red and black scales, and are designated by letters. The penetrator, the major load, and the scale vary with the kind of metal being tested. The scales, penetrators, major loads, and dial numbers to be read are listed in Table 2-19-1.

The metal to be tested in the Rockwell tester must be ground smooth on two opposite sides and be free of scratches and foreign matter. The surface should be perpendicular to the axis of penetration, and the two opposite ground surfaces should be parallel. If the specimen is tapered, the amount of error will depend on the taper. A curved surface will also cause a slight error in the hardness test. The amount of error depends on the curvature; i.e., the smaller the radius of curvature, the greater the error. To eliminate such error, a small flat should be ground on the curved surface if possible.

Clad aluminum-alloy sheets cannot be tested directly with any accuracy by a Rockwell hardness tester. If the hardness value of the base metal is desired, the pure aluminum coating must be removed from the area to be checked prior to testing.

Vickers Hardness Test

In this test, a small pyramidal diamond is pressed into the metal being tested. The Vickers Hardness number (HV) is the ratio of the load applied to the surface area of the indention.

The indenter is made of diamond, and is in the form of a square-based pyramid having an angle of 136 degrees between faces. The facets are highly-polished, free from surface imper-

diameter. A pressure of 3,000 kilograms is used for ferrous metals and 500 kilograms for nonferrous metals. The pressure must be maintained at least 10 seconds for ferrous metals and at least 30 seconds for nonferrous metals.

Pressure for the test is supplied by hydraulic pressure from either a hand pump or an electric motor, depending on the model of tester, and is monitored through a pressure gauge. A release mechanism is included in the hydraulic system for relieving the pressure after the test has been made, and a calibrated microscope is provided for measuring the diameter of the impression in millimeters.

The machine uses various shaped anvils for supporting the specimen, and an elevating screw for bringing the specimen in contact with the ball penetrator. The various anvils and other attachments are used for each of the variety of tests that the tester can perform.

The Brinell hardness number for a metal is determined by measuring the diameter of the impression left by the ball, using the calibrated microscope furnished with the tester. The measurement is converted into a Brinell hardness number using the conversion table furnished with the tester.

fections, and the point is sharp. The loads applied vary from 1 to 120 kg; the standard loads are 5, 10, 20, 30, 50, 100, and 120 kg. For most hardness testing, 50 kg is maximum.

A Vickers hardness tester should be calibrated to meet ASTM standard E1O specifications, acceptable for use over a loading range.

Webster Hardness Gauge

If a part is too large to use in a standard bench tester, the portable Webster style of tester can be used. In appearance a Webster hardness gauge looks like a pair of pliers with a dial attached.

Before use the gauge must be calibrated using a strip of the same material being tested, but with a known Rockwell hardness. The pliers are squeezed until they bottom out, and the hardness is read on the gauge.

The Webster gauge is especially useful in testing heat-treated aluminum.

Microhardness Testing

This is an indentation hardness test made with loads not exceeding 1 kg (1,000 g). Such hardness tests have been made with a load as light as 1 g, although the majority of microhardness tests are made with loads of 100 to 500 g. In general, the term is related to the size of the indentation rather than to the load applied.

Fields of Application

Microhardness testing is capable of providing information regarding the hardness characteristics of materials which cannot be obtained by hardness tests, such as the Brinell or Rockwell, and are as follows;

- Measuring the hardness of precision work pieces that are too small to be measured by more common hardness-testing methods.

- Measuring the hardness of product forms such as foil or wire that are too thin or too small in diameter to be measured by more conventional methods.

- Monitoring of carburizing or nitriding operations, which is sometimes accomplished by hardness surveys taken on cross sections of test pieces that accompanied the work pieces through production operations.

- Measuring the hardness of individual microconstituents.

- Measuring the hardness close to edges, thus detecting undesirable surface conditions such as grinding burn and decarburization.

- Measuring the hardness of surface layers such as plating or bonded layers.

Indenters

Microhardness testing can be performed with either the Knoop or the Vickers indenter. The Knoop indenter is used mostly in the United States; the Vickers indenter is the more widely used in Europe.

Knoop indentation testing is performed with a diamond, ground to pyramid form, that produces a diamond-shape indentation with an approximate ratio between long and short diagonals of 7 to 1. The indentation depth is about $1/30$ of its length. Due to the shape of the indenter, indentations of accurately measurable length are obtained with light loads.

The Knoop hardness number (HK) is the ratio of the load applied to the indenter to the unrecovered projected area of indentation.

Indentations

The Vickers indenter penetrates about twice as far into the work piece as does the Knoop indenter. The diagonal of the Vickers indentation is about $1/3$ of the total length of the Knoop indentation. The Vickers indenter is less sensitive to minute differences in surface conditions than is the Knoop indenter. However, the Vickers indentation, because of the shorter diagonal, is more sensitive to errors in measuring than is the Knoop indentation.

SCALE SYMBOL	PENETRATOR	MAJOR LEAD (kg)	DIAL NUMBER
A	Diamond	60	Black
B	$1/16$-inch ball	100	Red
C	Diamond	150	Black
D	Diamond	100	Black
E	$1/8$-inch ball	100	Red
F	$1/16$-inch ball	60	Red
G	$1/16$-inch ball	150	Red
H	$1/8$-inch ball	60	Red
K	$1/8$-inch ball	150	Red

Table 2-19-1. Standard Rockwell hardness scales

MATERIAL	HARDNESS	BRINELL NUMBER
COMMERCIAL DESIGNATION	TEMPER	500 kg LOAD 10 mm BALL
1100	0	23
-	H18	44
3003	0	28
-	H16	47
2014	0	45
-	T6	135
2017	0	45
-	T6	105
2024	0	47
-	T4	120
2025	T6	110
6151	T6	100
5052	0	47
-	H36	73
6061	0	30
-	T4	65
-	T6	95
7075	T6	135
7079	T6	135
195	T6	75
220	T4	75
C355	T6	80
A356	T6	70

Table 2-20-1. Hardness values for aluminum alloys

Section 20

Test For Distinguishing Heat-Treatable and Nonheat-Treatable Aluminum Alloys

Clad aluminum alloys have surface layers of pure aluminum or corrosion-resistant aluminum alloy bonded to the core material to inhibit corrosion. Presence of such a coating may be determined under a magnifying glass by examination of the edge surface which will show three distinct layers. In aluminum alloys, the properties of any specific alloy can be altered by work hardening (often called strain-hardening), heat treatment, or by a combination of these processes. Hardness values for aluminum alloys is shown in Table 2-20-1.

If for any reason the identification mark of the alloy is not on the material, it is possible to distinguish between some heat-treatable alloys and some nonheat-treatable alloys by immersing a sample of the material in a 10 percent solution of caustic soda (sodium hydroxide).

Those heat-treated alloys containing several percent of copper (2014, 2017, and 2024) will turn black due to the copper content. High-copper alloys when clad will not turn black on the surface, but the edges will turn black at the center of the sheet where the core is exposed.

If the alloy does not turn black in the caustic soda solution it is not evidence that the alloy is nonheat-treatable, as various high-strength heat-treatable alloys are not based primarily on the use of copper as an alloying agent. These include, among others 6053, 6061, and 7075 alloys. The composition and heat-treating ability of alloys which do not turn black in a caustic soda solution can be established by a testing laboratory.

All material ordered on the basis of Aluminum Company of America specifications will comply with corresponding Government specifications.

Section 21

Specifications and Inspection

Quantitative inspection items include chemical composition, mechanical properties, dimensional requirements (which sometimes include straightness), and packing and shipping requirements. The limits to which these factors must conform are set forth in detail in Government specifications.

Qualitative inspection items include general surface appearance, specific surface abrasions and blemishes, flatness and straightness. Government specifications discuss these items under workmanship. The following, among others, are not normally considered grounds for rejection:

- Surface discoloration of heat-treated materials. Alclad sheet is less susceptible than other heat-treated sheet.

- A few small surface blisters on heat treated Alclad sheet.

- Shallow scratches on Alclad sheet. The surface of Alclad sheet is relatively soft, and is therefore somewhat susceptible to handling scratches. Extensive investigations have shown that these scratches do not detract from the resistance to corrosion and do not have a measurable effect on the tensile strength, yield strength or elongation.

- Light die scratches and minor surface abrasions on extrusions, tubing, rods bars, and rolled shapes.

- Small residual heat-treating buckles and lack of perfect flatness, particularly on thin gauge (under 0.040″ thick) heat treated alloy sheet.

- Lack of perfect flatness on annealed sheets of any gauge.

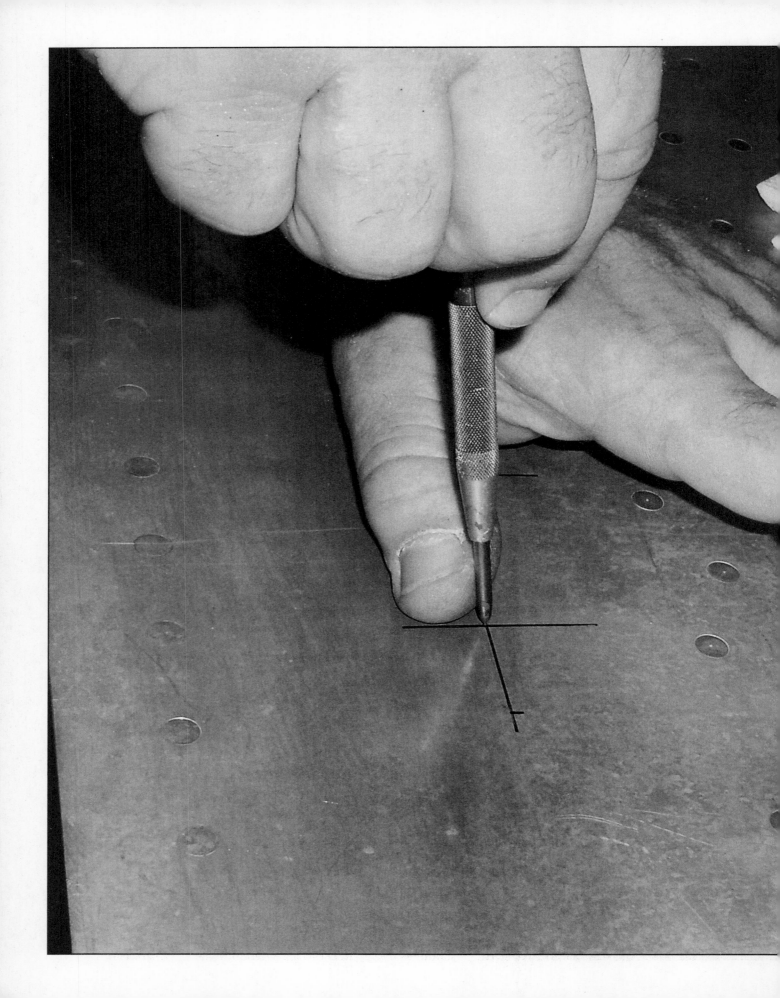

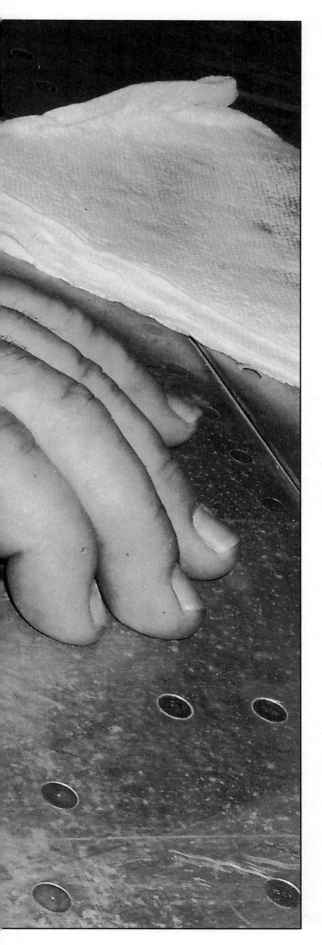

Hand Tools and Measuring Devices

This chapter contains information on some of the hand tools used by an aviation technician. It outlines the basic knowledge required in using the most common hand tools and measuring instruments used in aircraft repair work.

This information, however, cannot replace sound judgment on the part of the individual. There are many times when ingenuity and resourcefulness can supplement the basic rules. A sound knowledge is required of these basic rules and of the situations in which they apply. The use of tools may vary but good practices for safety, care, and storage of tools remain the same.

The technician must choose and use the proper tool for the job in order to do the work quickly and safely. Without the proper tools and the knowledge of how to use and maintain them, the technician wastes time, reduces efficiency, could cause injury to themselves or others, and could damage the aircraft.

Learning Objective

DESCRIBE
- the use of hammers and punches
- selection of turning tools
- metalworking tools

EXPLAIN
- types of pliers
- use of layout tools

APPLY
- select the proper cutting tool
- drill holes
- measure torque

Section 1

Types Of Hand Tools

Pounding Tools

Hammers and mallets are used to drive other tools or to form metal. Each type of hammer and mallet has a specific function. The misuse of these hammers or mallets can cause damage to equipment or injury to the technician. Figure 3-1-1 shows some of the types of hammers and mallets used in aviation. When

Left. Understanding proper tool usage is a critical skill for successful sheet metal technicians.

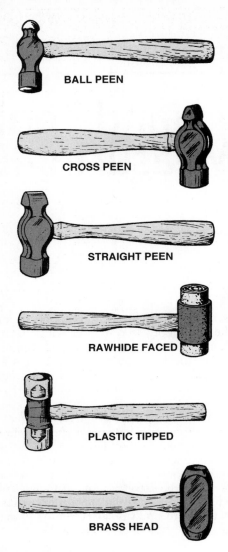

Figure 3-1-1. Pounding tools

using a hammer or mallet, choose the one best suited for the job. Ensure that the handle is tight. When striking a blow with the hammer, use the forearm as an extension of the handle. Swing the hammer by bending the elbow, not the wrist. Always strike the work squarely with the full face of the hammer. Always keep the faces of hammers and mallets smooth and free from dents to prevent marring the work.

Peening Hammers

Ball-Peen

The ball-peen hammer, Figure 3-1-1, has a rounded ball-shaped head used for forming soft metal, peening rivet heads, and striking metal in out-of-the-way places. The ball-peen hammer is classed by weight of the head. The weights range from two ounces to three pounds.

Cross-Peen

The cross-peen hammer, Figure 3-1-1, has a dull chisel head at right angles to the handle and is used to spread or draw metal out, removing rivet heads (not generally used for this in aviation), and bending metal. This hammer comes in weights ranging from 3 to 12 pounds.

Straight-Peen

The straight-peen hammer, Figure 3-1-1, is used like the cross-peen hammer. The difference is the straight-peen is parallel to the handle and keeps the striking edge parallel to the surface.

Carpenters Hammers

This type of hammer is better known as a claw hammer. The claw hammer has a striking face of two different designs and has claws for removing nails. One type is called the plain-faced claw hammer, the other is the convex face hammer known as the bell-faced claw hammer. This type of hammer is used in the crating and uncrating of parts, and should not be used as a substitute for the ball-peen hammer or vise versa. It should be noted that when using a flat-faced hammer, the nail head must be hit square with the hammer's face.

Sledge Hammer

Sledge hammers are similar to ball-peen hammers except they are heavier (see Figure 3-1-1). Sledge hammers have limited use in aircraft maintenance. Generally, short handled sledge hammers are used to drive large bolts, pins, nails, or chisels. Long handled sledge hammers are used to break concrete, rocks, or to drive rock drills. Sledge hammers can be double faced or have the same types of peens as the machinists ball-peen hammers.

Body Hammers

Made of metal, these hammers are used for riveting, setting, stretching, and planishing sheet metal and are classified according to their usage.

Stretching

Stretching hammers are used for making small depressions or forming concave or convex shapes in soft and semisoft metal. They are available in weights ranging from 20 to 90 ounces.

Planishing

Planishing hammers have metal heads with slightly convex faces. They are lighter than the stretching hammers and are used to smooth (or planish) the surfaces of parts which have already been formed. In many cases, the flat-faced wooden, plastic, or rawhide mallet is used for planishing purposes.

Riveting

Riveting hammers are used for driving rivets and for light chiseling. One end of the hammer head is cross peened, and the other end may have either a square or chamfered face. The sizes obtainable range from $5/8$ inch to $1^1/8$ inches, measured across the face.

Setting

Setting hammers are similar to riveting hammers, except in the shape of the peen (the pointed end). These hammers are used for setting down, clinching, or tucking the edges of sheet metal, and are made with either square or chamfered faces.

Mallets

Mallets are short handled, soft-faced striking tools used to drive wood-handled chisels, gouges, or wooden pins, to form or shape soft metal, and remove dents. The mallet is used because the soft face will not mar the metal's surface.

The mallet's handle is usually made of a hard wood. The soft face of the mallet can be made from a variety of materials. Some of the materials are rawhide, lead, brass, copper, rubber, or plastic (see Figure 3-1-1).

Replaceable plastic head inserts used on some mallets are color coded to assist in selecting the proper hardness for the task. Table 3-1-1 shows the color codes.

Section 2

Punches

Special types of punches are designed to install grommets and fasteners. Punches are used to locate centers for drawing circles, to start holes for drilling, to punch holes in sheet metal, to transfer location of holes in patterns, and to

remove damaged rivets, pins, or bolts. Solid or hollow punches are the two types generally used. Solid punches are classified according to the shape of their points. Figure 3-2-1 shows

USE THIS CONVERSION CHART FOR FACE SELECTION						
TYPE	SOFT	MEDIUM	TOUGH	MEDIUM HARD	HARD	EXTRA HARD
SOFT RUBBER	S	–	–	–	–	–
WOOD	S	M	–	N	–	–
RUBBER	–	M	–	–	–	–
HARD WOOD	–	–	T	–	–	–
LEAD	–	–	T	N	–	–
PLASTIC	–	–	T	–	H	–
RAWHIDE	–	M	T	N	H	XH
MICARTA	–	–	–	–	H	XH
FIBER	–	–	–	–	H	XH
COPPER	–	–	–	–	–	XH

HARDNESS	SYMBOL	COLOR
Soft	S	Brown
Medium	M	Red
Tough	T	Green
Medium Hard	N	Cream
Hard	H	Black
Extra Hard	XH	Yellow

Table 3-1-1. Face selection chart

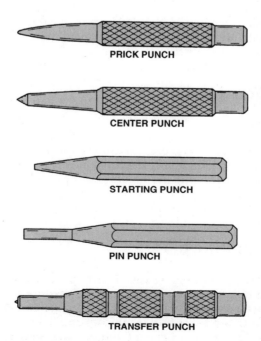

PRICK PUNCH

CENTER PUNCH

STARTING PUNCH

PIN PUNCH

TRANSFER PUNCH

Figure 3-2-1. Punches

several types of punches. Solid punches are used to mark sheet metal, drive out straight pins and tapered pins, and align holes. Hollow punches are used to punch holes in canvas, fabrics, or similar material. They are also used to set grommets and fasteners.

Prick Punch

Prick punches are used to place reference marks on metal. This punch is often used to transfer dimensions from a paper pattern directly on the metal. To do this, first place the paper pattern directly on the metal. Then go over the outline of the pattern with the prick punch, tapping it lightly with a small hammer and making slight indentations on the metal at the major points on the drawing. These indentations can then be used as reference marks for cutting the metal.

A prick punch should never be struck a heavy blow with a hammer because it may bend the punch or cause excessive damage to the material being worked.

Center Punch

A center punch creates indentations in metal which are necessary to hold the point of a twist drill when first starting to drill a hole. It should never be struck with enough force to dimple the material around the indentation or to cause the metal to protrude through the other side of the sheet. A center punch has a heavier body than a prick punch and is ground to a point with an angle of about 60 degrees.

Never use a prick punch or center punch to remove objects from holes, because the point of the punch will spread the object and cause it to bind even more.

Starting Punch

The starting punch, which is often called a drive or tapered punch, is used for driving out damaged rivets, pins, and bolts which sometimes bind in holes. The drive punch is therefore made with a flat face instead of a point. The size of the punch is determined by the width of the face, which is usually $1/8$ to $1/4$ inch.

Pin Punch

Pin punches, often called drift punches, are similar to drive punches and are used for the same purposes. The difference in the two is that the sides of a drive punch taper all the way to the face while the pin punch has a straight shank. Pin punches are sized by the diameter of the face, in thirty-seconds of an inch, and range from 1/16 to 3/8 inch in diameter.

Transfer Punch

The transfer punch is usually about 4 inches long. It has a point that tapers, then turns straight for a short distance in order to fit a drill-locating hole in a template. The tip has a point similar to that of a prick punch. As its name implies, the transfer punch is used to transfer the location of holes through the template or pattern to the material.

Section 3

Holding Tools

Pliers

There are several types of pliers, but those used most frequently in aircraft repair work are the diagonal, adjustable combination, needlenose, and duckbill. The size of pliers indicates their overall length, usually ranging from five to twelve inches.

Slip-Joint

The six-inch slip-joint pliers, Figure 3-3-1A, is the preferred size for use in repair work. The slip-joint permits the jaws to be opened wider at the hinge for gripping objects with large diameters. Slip-joint pliers come in sizes from five to ten inches. The better grades are drop-forged steel.

Slip-joint pliers or water pump pliers should not be used to install or remove cannon plugs. The jaws are not contoured to fit the cannon plug and will cause damage to the plug.

Water Pump

Water pump pliers, Figure 3-3-1B, are slip-joint pliers with the jaws set at an angle to the handles. These are used to grasp packing nuts, pipe, and odd shaped parts.

Self-Locking (Vise Grip®)

Self-locking pliers, Figure 3-3-1C, when properly used, are an excellent holding tool. Do not use self-locking pliers to remove or install hardware. Self-locking pliers are a holding tool and

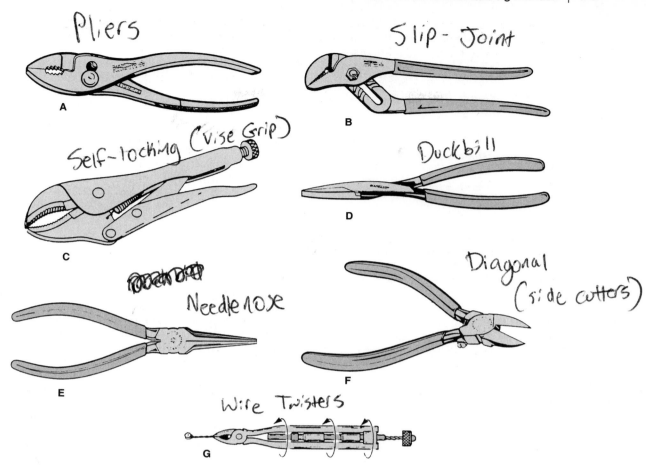

Figure 3-3-1. Pliers

should be used as such. The self-locking pliers has one stationary and one movable jaw. The movable jaw is adjusted by a screw in the base of the stationary handle. By turning the adjustable screw, the amount of clearance between the jaws can be changed. When the self-locking pliers closes, it also locks. This allows two pieces of material to be held tightly together. To open the self-locking pliers, pull up on the small handle inside the movable handle.

Duckbill

Duckbill pliers, Figure 3-3-1D, resemble a duck's bill in that the jaws are thin, flat, and shaped like a duck's bill. They are used exclusively for twisting safety wire.

Needlenose

Needlenose pliers, Figure 3-3-1E, have half-round jaws of varying lengths. They are used to hold objects and make adjustments in tight places.

Diagonal (Side Cutters)

Diagonal pliers, Figure 3-3-1F, are usually referred to as diagonals or dikes. The diagonal is a short-jawed cutter with a blade set at a slight angle on each jaw. This tool can be used to cut wire, rivets, small screws, or cotter pins, besides being practically indispensable in removing or installing safety wire. The duckbill pliers and the diagonal cutting pliers are used extensively in aviation for the job of safety wiring.

Wire Twisters

This is a special type of pliers used to twist safety wire, Figure 3-3-1G. These pliers hold, twist, and cut safety wire. They are used to reduce the time it takes to safety nuts, bolts, or cannon plugs. The wire is held in the serrated jaws and locked in place with a slide lock located between the handles. As the handle is pulled, the pliers rotate about a spiral rod. This motion twists the wire. Squeezing the handles together will release the lock. Care must be used not to stress the safety wire when using this type of pliers.

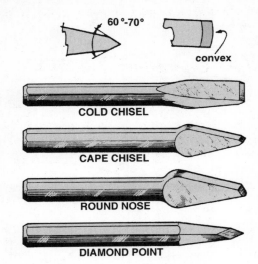

Figure 3-4-1. Chisels

Section 4

Cutting Tools

Chisels

A chisel is a hard steel cutting tool which can be used for cutting and chipping any metal softer than the chisel itself. It can be used in restricted areas and for such work as shearing rivets, or splitting seized or damaged nuts from bolts (Figure 3-4-1).

Chisels are usually made of eight-sided tool steel bar stock, carefully hardened and tempered. Since the cutting edge is slightly convex, the center portion receives the greatest shock when cutting, and the weaker corners are protected. The cutting angle should be 60° to 70° for general use, such as for cutting wire, strap iron, or small bars and rods.

When using a chisel, hold it firmly in one hand. With the other hand, strike the chisel head squarely with a ball-peen hammer.

The size of a flat cold chisel is determined by the width of the cutting edge. Lengths will vary, but chisels are seldom under 5 inches or over 8 inches long.

When cutting square corners or slots, a special cold chisel called a cape chisel should be used. It is like a flat chisel except the cutting edge is very narrow. It has the same cutting angle and is held and used in the same manner as any other chisel.

The diamond point chisel is tapered square at the cutting end, then ground at an angle to provide the sharp diamond point. It is used for cutting V-grooves and inside sharp angles.

Files

Most files are made of high-grade tool steels that are hardened and tempered. Files are manufactured in a variety of shapes and sizes. They are known either by the cross section, the general shape, or by their particular use. The cuts of files must be considered when selecting them for various types of work and materials.

Files are used to square ends, file rounded corners, remove burrs and slivers from metal, straighten uneven edges, file holes and slots, and smooth rough edges.

Files have three distinguishing features: (a) their length, measured exclusive of the tang (Figure 3-4-2), (b) their kind or name, which has reference to the relative coarseness of the teeth, and (c) their cut.

Mill Files

These are usually tapered slightly in thickness and in width for about one-third of their length. The teeth are ordinarily single-cut. These files are used for drawfiling and to some extent for filing soft metals (see Figure 3-4-3).

Hand Files

These are parallel in width and tapered in thickness. They have one safe edge (smooth edge) which permits filing in corners, and

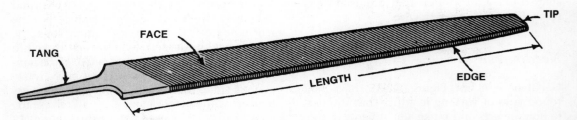

Figure 3-4-2. Hand file

on other work where a safe edge is required. Hand files are double-cut and used principally for finishing flat surfaces and similar work (see Figure 3-4-3).

Half-Round Files

These files cut on both the flat and round sides. They may be single- or double-cut. Their shape permits them to be used where other files would be unsatisfactory (see Figure 3-4-3).

Triangular and Three-Square Files

These files are triangular in cross section. Triangular files are single-cut and are used for filing the gullet between saw teeth. Three-square files, which are double-cut, may be used for filing internal angles, clearing out corners, or filing taps and cutters (see Figure 3-4-3).

Knife File

While the working faces of other flat files are parallel to each other, the knife file is a type of flat file whose faces are not parallel. The faces of a knife file are set at an angle so that they meet at one edge, similar to the way a knife blade is designed. By having one very narrow edge, tool and die makers, among others, are able to do work involving acute angles (see Figure 3-4-3).

Round or Rattail Files

These are circular in cross section and may be either tapered or blunt and single- or double-cut. They are used principally for filing circular openings or concave surfaces (see Figure 3-4-3).

Wood File

Same section as flat and half round files. They have coarser teeth and are especially adapt-

able for use on wood. Commonly called wood rasps.

Vixen (Curved-Tooth Files)

Curved-tooth files are especially designed for rapid filing and smooth finish on soft metals or wood. The regular cut is adapted for tough work on cast iron, soft steel, copper, brass, aluminum, wood, slate, marble, fiber, rubber, etc. The fine cut gives excellent results on steel, cast iron, phosphor bronze, white brass, and all hard metals. The smooth cut is used where the amount of material to be removed is very slight, but where a superior finish is desired. In the automotive trade a vixen file is called a body file (see Figure 3-4-3).

The length of files and rasps is found by measuring from the tip to the heel of the file. The tang is never included in the length.

Cut of files refers to both the character of the teeth or the coarseness; rough, coarse, or bastard for use on heavier classes of work and second cut, smooth, or dead smooth for finishing work. Files are usually made in two types of cuts, single-cut or double-cut.

The single-cut file has a single row of teeth extending across the face at an angle of 65° to 85° with the length of the file. The size of the cuts depends on the coarseness of the file.

The double-cut file has two rows of teeth which cross each other. For general work, the angle of the first row is 40° to 45°. The first row is generally referred to as overcut, and the second row as upcut; the upcut is somewhat finer and not so deep as the overcut.

Care and Use of Files

There are several precautions that any good craftsman will take in caring for files.

- Choose the right file for the material and work to be performed.

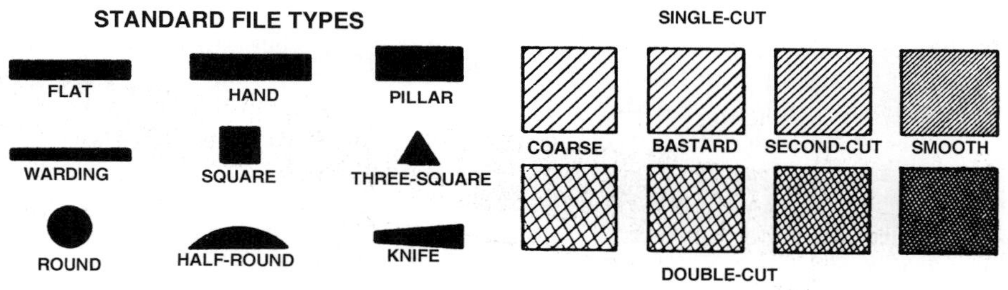

STANDARD FILE TYPES

FLAT HAND PILLAR

WARDING SQUARE THREE-SQUARE

ROUND HALF-ROUND KNIFE

SINGLE-CUT

COARSE BASTARD SECOND-CUT SMOOTH

DOUBLE-CUT

Figure 3-4-3. File Types

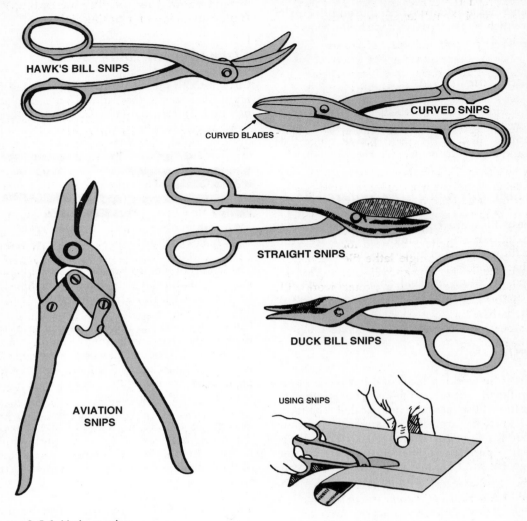

Figure 3-5-1. Various snips

- Keep all files racked and separated so they do not bear against each other.

- Keep the files in a dry place. Rust will corrode the teeth points.

- Keep files clean. Tap the end of the file against the bench after every few strokes, to loosen and clear the filings. Use a file card to keep files clean; a dirty file is a dull file.

The following methods are recommended for using files.

Crossfiling. Before attempting to use a file, place a handle on the tang of the file. This is essential for proper guiding and safe use. In moving the file endwise across the work (commonly known as crossfiling), grasp the handle so that its end fits into and against the fleshy part of the palm with the thumb lying along the top of the handle in a lengthwise direction. Grasp the end of the file between the thumb and first two fingers. To prevent undue

wear, relieve the pressure during the return stroke.

Drawfiling. A file is sometimes used by grasping it at each end, crosswise to the work, then moving it lengthwise with the work. When done properly, work may be finished somewhat finer than when crossfiling with the same file. In drawfiling, the teeth of the file produce a shearing effect. To accomplish this shearing effect, the angle at which the file is held with respect to its line of movement varies with different files, depending on the angle at which the teeth are cut. Pressure should be relieved during the backstroke.

Rounding corners. The method used in filing a rounded surface depends upon its width and the radius of the rounded surface. If the surface is narrow or only a portion of a surface is to be rounded, start the forward stroke of the file with the point of the file inclined downward at approximately a 45° angle. Using a rocking chair motion, finish the stroke with the heel of the file near the curved surface. This method allows use of the full length of the file.

Removing burred or slivered edges. Practically every cutting operation on sheet metal produces burrs or slivers. These must be removed to avoid personal injury and to prevent scratching and marring of parts to be assembled. Burrs and slivers will prevent parts from fitting properly and should always be removed from the work as a matter of habit.

Lathe filing. This method requires that the file be held against the work revolving in the lathe. The file should not be held rigid or stationary but should be stroked constantly with a slight gliding or lateral motion along the work. A standard mill file may be used for this operation, but the long angle lathe file provides a much cleaner shearing and self-clearing action. Use a file with safe edges to protect work with shoulders from being marred. Performed properly, lathe filing can be very accurate. It can also be very dangerous for the person wearing loose clothing.

Section 5

Hand Snips

There are several kinds of hand snips, each of which serves a different purpose. Straight, curved, hawksbill, and aviation snips are in common use (see Figure 3-5-1). Straight snips are used for cutting straight lines when the distance is not great enough to use a squaring shear and for cutting the outside of a curve. The other types are used for cutting the inside of curves or radii. Snips should never be used to cut heavy sheet metal.

Aviation Snips (Dutchmen)

Aviation snips are designed especially for cutting heat-treated aluminum alloy and stainless steel. They are also adaptable for enlarging small holes. The blades have small teeth on the cutting edges and are shaped for cutting very small circles and irregular outlines. The handles are the compound leverage type, making it possible to cut material as thick as 0.051 inch. Aviation snips are available in three types, those which cut from right to left, those which cut from left to right, and those designed to cut straight. Styles with offset handles are also available.

The handles of aviation snips are color coded for easy recognition: yellow handles are for straight cutting, red handles for cutting left, and green handles for cutting right.

Tin Snips

Available is many sizes, tin snips make clean cuts that do not need as much clean up before use as cuts made with aviation snips. They are best for straight cuts in metal within their capacity. Tin snips have the additional advantage of being able to be sharpened with a good mill file and a whetstone. This greatly extends their useful life.

Unlike the hacksaw, snips do not remove any material when the cut is made, but minute fractures often occur along the cut. Therefore, cuts should be made about one thirty-second inch from the layout line and finished by hand-filing down to the line. This is especially true of aviation snips with their serrated cutting edge. Metal cut with aviation snips cannot be used as cut. The cut edge must be cleaned up first.

With all snips, do not cut to the end of the blade. Doing so will surely produce a crack and a tear in the metal where the end of the blade stops cutting. Many times this can be enough to require scrapping the part you are forming.

Section 6

Wood Saws

Saws are tools with thin, flat blades with a row of teeth along one edge. Saws are made for various uses and come in many sizes. There are two general types of saws; those that cut wood and those that cut metal.

The most common types of wood saws are the crosscut and the rip saw. There are other types for special purposes, like the back-saw and the keyhole saw.

The rip saw, Figure 3-6-1A shows the tooth arrangement. This type of tooth arrangement is used to cut wood with the grain.

The crosscut and rip refer to the arrangement of the teeth on the edge of the saw. Figure 3-6-1B shows the tooth arrangement for a crosscut saw. This saw is used to cut across the grain.

The backsaw, Figure 3-6-2, has a straight blade with the top edge reinforced with a metal strip or cap to keep the blade from flexing. This saw

A

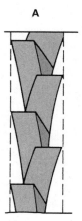

B

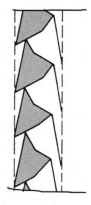

Figure 3-6-1. Saw tooth arrangement

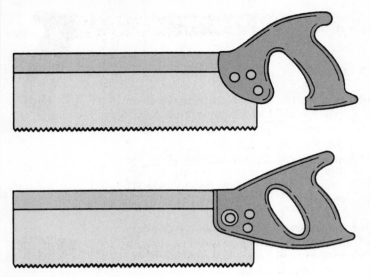

Figure 3-6-2. Backsaws

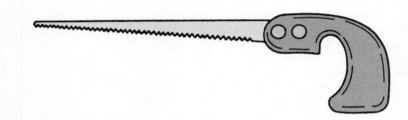

Figure 3-6-3. Keyhole saw

is used to cut straight cuts and is also used in conjunction with a miter box to cut angles.

The keyhole saw, Figure 3-6-3, has a highly tapered blade. The point of the blade is small enough to fit into a $1/4$-inch hole. This makes the keyhole saw excellent for use in close quarters.

Section 7

Metal Saws

The common hacksaw has a blade, a frame, and a handle. The handle can be obtained in two styles, pistol grip and straight (Figure 3-7-1).

Hacksaw blades have holes in both ends; they are mounted on pins attached to the frame. When installing a blade in a hacksaw frame, mount the blade with the teeth pointing forward, away from the handle.

Blades are made of high-grade tool steel or tungsten steel and are available in sizes from

6 to 16 inches in length. The 10-inch blade is most commonly used. There are two types, the all-hard blade and the flexible blade. In flexible blades, only the teeth are hardened. Selection of the best blade for the job involves finding the right type and pitch. An all-hard blade is best for sawing brass, tool steel, cast iron, or heavy cross-section materials. A flexible blade is usually best for sawing hollow shapes or metals having a thin cross section.

The pitch of a blade indicates the number of teeth per inch. Pitches of 14, 18, 24, and 32 teeth per inch are available. A blade with 14 teeth per inch is preferred when cutting machine steel, cold-rolled steel, or structural steel. A blade with 18 teeth per inch is preferred for solid stock aluminum, bearing metal, tool steel, or cast iron. Use a blade with 24 teeth per inch when cutting thick-walled tubing, pipe, brass, copper, channel, or angle iron. Use a 32-teeth-per-inch blade for cutting thin-walled tubing or sheet metal.

When using a hacksaw, observe the following procedures:

1. Select an appropriate saw blade for the job.

2. Assemble the blade in the frame so that the cutting edge of the teeth points away from the handle.

3. Adjust tension of the blade in the frame to prevent the saw from buckling and drifting.

4. Clamp the work in the vise in such a way that will provide as much bearing surface as possible and will engage the greatest number of teeth.

5. Indicate the starting point by nicking the surface with the edge of a file to break any sharp corner that might strip the teeth. This mark will also aid in starting the saw at the proper place.

6. Hold the saw at an angle that will keep at least two teeth in contact with the work at all times. Start the cut with a light, steady, forward stroke just outside the cutting line. At the end of the stroke, relieve the pressure and draw the blade back. The cut is made on the forward stroke.

7. After the first few strokes, make each stroke as long as the hacksaw frame will allow. This will prevent the blade from overheating. Apply just enough pressure on the forward stroke to cause each tooth to remove a small amount of metal. The strokes should be long and steady with a speed not more than 40 to 50 strokes per minute.

Section 8

Drills

There are generally four types of portable drills used in aviation for holding and turning twist drills. Three of these are hand drills.

Hand Drills

Holes $1/4$ inch in diameter and under can be drilled using a hand drill. This drill is commonly called an egg beater. The breast drill is designed to hold larger size twist drills than the hand drill. In addition, a breastplate is affixed at the upper end of the drill to permit the use of body weight to increase the cutting power of the drill. The most common of the hand drills is t he carpenters brace and bit that uses a square shanked bit.

Drill Motors

Electric and pneumatic drill motors make up the forth kind of portable drill. They are available in various shapes and sizes to satisfy almost any requirement. Pneumatic drill motors are preferred for use around flammable materials, since sparks from an electric drill are a fire or explosion hazard.

Wood Bits

There are a number of woodworking bits that are used in aviation maintenance.

Auger bits are the most generally used bits. The two types of auger bits are the Jennings and the solid center bit.

The Jennings bit, Figure 3-8-1A, is a double-spiral design which allows for easier chip removal and leaves a cleaner hole.

The solid center bit, Figure 3-8-1B, has a single spiral and is a stiffer bit. This bit is used in drilling deep holes and in wood with wavy grain.

The spade bit, Figure 3-8-1C, costs less than the auger bits. The spade bit has a tapered pilot to help keep the cutting edge centered in the hole.

An expansion bit, Figure 3-8-1D, is used to drill larger diameter holes. The adjustment in the radius of the hole is accomplished by lengthening or shortening the cutting arm. A centering pilot helps keep the bit straight as it cuts.

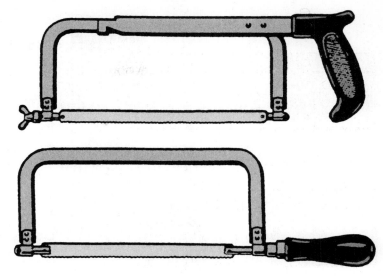

Figure 3-7-1. Hacksaws

The Forstner bit, Figure 3-8-1E, is used in drilling shallow, flat bottomed holes. This bit must be located carefully on the work and then tapped lightly into the work before starting to drill.

Twist Drills

A twist drill is a pointed tool that is rotated to cut holes in material. It is made of a cylindrical hardened steel bar having spiral flutes (grooves) running the length of the body, and a conical point with cutting edges formed by the ends of the flutes.

The principal parts of a twist drill are the shank, the body, and the point, illustrated in

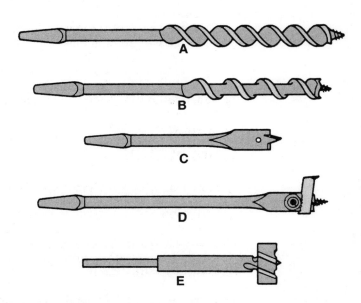

Figure 3-8-1. Wood bits

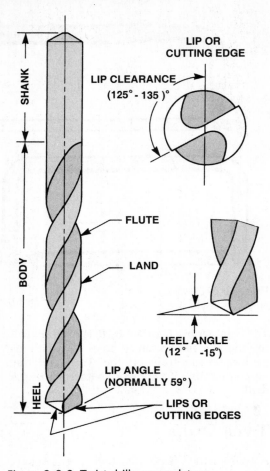

Figure 3-8-2. Twist drill nomenclature

Figure 3-8-2. The diameter of a twist drill may be given in one of four ways: by fractions, letters, numbers, or metric. Fractionally, they are classified by sixteenths of an inch (from $1/16$ to $3^1/_2$ inch), by thirty-seconds (from $1/32$ to $2^1/_2$ inch), or by sixty-fourths (from $1/64$ to $1^1/4$ inch). For a more exact measurement a letter system is used with decimal equivalents: A (0.234 inch) to Z (0.413 inch). The number system of classification is most accurate: No. 80 (0.0314 inch) to No. 1 (0.228 inch). Metric drills are available numbered by their actual size in millimeters, or decimals thereof. Drill sizes and their decimal equivalents are shown in Table 3-8-1.

Types of Drills

Drills come in different types according to the usage. Most are available in all materials and with all points.

A standard commercial drill is called a jobber length drill. When you go to the hardware store and buy a drill, this is what you will get.

A taper length drill is a bit longer than a jobber drill and has a longer shank. This gives more

material for the drill motor chuck to grip. The web thickness is greater for increased deep hole strength.

A stub screw machine drill is designed for machine drilling, but is useful for flat sheet drilling. Being half as long as a jobber drill, they are stiffer in comparison to their length. This gives less flexing and reduced chatter. They are more difficult to hold vertical when used in a hand held drill motor.

Aircraft extension drills are available in many lengths, with 6 inch and 12 inch being the most common. They are made from high speed steel (HHS) and are relatively expensive. They are normally used with a drill guide made from a piece of tubing that is held with the free hand. Used unsupported, there is a tendency to whip.

Material Content

Drills are made from various materials according to their intended use.

Carbon steel is not used much in quality drills. Their are generally prone to breakage and will lose their temper rapidly if not cooled with a cutting fluid. Carbon steel will, however, hold a sharper edge that other alloys. It will also lose the edge quicker. Most carbon steel drills are bright polished metal. When blued, the finish will again be bright.

High Speed Steel (HSS) is the most common material used for drills. HSS has good strength and heat tolerance along with a reasonable cost. Most HSS drills are finished in a standard blue (not bright) and are marked HSS or HS on the shank.

Cobalt drills are colored gold and are more expensive. They are also more heat tolerant and work better for corrosion resistant and hard to drill metals. They are normally available in jobber length.

Drills are also available made from, or tipped with, carbide. A carbide drill is used for very hard or abrasive materials. They are expensive, but will cut most metals. While carbide drills can tolerate extreme heat, they cannot tolerate rough usage and very little side pressure. Carbide will break very easily when used in a hand held drill motor.

Drill Shank

The drill shank is the end that fits into the chuck of a hand or power drill. The three shank shapes most commonly used in hand drills are the straight, tapered, and the square or bit stock

MM	Decimal	Fraction	No. or Letter	MM	Decimal	Fraction	No. or Letter	MM	Decimal	Fraction	No. or Letter
0.1	0.0039	-	-	1.4	0.0551	-	-	3.1	0.1220	-	-
0.15	0.0059	-	-	1.45	0.0570	-	-	3.18	0.1250	1/8	-
0.2	0.0079	-	-	1.5	0.0591	-	-	3.2	0.1260	-	-
0.25	0.0098	-	-	-	0.0595	-	53	3.25	0.1279	-	-
0.3	0.0118	-	-	1.55	0.0610	-	-	-	0.1285	-	30
-	0.0135	-	80	1.59	0.0625	1/16	-	3.3	0.1299	-	-
0.35	0.0138	-	-	1.6	0.0629	-	-	3.4	0.1338	-	-
-	0.0145	-	79	-	0.0635	-	52	-	0.1360	-	29
0.39	0.0156	1/64	-	1.65	0.0649	-	-	3.5	0.1378	-	-
0.4	0.0157	-	-	1.7	0.0669	-	-	-	.01405	-	28
-	0.0160	-	78	-	0.0670	-	51	3.57	0.1406	9/64	-
0.45	0.0177	-	-	1.75	0.0689	-	-	3.6	0.1417	-	-
-	0.0180	-	77	-	0.0700	-	50	-	0.1440	-	27
0.5	0.0197	-	-	1.8	0.0709	-	-	3.7	0.1457	-	-
-	0.0200	-	76	1.85	0.0728	-	-	-	0.1470	-	26
-	0.0210	-	75	-	0.0730	-	49	3.75	0.1476	-	-
0.55	0.0217	-	-	1.9	0.0748	-	-	-	0.1495	-	25
-	0.0225	-	74	-	0.0760	-	48	3.8	0.1496	-	-
0.6	0.0236	-	-	1.95	0.0767	-	-	-	0.1520	-	24
-	0.0240	-	73	1.98	0.0781	5/64	-	3.9	0.1535	-	-
-	0.0250	-	72	-	0.0785	-	47	-	0.1540	-	23
0.65	0.0256	-	-	2.0	0.0787	-	-	3.97	0.1562	5/32	-
-	0.0260	-	71	2.05	0.0807	-	-	-	0.1570	-	22
-	0.0280	-	70	-	0.0810	-	46	4.0	0.1575	-	-
0.7	0.0276	-	-	-	0.0820	-	45	-	0.1590	-	21
-	0.0292	-	69	2.1	0.0827	-	-	-	0.1610	-	20
0.75	0.0295	-	-	2.15	0.0846	-	-	4.1	0.1614	-	-
-	0.0310	-	68	-	0.0860	-	44	4.2	0.1654	-	-
0.79	0.0312	1/32	-	2.2	0.0866	-	-	-	0.1660	-	19
0.8	0.0315	-	-	2.25	0.0885	-	-	4.25	0.1673	-	-
-	0.0320	-	67	-	0.0890	-	43	4.3	0.1693	-	-
-	0.0330	-	66	2.3	0.0905	-	-	-	0.1695	-	18
0.85	0.0335	-	-	2.35	0.0925	-	-	4.37	0.1719	11/64	-
-	0.0350	-	65	-	0.0935	-	42	-	0.1730	-	17
0.9	0.0354	-	-	2.38	0.0937	3/32	-	4.4	0.1732	-	-
-	0.0360	-	64	2.4	0.0945	-	-	-	0.1770	-	16
-	0.0370	-	63	-	0.0960	-	41	4.5	0.1771	-	-
0.95	0.0374	-	-	2.45	0.0964	-	-	-	0.1800	-	15
-	0.0380	-	62	-	0.0980	-	40	4.6	0.1811	-	-
-	0.0390	-	61	2.5	0.0984	-	-	-	0.1820	-	14
1.0	0.0394	-	-	-	0.0995	-	39	4.7	0.1850	-	13
-	0.0400	-	60	-	0.1015	-	38	4.75	0.1870	-	-
-	0.0410	-	59	2.6	0.1024	-	-	4.76	0.1875	3/16	-
1.05	0.0413	-	-	-	0.1040	-	37	4.8	0.1890	-	12
-	0.0420	-	58	2.7	0.1063	-	-	-	0.1910	-	11
-	0.0430	-	57	-	0.1065	-	36	4.9	0.1929	-	-
1.1	0.0433	-	-	2.75	0.1082	-	-	-	0.1935	-	10
1.15	0.0452	-	-	2.78	0.1094	7/64	-	-	0.1960	-	9
-	0.0465	-	56	-	0.1100	-	35	5.0	0.1968	-	-
1.19	0.0469	3/64	-	2.8	0.1102	-	-	-	0.1990	-	8
1.2	0.0472	-	-	-	0.1110	-	34	5.1	0.2008	-	-
1.25	0.0492	-	-	-	0.1130	-	33	-	0.2010	-	7
1.3	0.0512	-	-	2.9	0.1141	-	-	5.16	0.2031	13/64	-
-	0.0520	-	55	-	0.1160	-	32	-	0.2040	-	6
1.35	0.0531	-	-	3.0	0.1181	-	-	5.2	0.2047	-	-
-	0.0550	-	54	-	0.1200	-	31	-	0.2055	-	5

Table 3-8-1A. Twist drill sizes

MM	Decimal	Fraction	No. or Letter
5.25	0.2067	-	-
5.3	0.2086	-	-
-	0.2090	-	4
5.4	0.2126	-	-
-	0.2130	-	3
5.5	0.2165	-	-
5.56	0.2187	1/32	-
5.6	0.2205	-	-
-	0.2210	-	2
5.7	0.2244	-	-
5.75	0.2263	-	-
-	0.2280	-	1
5.8	0.2383	-	-
5.9	0.2323	-	-
-	0.2340	-	A
5.95	0.2344	15/64	-
6.0	0.2362	-	-
-	0.2380	-	B
6.1	0.2401	-	-
-	0.2420	-	C
6.2	0.2441	-	-
6.25	0.2460	-	D
6.3	0.2480	-	-
6.35	0.2500	1/4	E
6.4	0.2520	-	-
6.5	0.2559	-	-
-	0.2570	-	F
6.6	0.2598	-	-
-	0.2610	-	G
6.7	0.2638	-	-
6.75	0.2657	17/64	-
6.75	0.2657	-	-
-	0.2660	-	H
6.8	0.2677	-	-
6.9	0.2716	-	-
-	0.2720	-	I
7.0	0.2756	-	-
-	0.2770	-	J
7.1	0.2795	-	-
-	0.2811	-	K
7.14	0.2812	9/32	-
7.2	0.2835	-	-
7.25	0.2854	-	-
7.3	0.2874	-	-
-	0.2900	-	L
7.4	0.2913	-	-
-	0.2950	-	M
7.5	0.2953	-	-
7.54	0.2968	19/64	-
7.6	0.2992	-	-
-	0.3020	-	N
7.7	0.3031	-	-
7.75	0.3051	-	-
7.8	0.3071	-	-
7.9	0.3110	-	-
7.94	0.3125	5/16	-
8.0	0.3150	-	-
-	0.3160	-	O
8.1	0.3189	-	-
8.2	0.3228	-	-
-	0.2330	-	P
8.25	0.3248	-	-
8.3	0.3268	-	-
8.33	0.3281	21/64	-
8.4	0.3307	-	-
-	0.3320	-	Q
8.5	0.3346	-	-
8.6	0.3386	-	-
-	0.3390	-	R
8.7	0.3425	-	-
8.73	0.3437	11/32	-
8.75	0.3445	-	-
8.8	0.3465	-	-
-	0.3480	-	-
8.9	0.3504	-	-
9.0	0.3543	-	-
-	0.3580	-	T
9.1	0.3583	-	-
9.13	0.3594	23/64	-
9.2	0.3622	-	-
9.25	0.3641	-	-
9.3	0.3661	-	-
-	0.3680	-	U
9.4	0.3701	-	-
9.5	0.3740	-	-
9.53	0.3750	3/8	-
-	0.3770	-	V
9.6	0.3780	-	-
9.7	0.3819	-	-
9.75	0.3838	-	-
9.8	0.3858	-	-
-	0.3860	-	W
9.9	0.3898	-	-
9.92	0.3906	25/64	-
10.0	0.3937	-	-
-	0.3970	-	X
-	0.4040	-	Y
10.32	0.4062	13/32	-
-	0.4130	-	Z
10.5	0.4134	-	-
10.72	0.4219	27/64	-
11.0	0.4330	-	-
11.11	0.4375	7/16	-
11.5	0.4528	-	-
11.51	0.4531	29/64	-
11.91	0.4687	15/32	-
12.0	0.4724	-	-
12.30	0.4843	31/64	-
12.5	0.4921	-	-
12.7	0.5000	1/2	-
13.0	0.5118	-	-
13.10	0.5156	33/64	-
13.49	0.5312	17/32	-
13.5	0.5315	-	-
13.89	0.5469	35/64	-
14.0	0.5512	-	-
14.29	0.5625	9/16	-
14.5	0.5709	-	-
14.68	0.5781	37/64	-
15.0	0.5906	-	-
15.08	0.5937	19/32	-
15.48	0.6094	39/64	-
15.5	0.6102	-	-
15.88	0.6250	5/8	-
16.0	0.6299	-	-
16.27	0.6406	41/64	-
16.5	0.6496	-	-
16.67	0.6562	21/32	-
17.0	0.6693	-	-
17.06	0.6719	43/64	-
17.46	0.6875	11/16	-
17.5	0.6890	-	-
17.86	0.7031	45/64	-
18.0	0.7087	-	-
18.26	0.7187	23/32	-
18.5	0.7283	-	-
18.65	0.7344	47/64	-
19.0	0.7480	-	-
19.05	0.7500	3/4	-
19.45	0.7656	49/64	-
19.5	0.7677	-	-
19.84	0.7812	25/32	-
20.0	0.7874	-	-
20.24	0.7969	51/64	-
20.5	0.8071	-	-
20.64	0.8125	13/16	-
21.0	0.8268	-	-
21.03	0.8281	53/64	-
21.43	0.8437	27/32	-
21.5	0.8465	-	-
21.83	0.8594	55/64	-
22.0	0.8661	-	-
22.23	0.8750	7/8	-
22.5	0.8858	-	-
22.62	0.8906	57/64	-
23.0	0.9055	-	-
23.02	0.9062	29/32	-
23.42	0.9219	59/64	-
23.5	0.9252	-	-
23.81	0.9375	15/16	-
24.0	0.9449	-	-
24.21	0.9531	61/64	-
24.5	0.9646	-	-
24.61	0.9687	31/32	-
25.0	0.9843	-	-
25.03	0.9844	63/64	-
25.4	1.000	1	-

Table 3-8-1B. Twist drill sizes

shank (Figure 3-8-3). The straight shank generally is used in hand, breast, or portable electric drills; the square shank is made to fit into a carpenter's brace. Tapered shanks generally are used in machine shop drill presses. A drill with a reduced size shank is called a Silver and Deming drill. It will allow a larger drill to fit in a smaller chuck.

Drill Body

The metal column forming the core of the drill is the body. The body clearance area lies just back of the margin, slightly smaller in diameter than the margin, to reduce the friction between the drill and the sides of the hole. Always make sure the body is held tightly in the chuck of the drill motor or drill press. Any slippage while drilling will scar the body and make accurate centering in the chuck difficult, if not impossible.

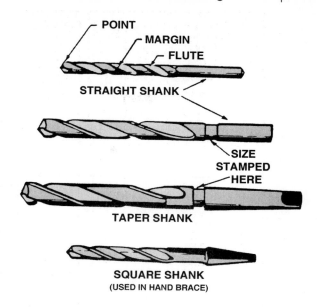

Figure 3-8-3. Twist drill shanks

Drill Points

The angle at which the drill point is ground is the lip clearance angle. On standard drills used to cut steel and cast iron, the angle should be 59 degrees from the axis of the drill. This is an included angle of 118 degrees.

For soft materials the most common included angle is 90 degrees. This angle works good for copper, lead, pure nickel, and material of this type. It does not advance rapidly and produces a stringly chip. A 90-degree included angle will also produce more burrs on the back side of a hole.

For hard or tough material, including aluminum alloy sheet metal, an included angle of 135 degrees is good. This angle has a shorter, stronger, lip and will advance rapidly. A drawback to a 135-degree point is it's tendency to walk across the work instead of starting to drill quickly and cleanly. This makes the use of a center punch mandatory. 135-degree points also leave a smaller burr on exiting the material and have a reduced tendency to chatter on exiting the back side. Because of a tendency to clog with chips, this type of drill point should not be used for deep holes.

The most desirable drill for sheet metal is a 135-degree drill point ground with a split point. On a split point the back side if the lip, or heel, has been relief ground to produce a sharper point by thinning the web and thus splitting the size of the point in half. This makes the drill start with less tendency to walk, and less tendency for the heel to drag on the material being drilled. This produces a better hole, faster, and with less heat on the drill point.

Use of Twist Drills

While twist drills may be used to bore through a variety of materials such as soft or hard materials, plastics, or hard rubber, the efficiency of the drill and smoothness of the resultant hole are based on the speed of the drill. Another factor in using a twist drill is whether a hand held manual, electric, or pneumatic drill is used, or if a drill press is used.

Before using a twist drill, determine what material is being drilled. This will affect the material from which the drill is made. It makes no sense to try and drill stainless steel with a carbon bit.

Ensure that the object to be bored is secured. If the twist drill catches on the material, the object being bored will rotate with the drill bit. Objects held by hand that catch on the drill can rip flesh and break bones in fractions of a second. Holding devices for securing objects being bored can be purchased or manufactured, and are an investment in safety.

Make an indentation in the material to be drilled with a center punch. This indentation should be made at the exact point at which the hole is to be drilled. This indentation provides a starting point for the drill, and prevents the bit from moving across the face of the material. Do not use a prick punch as the angle will be incorrect and may still allow the drill to walk. Do not strike the center punch too hard as it can stretch the metal.

Select the proper speed from a drill speed chart, such as the one in Table 3-8-2, based on the size of the drill and material being drilled.

Diameter of Drill	Soft Metals *300 sfpm	Plastic or Hard Rubber *200 sfpm	Annealed Cast Iron *140 sfpm	Mild Steel *100 sfpm	Malleable Iron *90 sfpm	Hard Cast Iron *80 sfpm	Tool Steel *60 sfpm	Cast Alloy Steel *40 sfpm
1/16 (No. 53 to 80)	18320	2217	8554	6111	5500	4889	3667	2445
3/32 (No. 42 to 52)	12212	8142	5702	4071	3666	3258	2442	1649
1/8 (No. 31 to 41)	9160	6112	4278	3056	2750	2445	1833	1222
5/32 (No. 23 to 30)	7328	4888	3420	2444	2198	1954	1465	977
3/16 (No. 13 to 22)	6106	4075	2852	2037	1833	1630	1222	815
7/32 (No. 1 to 12)	5234	3490	2444	1745	1575	1396	1047	698
1/4 (A to E)	4575	3055	2139	1527	1375	1222	917	611
9/32 (G to K)	4071	2712	1900	1356	1222	1084	814	542
9/16 (L, M, N)	3660	2445	1711	1222	1100	978	733	489
11/32 (O to R)	3330	2220	1554	1110	1000	888	666	444
3/8 (S, I, U)	3050	2037	1426	1018	917	815	611	407
13/32 (V to Z)	2818	1878	1316	939	846	752	563	376
7/16	2614	1746	1222	873	786	698	524	349
15/32	2442	1628	1140	814	732	652	488	326
1/2	2287	1528	1070	764	688	611	458	306
9/16	2035	1357	950	678	611	543	407	271
3/8	1830	1222	856	611	550	489	367	244
11/16	1665	1110	777	555	500	444	333	222
3/4	1525	1018	713	509	458	407	306	204

NOTES:

The chart indicates the high range of r.p.m.'s for each drill size.

Figures are for high-speed drills. The speed of carbon drills should be reduced one-half. Use drill speed nearest to figure given.

*sfpm – Surface speed in feet per minute of the outer lip of the drill. The idea is to maintain the sfpm by reducing the drill r.p.m. as the diameter increases.

Table 3-8-2. Drill speeds and feeds

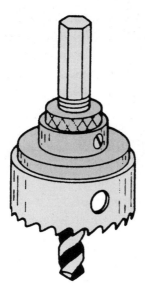

Figure 3-9-1. Hole saw

Figure 3-9-2. Fly cutter

Section 9

Hole Cutters

There are two types of hole cutters used to cut holes in sheet metal. These are the circular hole saw and the fly cutter. Each has its advantages and disadvantages.

The circular hole cutter, Figure 3-9-1, has a pilot drill used to center the hole cutter and provide stability when the circular cutter contacts the sheet metal.

The fly cutter, Figure 3-9-2, is an adjustable hole cutter. The pilot drill provides the same functions as it does on the circular hole cutter. The radius is adjusted by moving the arm with the cutting bit attached. When using this type of cutter, use a drill press with the sheet metal backed by a piece of wood, and feed the bit very slowly into the metal. By reversing the bit in the arm, a bevel can be put on the hole.

Section 10

Countersink

A countersink is a tool which cuts a cone-shaped depression around the hole to allow a rivet or screw to set flush with the surface of the material. Countersinks are made with various angles to correspond to the various angles of the countersunk rivet or screwheads. The

angle of the standard countersink shown in Figure 3-10-1 is 100 degrees. Most commercial countersinks are 82 degrees.

Special stop countersinks are available. Stop countersinks (Figure 3-10-1) are adjustable to any desired depth, and the cutters are interchangeable so that holes of various counter-

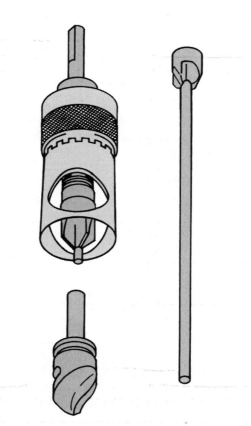

Figure 3-10-1. Countersinks

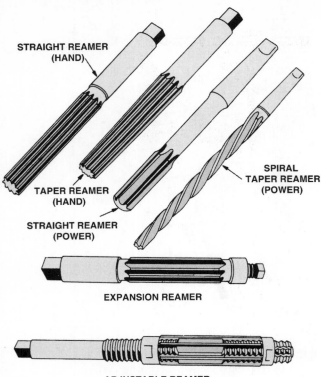

Figure 3-11-1. Reamers

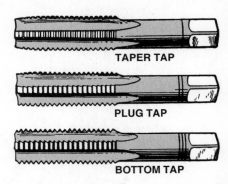

Figure 3-12-1. Hand taps

sunk angles may be made. Some stop countersinks have a micrometer set arrangement (in increments of 0.001 inch) for adjusting the cutting depths.

When using a countersink, care must be taken not to remove an excessive amount of material since this reduces the strength of flush joints.

Section 11

Reamers

Hand reamers have square end shanks so they can be turned with a tap wrench or similar handle. The various types of reamers are illustrated in Figure 3-11-1.

A hole that is to be reamed to exact size must be drilled about 0.003 to 0.007 inches undersize. A cut that removes more than 0.007-inch places too much load on the reamer and should not be attempted.

Reamers are made of either carbon tool steel or high-speed steel. The cutting blades of a high-speed steel reamer lose their original keenness sooner than those of a carbon steel reamer; however, after the first super-keenness is gone, they are still serviceable. The high-speed

reamer usually lasts much longer than the carbon steel type.

Reamer blades are hardened to the point of being brittle and must be handled carefully to avoid chipping them. When reaming a hole, rotate the reamer in the cutting direction only. Turn the reamer steadily and evenly to prevent chattering or marking and scoring of the hole walls.

Reamers are available in any standard size. The straight-fluted reamer is less expensive than the spiral-fluted reamer, but the spiral type has less tendency to chatter. Both types are tapered for a short distance back of the end to aid in starting. Bottoming reamers have no taper and are used to complete the reaming of blind holes.

For general use, an expansion reamer is the most practical. This type is furnished in standard sizes from $1/4$ inch to 1 inch, increasing in diameter by $1/32$ inch increments.

Taper reamers, both hand- and machine-operated, are used to smooth and true tapered holes and recesses.

Pick the type of reamer for the job. The solid straight hole reamer is the most accurate.

If you use the taper, expansion, or adjustable type of reamers, make a number of small cuts, not one big one. Check the hole after each cut. Never force the reamer into a hole.

Section 12

Taps And Dies

A tap is used to cut threads on the inside of a hole, while a die is for cutting external threads

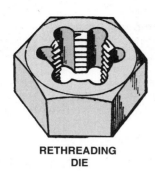

RETHREADING DIE

ROUND ADJUSTABLE DIE

Figure 3-12-2. Dies

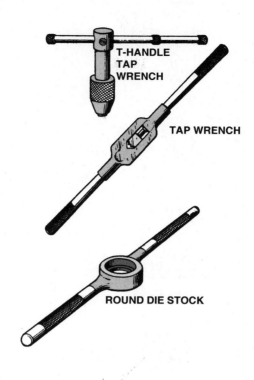

T-HANDLE TAP WRENCH

TAP WRENCH

ROUND DIE STOCK

Figure 3-12-3. Diestock and tap wrenches

on round stock. They are made of hard-tempered steel and ground to an exact size. There are five types of threads that can be cut with standard taps and dies. They are National Coarse, National Fine, National Extra Fine, National Pipe, and metric.

Hand taps are usually provided in sets of three taps for each diameter and thread series. Each set contains a taper tap, a plug tap, and a bottoming tap. The taps in a set are identical in diameter and cross section; the only difference is the amount of taper (Figure 3-12-1).

The taper tap is used to begin the tapping process, because it is chamfered back for 6 to 10 threads. This tap cuts a complete thread when it is cutting above the taper. It is the only tap needed when tapping holes that extend through thin sections. The plug tap supplements the taper tap for tapping holes in thick or hard stock.

The bottoming tap has a one- to two-thread chamfer. It is used to cut full threads to the bottom of a blind hole.

Dies may be classified as solid and as adjustable round split die, or plain round split die (Figure 3-12-2). The adjustable-split die has an adjusting screw that can be tightened so that the die is spread slightly. By adjusting the die, the diameter and fit of the thread can be controlled.

Solid dies are not adjustable; therefore, a variety of thread fits cannot be obtained with this type.

There are many types of wrenches for turning taps, as well as turning dies. The T-handle, the adjustable tap wrench, and the diestock for round split dies shown in Figure 3-12-3 are a few of the more common types.

Taps or dies should never be used without a suitable lubricant. They will have a tendency to grab or tear the material being threaded. Make sure the lubricant is approved for the material being threaded.

Information on thread sizes, fits, types, etc., is shown in Tables 3-12-1 and 3-12-2.

Section 13

Turning Tools

Screwdrivers

The screwdriver may be classified by its shape, type of blade, or blade length. It is made for only one purpose, i.e., for loosening or tightening screws or screwhead bolts. Figure 3-13-1

NATIONAL COURSE THREAD SERIES MEDIUM FIT, CLASS 3 (NC)					NATIONAL FINE THREAD SERIES MEDIUM FIT, CLASS 3 (NF)				
			Tap Drill					Tap Drill	
Size and Threads	Body Diameter	Desired Hole Diameter	Best Hole Diameter	Standard Drill Size	Size and Threads	Body Diameter	Desired Hole Diameter	Best Hole Diameter	Standard Drill Size
					0-80	0.060	52	0.0472	$3/64$
1-64	0.073	47	0.0575	#53	1-72	0.073	47	0.0591	#53
2-56	0.086	42	0.0682	#51	2-64	0.086	42	0.0700	#50
3-48	0.099	37	0.078	$5/64$	3-56	0.099	37	0.0810	#46
4-40	0.112	31	0.0866	#44	4-48	0.112	31	0.0911	#42
5-40	0.125	29	0.0995	#39	5-44	0.125	25	0.1024	#38
6-32	0.138	27	0.1063	#36	6-40	0.138	27	0.113	#33
8-32	0.164	18	0.1324	#29	8-36	0.164	18	0.136	#29
10-24	0.190	10	0.1472	#26	10-32	0.190	10	0.159	#21
12-24	0.216	2	0.1732	#17	12-28	0.216	2	0.180	#15
$1/4$-20	0.250	$1/4$	0.1990	#8	$1/4$-28	0.250	F	0.213	#3
$5/16$-18	0.3125	$5/16$	0.2559	#F	$5/16$-24	0.3125	$5/16$	0.2703	I
$3/8$-16	0.375	$3/8$	0.3110	$5/16$"	$3/8$-24	0.375	$3/8$	0.332	Q
$7/16$-14	0.4375	$7/16$	0.3642	U	$7/16$-20	0.4375	$7/16$	0.386	W
$1/2$-13	0.500	$1/2$	0.4219	$27/64$"	$1/2$-20	0.500	$1/2$	0.449	$7/16$"
$9/16$-12	0.5625	$9/16$	0.4776	$31/64$"	$9/16$-18	0.5625	$9/16$	0.506	$1/2$"
$5/8$-11	0.625	$5/8$	0.5315	$17/32$"	$5/8$-18	0.625	$5/8$	0.568	$9/16$"
$3/4$-10	0.750	$3/4$	0.6480	$41/64$"	$3/4$-16	0.750	$3/4$	0.6688	$11/16$"
$7/8$-9	0.875	$7/8$	0.7307	$49/64$"	$7/8$-14	0.875	$7/8$	0.7822	$51/64$"
1-8	1.000	1	0.8376	$7/8$"	1-14	1.000	1	0.9072	$59/64$"

Table 3-12-1. American (national) screw thread sizes

Nominal Size (In.)	No. of Threads per Inch	Pitch Diameter		Length		Pipe OD D (In.)	Depth of Thread (In.)	Tap Drills for Pipe Threads	
		A (In.)	B (In.)	L2 (In.)	L1 (In.)			Minor Diameter small end	Size drill
$1/8$	27	0.36351	0.37476	0.2638	0.180	0.405	0.02963	0.33388	R
$1/4$	18	0.47739	0.48989	0.4018	0.200	0.540	0.04444	0.43294	$7/16$
$3/8$	18	0.61201	0.62701	0.4078	0.240	0.675	0.04444	0.56757	$37/64$
$1/2$	14	0.75843	0.77843	0.5337	0.320	0.840	0.05714	0.70129	$23/32$
$3/4$	14	0.96768	0.98887	0.5457	0.339	1.050	0.05714	0.91054	$59/64$
1	11 $1/2$	1.21363	1.23863	0.6828	0.400	1.315	0.06957	1.14407	1 $5/32$
1 $1/4$	11 $1/2$	1.55713	1.58338	0.7068	0.420	1.660	0.06957	1.48757	1 $1/2$
1 $1/2$	11 $1/2$	1.79609	1.82234	0.7235	0.402	1.900	0.06957	1.72652	1 $47/64$
2	11 $1/2$	1.26902	2.29627	0.7565	0.436	2.375	0.06957	2.19946	2 $7/32$
2 $1/2$	8	2.71953	2.76216	1.1375	0.682	2.875	0.1000	2.61953	2 $5/8$
3	8	3.34062	3.38850	1.2000	0.766	3.500	0.1000	3.24063	3 $1/4$
3 $1/2$	8	3.83750	3.88881	1.2500	0.821	4.000	0.1000	3.73750	3 $3/4$
4	8	4.33438	4.38712	1.3000	0.844	4.500	0.1000	4.23438	4 $1/4$

Table 3-12-2. American (national) pipe thread dimensions and tap drill sizes

shows several different types of screwdrivers. When using the common screwdriver, select the largest screwdriver whose blade will make a good fit in the screw which is to be turned.

A common screwdriver must fill at least 75 percent of the screw slot. If the screwdriver is the wrong size, it cuts and burrs the screw slot, making it worthless. A screwdriver with the wrong size blade may slip and damage adjacent parts of the structures.

The two types of recessed head screws in common use are the Phillips and the Reed and Prince. Coming into popular usage is the Torx-type recessed screw. Other recessed type screws include the less popular Butterfly, TriWing, and the Posidriv screws.

Both the Phillips and Reed and Prince recessed heads are optional on several types of screws. As shown in Figure 3-13-2, the Reed and Prince recessed head forms a perfect cross. The screwdriver used with this screw is pointed on the end. Since the Phillips screw has a slightly larger center in the cross, the Phillips screwdriver is blunt on the end. The Phillips screwdriver is not interchangeable with the Reed and Prince. The use of the wrong type screwdriver results in mutilation of the screwdriver and the screwhead. When turning a recessed head screw, use only the proper recessed head screwdriver of the correct size.

The Torx screwdriver, used to install and remove Torx-type screws, consists of a six-pointed blade. An example can be seen in Figure 3-13-2A. Care should be taken not to attempt to remove Allen head screws with a Torx screwdriver. While they may at first appear to be the same, they are not. The same is true with the screw. By using an Allen wrench on a Torx screw, or using a Torx screwdriver on an Allen head, something will be destroyed; either the screw head or the Torx screwdriver, or both.

There are a number of specialized types of screwdrivers in use. Among them are the clutch head, better known as the Butterfly, Figure 3-13-2B; the TriWing, Figure 3-13-2C; and the Posidriv, Figure 3-13-2D. All of these screwdrivers provide a tighter connection with the screw.

An offset screwdriver, Figure 3-13-1, may be used when vertical space is limited. Offset screwdrivers are constructed with both ends bent 90° to the shank handle. By using alternate ends, most screws can be seated or loosened even when the swinging space is limited. Offset screwdrivers are made for both standard and recessed head screws.

The ratchet or spiral screwdriver, Figure 3-13-1, is fast acting in that it turns the screw when the

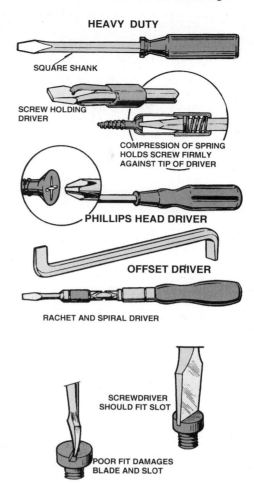

Figure 3-13-1. Screwdrivers

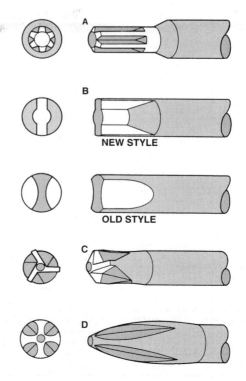

Figure 3-13-2. Specialized screwdrivers

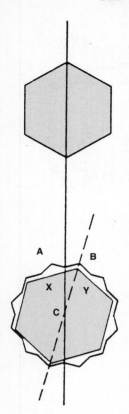

Figure 3-13-3. Box-end wrench use

handle is pulled back and then pushed forward. It can be set to turn the screw either clockwise or counterclockwise, or it can be locked in position and used as a standard screwdriver. The ratchet screwdriver is not a heavy-duty tool and should be used only for light work. A word of caution: When using a spiral or ratchet screwdriver, extreme care must be used to maintain constant pressure and prevent the blade from slipping out from the slot in the screw head. If this occurs, the surrounding structure is subject to damage. The common name for this type of screwdriver is a Yankee screwdriver, after the original manufacturer. Battery powered portable screwdrivers have generally replaced the Yankee screwdriver because of their greater speed and versatility.

Special Use Screwdrivers

There are many special use screwdrivers that have specific applications. A good example is a screwdriver designed to remove difficult or frozen screws from cowling and structural members. Most are designed to be used with power drivers, drill motors, or air hammers. Their use can greatly reduce damage to surrounding parts and make a hard job easy. However, there are times when nothing works and the screw must be drilled out and replaced from scratch.

Wrenches

The wrenches most often used in aircraft maintenance are classified as open-end, box-end, socket, adjustable, or special wrenches. The Allen wrench, although seldom used,

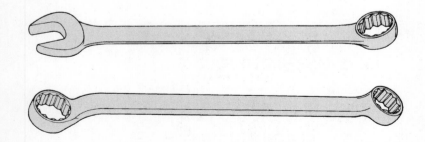

Figure 3-13-4. Box-end and combination wrenches

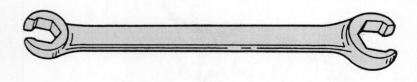

Figure 3-13-5. Flare nut wrench

is required on one special type of recessed screw. One of the most widely used metals for making wrenches is chrome-vanadium steel. Wrenches made of this metal are almost unbreakable.

Open-End

Open-end wrenches are solid, nonadjustable wrenches with open parallel jaws on one or both ends. These wrenches may have their jaws parallel to the handle or at an angle up to 90 degrees; most are set at an angle of 15 degrees. Basically, the wrenches are designed to fit a nut, bolt head, or other object which makes it possible to exert a turning action.

Box-End

Box-end wrenches are popular tools because of their usefulness in close quarters. They are called box wrenches since they box, or completely surround, the nut or bolt head. Practically all box-end wrenches are made with 12 points so they can be used in places having as little as 15-degree swing. In Figure 3-13-3, point A on the illustrated double broached hexagon wrench is nearer the centerline of the head and the wrench handle than point B, and also the center line of nut C. If the wrench is inverted and installed on the six point nut, A will be centered over side Y instead of side X. The centerline of the handle will now be in the dotted line position. It is by reversing (turning the wrench over) the position of the wrench, that a 15-degree arc may be made with the wrench handle. Although box-end wrenches are ideal to break loose tight nuts or pull tight nuts tighter, time is lost turning the nut off the bolt once the nut is broken loose. Only when there is sufficient clearance to rotate the wrench in a complete circle can this tedious process be avoided.

Combination Wrench

After a tight nut is broken loose, it can be completely backed off or unscrewed more quickly with an open-end than with a box-end wrench. In this case, a combination wrench is needed, which has a box-end on one end and an open-end of the same size on the other. Both the box-end and combination wrenches are shown in Figure 3-13-4.

Flare Nut Wrench

The flare nut wrench, Figure 3-13-5, is a thin walled split box wrench used for tightening nuts on tubing. The wrench can be slipped over the tube and moved on to the nut. It is especially useful in the installation and removal of tubing in hydraulic, fuel, and oil systems.

Open and Box-End Racheting Wrenches

The open-end ratchet wrench, Figure 3-13-6A, is an open-end wrench with one jaw partially removed. Enough of the jaw is left to engage the flat surface of the nut or bolt. As the turn is completed on the hardware the wrench can be slipped around to the next flat without removing the wrench. This type of wrench is used in tight places to run down hardware but is not used to apply torque.

The box-end ratchet wrench, Figure 3-13-6B, can be used in small openings where the open-end wrench would normally be used. The racheting allows for faster removal and installation of nuts and bolts. The ratchet works in only one direction. To turn the nut or bolt in the opposite direction, turn over the wrench.

Socket Wrench

A socket wrench is made of two parts: (a) the socket, which is placed over the top of a nut or bolt head, and (b) a handle, which is attached to the socket. Many types of handles, extensions, and attachments are available to

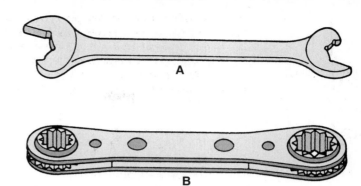

Figure 3-13-6. Open-end and box-end ratchet wrenches

make it possible to use socket wrenches in almost any location or position. Sockets are made with either fixed or detachable handles. Socket wrenches with fixed handles are usually furnished as an accessory to a machine. They have either a 4-, 6- or 12-sided recess to fit a nut or bolt head that needs regular adjustment.

Sockets

A socket wrench is a round metal sleeve with a square drive opening on one end for attaching to a handle and a 6- or 12-point opening on the other for fitting on a nut or bolt. The socket wrench can be a short reach socket or a long reach socket (deep reach), Figure 3-13-7.

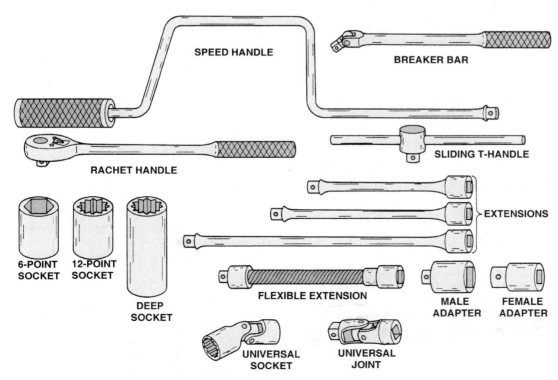

Figure 3-13-7. Socket set

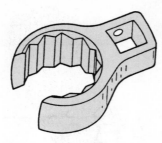

Figure 3-13-8. Crowfoot socket

The square drive end comes in various sizes. Generally in aviation the drive sizes are $1/4$, $3/8$, $1/2$, or $3/4$ inch.

The socket wrench opening comes in various sizes also. Most common are sets starting with $3/8$ inch to 1 inch. The short and deep reach sockets each have their uses when removing nuts or bolts. The short reach socket works well for removing most nuts and bolts.

The deep-reach socket is used when the nut or bolt is recessed, or when the nut is on a bolt with long extended threads. The six or twelve points in the socket wrench allows for gripping the nut or bolt at various angles in relation to the drive end. This allows for a handle to be positioned for the best amount of rotation.

Flex Socket

A newer type of socket is the flex socket. This socket works like the universal. The flex is allowed by the use of a ball and socket attaching the drive end to the socket end. This allows for smoother operation.

Crowfoot Socket

A crowfoot socket, Figure 3-13-8, is an open-end wrench with a square drive attached to the side. The crowfoot socket is used in tight areas where other wrenches cannot be used. They range in size from $3/8$ inch to $2^1/2$ inches.

Handles

There are a number of handles in a socket wrench set. Each handle has its uses. Each handle has a spring loaded ball on the drive end to hold the socket wrench.

Ratchet Handle

The ratchet handle, Figure 3-13-7, allows a socket wrench to turn in both directions. A lever on the ratchet operates a pawl inside of the ratchet head. Pulling on the handle in one direction engages the pawls and turns the socket. Moving the handle in the opposite direction allows the pawls to slide without engaging and the socket wrench does not turn. Moving the lever on the ratchet head to the opposite position will reverse the operation, allowing the socket to rotate in the opposite direction. The ratchet handle can be used to tighten or loosen nuts and bolts.

Hinged Handle

The hinged handle, Figure 3-13-7, has a hinged adapter which will rotate 90 degrees left or right from the handle. To loosen a nut or bolt, place the hinge 90 degrees to the handle and install a socket wrench. In this position the technician has the greatest possible leverage to use in loosening the nut or bolt. After loosening the nut or bolt, rotate the handle above the socket wrench and turn the handle to remove the nut or bolt faster.

Speed Handle

The speed handle, Figure 3-13-7, is used to install or remove nuts or bolts that have little or no torque. The speed handle has a brace type shaft with a square drive on one end and a rotating handle on the other.

Sliding Bar Handle

The sliding bar handle, Figure 3-13-7, is used to increase leverage and to work around other objects. When the bar handle is moved to the end, the technician has the greatest amount of leverage available. Slide the handle to the center and turn the nut or bolt quickly.

Extensions

Extensions, Figure 3-13-7, can be either rigid or flexible. The length can range from 2 inches up. The extension is used to increase the reach of a socket wrench. Extensions can be used on any handle or in combination to gain clearance for the handle.

Universal Socket Wrenches

Universal socket wrenches, Figure 3-13-7, are so named because of the universal joint that connects the drive end to the socket wrench end. The universal joint allows the socket wrench to rotate while the drive end is at an angle to the socket wrench. This allows for installing or removing nuts or bolts that may be slightly recessed. A universal adapter can be used between a socket wrench and an extension.

Adapters

Adapters, Figure 3-13-7, are used to change drive sizes between the handle and the socket wrench. They can either increase or decrease the drive size from the handle to the socket wrench.

Allen Wrenches

Most headless set screws are the Allen type and must be installed and removed with an Allen wrench. Allen wrenches are six-sided bars in the shape of an L. They range in size from $3/64$ to $1/2$ inch and fit into a hexagonal recess in the set screw. Allen wrenches are also available with square and hex drive ends allowing them to be driven by standard drives.

Many MS and NAS close tolerance and high strength bolts and fasteners use an Allen head for installation and tightening.

Section 14

Impact Tools

Hand Impact Tools

Because of the conditions aircraft operate in, it may be necessary to remove nuts and bolts with hand impact tools. This must be done carefully or damage to the aircraft may result.

The hand impact driver, Figure 3-14-1, is used to remove hardware that resists other methods of removal. The impact driver has a heavy housing to accept blows from a hammer and an internal mechanism that converts the hammer blows into a twisting motion. It is the sudden twisting that loosens the fasteners.

The hand impact driver can accommodate bits or sockets.

Care must be used when using the impact driver. Safety glasses should be used.

Power Impact Tools

Power impact tools should not be used on aircraft for installation or removal of hardware.

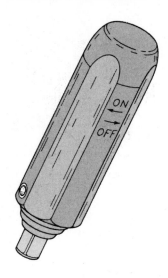

Figure 3-14-1. Hand impact driver

Power impact tools do not apply a smooth torque. It is this unequal torque that can lead to damage to aircraft or components.

The power impact tool applies torque in a series of jerks or impacts that are hard to measure. The application of this unknown value of torque can exceed the torque requirements of the part.

There are jobs power impact tools can be used for, but the results must be carefully considered.

Section 15

Measuring Devices

Torque Wrenches

There are times when definite pressure must be applied to a nut or bolt. In such cases a torque wrench must be used. The torque wrench is a precision tool consisting of a torque-indicating handle and appropriate adapter or attachments. It measures the amount of turning or twisting force applied to a nut, bolt, or screw.

The three most commonly used torque wrenches are the deflecting beam, dial-indicating, and micrometer-setting types. When using the deflecting beam and the dial-indicating torque wrenches, the torque is read visually on a dial or scale mounted on the handle of the wrench. The micrometer-setting torque wrench is preset to the desired torque. When

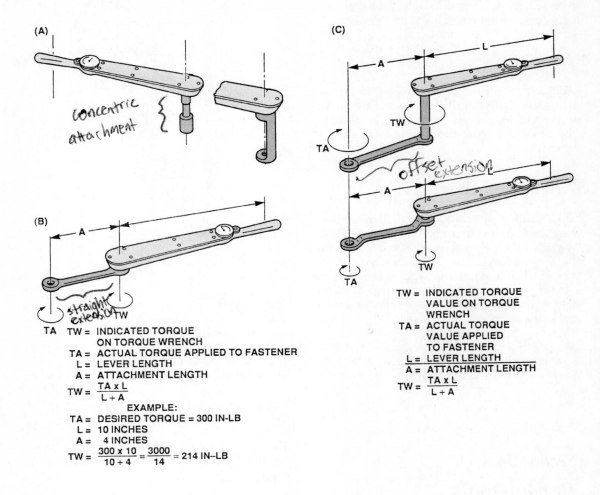

Figure 3-15-1. Straight and concentric torque wrench extensions and calculations

this torque is reached, a sharp impulse or breakaway is noticed by the operator.

Some torque wrench applications may require the use of an adapter or extension to reach a fastener or to allow the dial to be accurately read. These extensions may be concentric or non-concentric.

The concentric extensions present few problems because they do not change the effective length of the torque wrench.

Non-concentric extensions, as the name implies, change the effective length of the torque wrench. Calculations are required for these types of extensions. There are two types of non-concentric extensions; the straight extension and the reverse extension. The use of this type of extension will require the use of a formula. In using the formula, the lever length L is the critical factor. The point where the technician grips the torque wrench to the pivot point determines the length L.

A concentric attachment is shown in Figure 3-15-1A. When applying torque to a fastener, the torque is read from the dial or an audible indication is heard when the proper torque is reached. Figure 3-15-1B shows the straight extension attachment, Figure 3-15-1C shows the offset extension, Figure 3-15-2A the reverse extension, and Figure 3-15-2B the angle extension. Figure 3-15-2C indicates the differences in torque by the way the technician grips the torque wrench.

Before each use, the torque wrench should be visually inspected for damage. If a bent pointer, cracked or broken glass (dial type), or signs of rough handling are found, the wrench must be tested.

NOTE: *Torque wrenches must be tested at periodic intervals to ensure accuracy. Each Repair Station must keep a calibration record of the tests and their results. A torque wrench with an out of date calibration should be re-calibrated before use.*

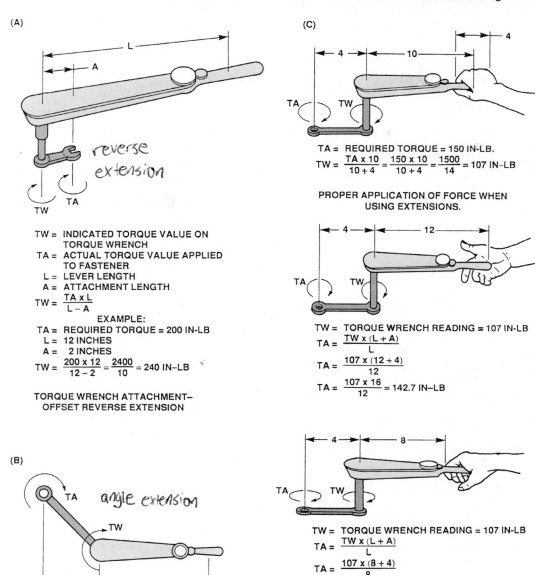

(A)

reverse extension

TW = INDICATED TORQUE VALUE ON TORQUE WRENCH
TA = ACTUAL TORQUE VALUE APPLIED TO FASTENER
L = LEVER LENGTH
A = ATTACHMENT LENGTH

$$TW = \frac{TA \times L}{L - A}$$

EXAMPLE:
TA = REQUIRED TORQUE = 200 IN-LB
L = 12 INCHES
A = 2 INCHES

$$TW = \frac{200 \times 12}{12 - 2} = \frac{2400}{10} = 240 \text{ IN-LB}$$

TORQUE WRENCH ATTACHMENT–
OFFSET REVERSE EXTENSION

(B)

angle extension

$$TW = \frac{TA \times L}{L + A}$$

ANGLE EXTENSION TORQUE
WRENCH ATTACHMENT

(C)

TA = REQUIRED TORQUE = 150 IN-LB.

$$TW = \frac{TA \times 10}{10 + 4} = \frac{150 \times 10}{10 + 4} = \frac{1500}{14} = 107 \text{ IN-LB}$$

PROPER APPLICATION OF FORCE WHEN
USING EXTENSIONS.

TW = TORQUE WRENCH READING = 107 IN-LB

$$TA = \frac{TW \times (L + A)}{L}$$

$$TA = \frac{107 \times (12 + 4)}{12}$$

$$TA = \frac{107 \times 16}{12} = 142.7 \text{ IN-LB}$$

TW = TORQUE WRENCH READING = 107 IN-LB

$$TA = \frac{TW \times (L + A)}{L}$$

$$TA = \frac{107 \times (8 + 4)}{8}$$

$$TA = \frac{107 \times 12}{8} = 160.5 \text{ IN-LB}$$

IMPROPER APPLICATION OF FORCE

Figure 3-15-2. Offset and reverse torque wrench extensions and calculations

Section 16

Measuring and Layout Tools

Layout and measuring devices are precision tools. They are carefully machined, accurately marked and, in many cases, are made up of very delicate parts. When using these tools, be careful not to drop, bend, or scratch them. The finished product will be no more accurate than the measurements or the layout; therefore, it is very important to understand how to read, use, and care for these tools.

Rules (Scales)

Rules are made of steel and are either rigid or flexible. The flexible steel rule will bend, but it should not be bent intentionally as it may be broken rather easily. In the machinist trade a rule is called a scale.

In aircraft work the unit of measure most commonly used is the inch. The inch may be divided into smaller parts by means of either common or decimal fraction divisions. The standard aircraft rule is divided in 100ths and 50ths of an inch.

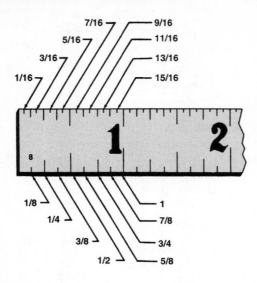 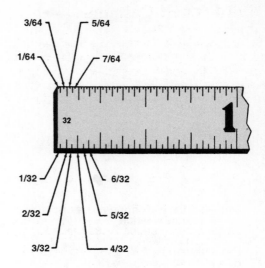

Figure 3-16-1. Rules

The fractions of an inch may be expressed in decimals, called decimal equivalents of an inch; for example, $1/8$ inch is expressed as 0.125 (one hundred twenty-five thousandths of an inch).

The fractional divisions for an inch are found by dividing the inch into equal parts halves ($1/2$), quarters ($1/4$), eighths ($1/8$), sixteenths ($1/16$), thirty-seconds ($1/32$), and sixty-fourths ($1/64$) as shown in Figure 3-16-1.

Rules are manufactured in two basic styles, those divided or marked in common fractions (Figure 3-16-1), and those divided or marked in decimals or divisions of one one-hundredth of an inch. A rule may be used either as a measuring tool or as a straightedge.

Combination Sets

The combination set (Figure 3-16-2), as its name implies, is a tool that has several uses. It can be used for the same purposes as an ordinary try square, but it differs from the try square in that the head slides along the blade and can be clamped at any desired place. Combined with the square, or stock, head are a level and scriber. The head slides in a central groove on the blade or scale, which can be used separately as a rule.

The spirit level in the stock head makes it convenient to square a piece of material with a surface and at the same time tell whether one or the other is plumb or level. The head can be used alone as a simple level. The combination of square head and blade can also be used as a marking gauge to scribe lines at a 45° angle, as a depth gauge, or as a height gauge. A convenient scriber is held frictionally in the head by a small brass bushing.

The protractor head can be used to check angles and also may be set at any desired angle to draw lines.

The center head is used to find the center of shafts or other cylindrical work.

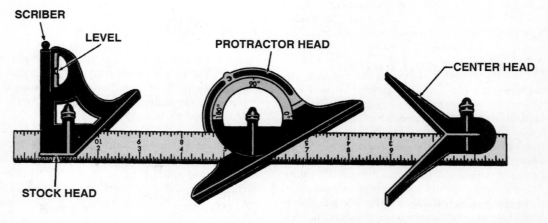

Figure 3-16-2. Combination set

Dividers and Calipers

Dividers and pencil compasses have two legs joined at the top by a pivot. They are used to scribe circles and arcs and for transferring measurements from the rule to the work. When using pencil compasses or dividers, the following procedures are suggested:

1. Inspect the points to make sure they are sharp.

2. To set the dividers or compasses, hold them with the point of one leg in the graduations on the rule. Turn the adjustment nut with the thumb and forefinger; adjust the dividers or compasses until the point of the other leg rests on the graduation of the rule which gives the required measurement.

3. To draw an arc or circle with either the pencil compasses or dividers, hold the thumb attachment on the top with the thumb and forefinger. With pressure exerted on both legs, swing the compass in a clockwise direction and draw the desired arc or circle.

4. The tendency for the legs to slip is avoided by inclining the compasses or dividers in the direction in which they are being rotated. In working on metals, the dividers are used only to scribe arcs or circles that will later be removed by cutting. All other arcs or circles are drawn with pencil compasses to avoid scratching the material.

5. On paper layouts, the pencil compasses are used for scribing arcs and circles. Dividers should be used to transfer critical measurements because they are more accurate than a pencil compass.

Calipers

Calipers are used for measuring diameters and distances or for comparing distances and sizes. The three common types of calipers are the inside, the outside, and the hermaphrodite calipers, such as gear-tool calipers (Figure 3-16-3).

Inside calipers have outward curved legs for measuring inside diameters, such as diameters of holes, the distance between two surfaces, the width of slots, or other similar jobs.

Outside calipers are used for measuring outside dimensions, for example, the diameter of a piece of round stock.

A hermaphrodite caliper is generally used as a marking gauge in layout work. It should not be used for precision measurement.

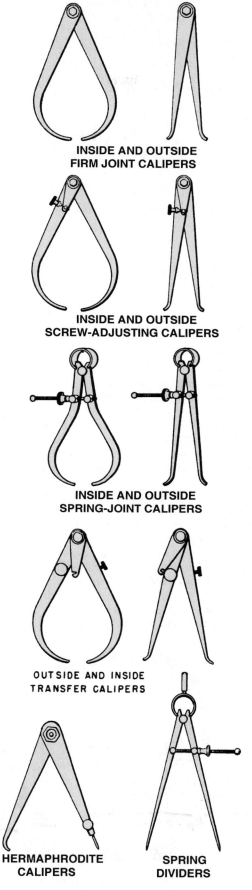

INSIDE AND OUTSIDE FIRM JOINT CALIPERS

INSIDE AND OUTSIDE SCREW-ADJUSTING CALIPERS

INSIDE AND OUTSIDE SPRING-JOINT CALIPERS

OUTSIDE AND INSIDE TRANSFER CALIPERS

HERMAPHRODITE CALIPERS

SPRING DIVIDERS

Figure 3-16-3. Calipers

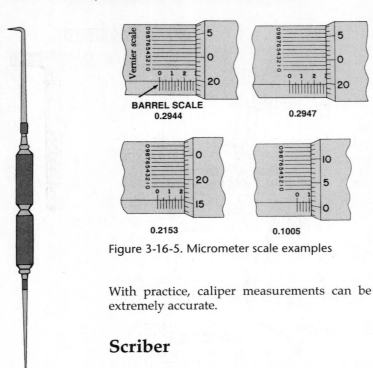

Figure 3-16-5. Micrometer scale examples

With practice, caliper measurements can be extremely accurate.

Scriber

The scriber is designed to serve the aviation technician in the same way a pencil or pen serves a writer. In general, it is used to scribe or mark lines on metal surfaces.

The scriber, shown in Figure 3-16-4, is made of tool steel, 4 to 12 inches long, and has two needle-pointed ends. One end is bent at a 90° angle for reaching and marking through holes.

Before using a scriber always inspect the points for sharpness. Be sure the straightedge is flat on the metal and in position for scribing. Tilt the scriber slightly in the direction toward which it will be moved, holding it like a pencil. Keep the scriber's point close to the guiding edge of the straightedge. The scribed line should be heavy enough to be visible, but no deeper than necessary to serve its purpose.

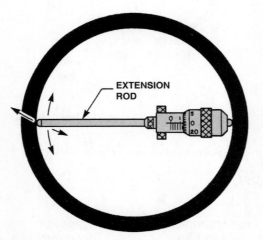

Figure 3-16-6. Using an inside micrometer with extension rod

Figure 3-16-4. Scriber

It must be used only to mark lines that will be removed by cutting or trimming.

Micrometer Calipers

There are four types of micrometer calipers, commonly called outside micrometer, inside micrometer, depth micrometer, and thread micrometer. Micrometers are available in a variety of sizes, either 0- to $\frac{1}{2}$-inch, 0- to 1-inch, 1- to 2-inch, 2- to 3-inch, 3- to 4-inch, 4- to 5-inch, or 5- to 6-inch sizes.

Vernier Scale

Some micrometers are equipped with a vernier scale which makes it possible to read directly the fraction of a division that may be indicated on the thimble scale. Typical examples of the vernier scale as it applies to the micrometer are shown in Figure 3-16-5.

All three scales on a micrometer are not fully visible without turning the micrometer; but the examples shown in Figure 3-16-5 are drawn as though the barrel and thimble of the micrometer were laid out flat so that all three scales can be seen at the same time. The barrel scale is the lower horizontal scale; the thimble scale is vertical on the right; and the long horizontal lines (0 through 9 and 0) make up the vernier scale.

Inside micrometers are used to measure inside diameters (ID). The inside micrometer set has a range from two to ten inches. This is accomplished by a series of extension rods within the set.

When using the inside micrometer, Figure 3-16-6, the normal procedure is to set the micrometer across the diameter or in between the inside surfaces. Note the arrows in Figure 3-16-6, these indicate the directions the technician is feeling for the largest dimension horizontally and the smallest dimension vertically. Inside micrometers have spherical contact points. This will require practice to feel for the full diameter.

The thimble on an inside micrometer is stiffer than other micrometers. When the micrometer is removed, it is read like any other micrometer. It is possible to use inside micrometers to measure deep holes by the use of a handle attachment.

In reading a micrometer, an excellent way to remember the relative scale values is to remember that the 0.025-inch barrel scale graduations are established by the lead screw (40 threads per inch). Next, the thimble graduations divide the 0.025 inch into 25 parts, each equal to 0.001 inch; then the vernier graduations divide the 0.001 inch into 10 equal parts, each equal to 0.0001 inch. Remembering the values of the various scale graduations, the barrel scale reading is noted. The thimble scale reading is added to it; then the vernier scale reading is added to get the final reading. The vernier scale line to be read is always the one aligned exactly with any thimble graduation.

In the first example in Figure 3-16-5, the barrel reads 0.275 inch and the thimble reads more than 0.019 inch. The number one graduation on the thimble is aligned exactly with the number four graduation on the vernier scale. Thus, the final reading is 0.2944 inch.

In the second example in Figure 3-16-5, the barrel reads 0.275 inch, and the thimble reads more than 0.019 inch and less than 0.020 inch. On the vernier scale, the number seven graduation coincides with a line on the thimble. This

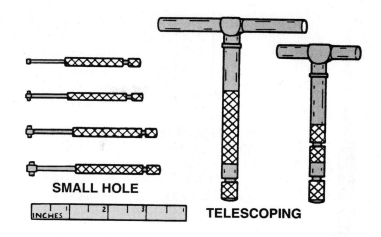

Figure 3-16-7. Small hole and telescoping gauges

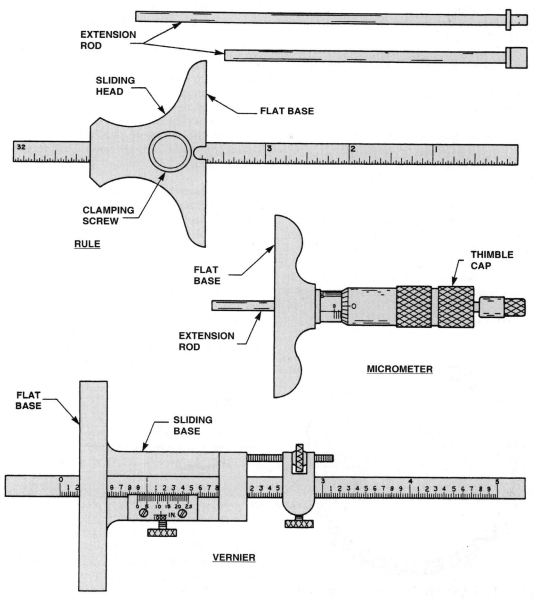

Figure 3-16-8. Types of depth gauges

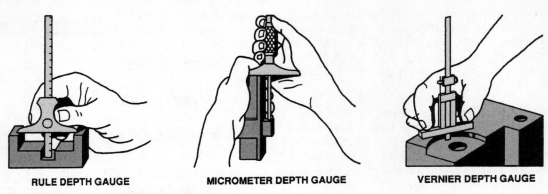

RULE DEPTH GAUGE　　**MICROMETER DEPTH GAUGE**　　**VERNIER DEPTH GAUGE**

Figure 3-16-9. Using depth gauges

means that the thimble reading would be 0.0197 inch. Adding this to the barrel reading of 0.275 inch gives a total measurement of 0.2947 inch.

The third and fourth examples in Figure 3-16-5 are additional readings that would require use of the vernier scale for accurate readings to ten-thousandths of an inch.

Newer electronic battery powered micrometer and calipers have direct reading readouts, eliminating the process of interpreting readings.

Small Hole Gauges

Small hole gauges and telescoping gauges are also used to measure inside diameters as shown by Figure 3-16-7.

The small hole gauge has an expandable measuring ball that is controlled by the knurled handle. The ball is inserted into the hole and the handle is turned to expand the ball. When the ball is removed, a micrometer is used to measure the diameter. The maximum size is $^1/_2$ inch.

The telescoping gauge is used to measure larger holes and other inside dimensions. This gauge has a fixed pin and a spring and plunger. The plunger is operated by the handle. As the handle is turned, it allows a spring to move the plunger. When the plunger contacts the surface, the measuring is completed. The handle is turned to hold the plunger in place and the gauge is removed. The measurement is transferred to a micrometer of sufficient size.

A depth gauge is used to measure the depth of holes, slots, recesses, and the distance from a surface to a recessed part. Figure 3-16-8 shows some of the types of depth gauges. Figure 3-16-9 shows the various ways a depth gauge can be used.

The outside micrometer (Figure 3-16-10) is used by the technician more often than any other type. It may be used to measure the outside dimensions of shafts, thickness of sheet metal stock, diameter of drills, or for many other applications.

The micrometer depth gauges are used to measure depths that are perpendicular from

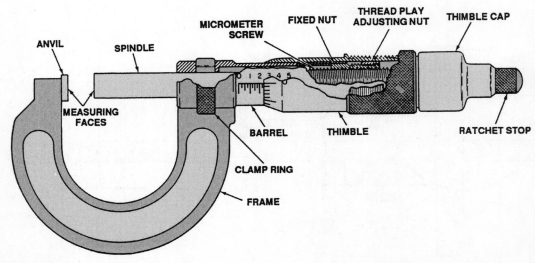

Figure 3-16-10. Outside micrometer

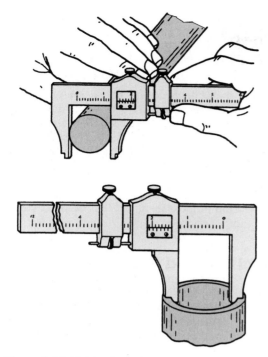

Figure 3-16-11. Vernier caliper

the measuring surface. The depth of the measurement can be varied by the use of extension rods.

Vernier Calipers

Vernier calipers are used when very accurate inside or outside measurements are needed. The graduations can be in inches or millimeters.

The vernier caliper has an L-shaped stationary body with the scale engraved on it and a stationary jaw. The sliding member has a jaw that matches the stationary jaw and contains the vernier scale. Both the stationary and sliding jaws are marked IN and OUT indicating which part of the jaw is used for measuring inside dimensions and outside dimensions.

The vernier caliper is used by unlocking the movable jaw and the vernier scale. Move the jaws to the desired position, either using the IN or OUT position, Figure 3-16-11, on the jaws. Lock the movable jaw and make any fine adjustments by using the fine adjustment on the vernier scale. When this adjustment is made, lock the vernier scale, remove and read the caliper. To interpret what the vernier caliper is indicating, an understanding is needed of what the scale and vernier scale are showing.

Figure 3-16-12 shows the readings on vernier calipers. Number one in the figure marks the scale on the stationary body and it is graduated in 0.025-inch increments. Every fourth increment represents a tenth of an inch and is numbered one through nine. This is marked in the figure by the number two.

The vernier scale has 25 increments (number three of Figure 3-16-12), numbered 0, 5, 10, 15, 20, and 25. These 25 increments are equal to the 24 increments on the stationary body scale (number four of Figure 3-16-12). The difference between the 25 increments on the stationary body and the 24 increments on the vernier scale is $1/1000$ inch.

After measuring the work, the locks are engaged, the caliper is removed from the work, and the scale is read by:

1. Read the number of whole inches (number five of Figure 3-16-12) on the fixed scale to the left of the vernier scale zero index (number six of Figure 3-16-12). Write it down: 1.00 inches.

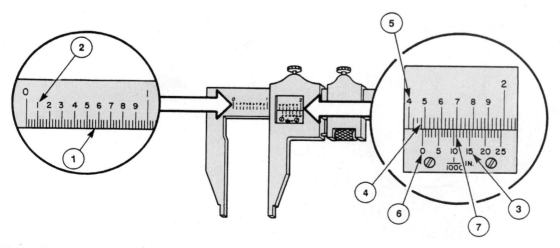

Figure 3-16-12. Reading the vernier caliper

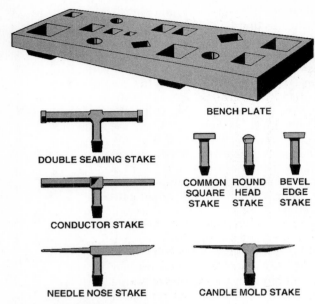

Figure 3-17-1. Stake table and stakes

2. Read the tenths on the fixed scale (number four of Figure 3-16-12), to the left of the vernier scale zero index (number six of Figure 3-16-12). Write it down: 0.40 inch.

3. Read the number of 25ths on the fixed scale (number four of Figure 3-16-12), adjacent to the vernier scale zero. Write it down: 0.075 inch.

4. Read the line on the vernier scale (number seven of Figure 3-16-12), that lines up with a line on the fixed scale. Remember that each of the 25 increments is $1/1000$ inch. Write it down: 0.011 inch.

5. Total the individual readings: 1.486 inches.

As with all micrometers, modern calipers have gone electronic. An electronic caliper provides direct digital readouts for both inside and outside measurements. They are also automatically calibrated.

Although expensive, digital calipers can be worth the cost if they are to be used regularly.

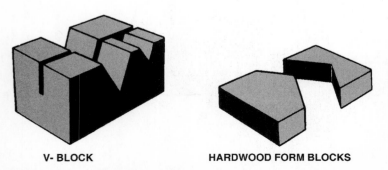

Figure 3-17-2. Hardwood V-blocks and hardwood form blocks.

Section 17
Special Sheet Metal Tools

Sheet metal technicians use a lot of special tools and devices that have been developed to make their work faster, simpler, and better. These special tools and devices include both hand and power tools. Some are multi-use tools, while some have been developed for specific aircraft applications. In this chapter we will cover the basics of these tools, with actual operation of most forming tools being covered in another chapter.

Dollies And Stakes

Sheet metal is often formed or finished (planished) over variously shaped anvils called dollies or stakes. These are used for forming small, odd-shaped parts, or for putting on finishing touches for which a large machine may not be suited.

Dollies are meant to be held in the hand, whereas stakes are designed to be supported by a flat cast iron bench plate fastened to the workbench (Figure 3-17-1). While not essential, these tools are extremely handy in a busy shop. They are derived from the old time traveling tinsmiths trade.

Most stakes have machined, polished surfaces which have been hardened. Do not use stakes to back up material when chiseling, or when using any similar cutting tool because this will deface the surface of the stake and make it useless for finish work.

V-Blocks

V-blocks made of hardwood are widely used in airframe metalwork for shrinking and stretching metal, particularly angles and flanges. The size of the block depends on the work being done and on personal preference. Although any type of hardwood is suitable, maple and ash are recommended for best results when working with aluminum alloys.

Hardwood Form Blocks

Hardwood form blocks can be constructed to duplicate practically any aircraft structural or non-structural part. The wooden block or form is shaped to the exact dimensions and contour of the part to be formed. Form blocks are used for hand forming as well as for hydro-press dies (Figure 3-17-2).

Shrinking Blocks

A shrinking block, Figure 3-17-3, consists of two metal blocks and some device for clamping them together. One block forms the base, and the other is cut away to provide space where the crimped material can be hammered. The legs of the upper jaw clamp the material to the base block on each side of the crimp so that the material will not creep away but will remain stationary while the crimp is hammered flat (being shrunk). This type of crimping block is designed to be held in a bench vise.

Shrinking blocks can be made to fit any specific need. The basic form and principle remain the same, even though the blocks may vary considerably in size and shape.

Sandbags

A sandbag is generally used as a support during the bumping process. A serviceable bag can be made by sewing heavy canvas or soft leather to form a bag of the desired size, and filling it with sand which has been sifted through a fine mesh screen.

Before filling canvas bags with sand, use a brush to coat the inside of it with softened paraffin or beeswax, which forms a sealing layer and prevents the sand from working through the pores of the canvas.

Sandbag forming takes a considerable amount of practice to do well. Most items that can be formed by the sandbag method are currently formed using an English Wheel machine.

Section 18

Holding Devices

Vises

Vises and clamps are tools used for holding materials of various kinds on which some type of operation is being performed. The type of operation being performed and the type of metal being used determine the holding device to be used.

The most commonly used vises are shown in Figure 3-18-1. The machinist's vise has flat jaws and usually a swivel base, whereas the utility bench vise has scored, removable jaws and an anvil-faced back jaw. This vise will hold

Figure 3-17-3. Shrinking block

heavier material than the machinist's vise and will also grip pipe or rod firmly. The back jaw can be used for an anvil if the work being done is light. To be useful for sheet metal work, a utility vise will have to use jaw protectors, or have smooth jaws made to replace the toothed jaws. Jaws can be fabricated from most any metal and drilled on a drill press.

A good woodworking vise with maple jaws is an excellent holding tool that will not damage the work being held.

C-Clamps

The carriage clamp, or C-clamp, as it is commonly called, is shaped like a large C and has three main parts: the threaded screw, the jaw, and the swivel head. The swivel plate, which is at the bottom of the screw, prevents the end

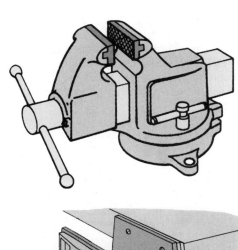

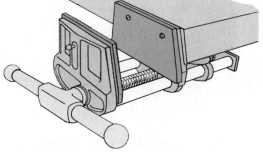

Figure 3-18-1. Machinist and woodworkers vises

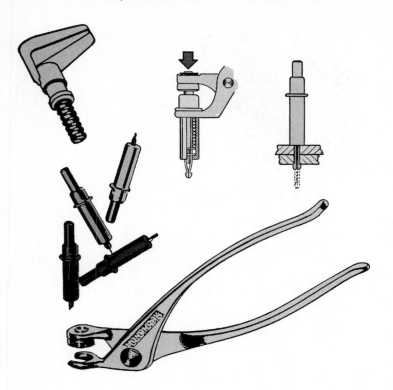

Figure 3-18-2. Clecos, cleco pliers, and an edge clamp for holding sheet metal during assembly

from turning directly against the material being clamped. Although C-clamps vary in size from 2 in. upward, their function is always that of clamping or holding.

The shape of the C-clamp allows it to span obstructions near the edge of a piece of work. The greatest limitation in the use of the carriage clamp is its tendency to spring out of shape. It should never be tightened more than hand-tight. Masking tape covering each jaw is a good method of not marring the work. The tape can be frequently replaced to prevent accumulated dirt and shavings from marring the work.

Clecos

The most commonly used sheet-metal holder is the Cleco fastener (Figure 3-18-2) manufactured by Monogram. It is used to keep drilled parts made from sheet stock pressed tightly together. Unless parts are held tightly together they will separate while being riveted.

This type of fastener is available in six different sizes: $3/32$, $1/8$, $5/32$, $3/16$, $1/4$, and $3/8$ inch. Special pliers are used to insert the fastener in a drilled hole. One pair of pliers will fit all six different sizes.

Screws

Sheet-metal screws are sometimes used as temporary holders. The metal sheets must be held tightly together before installing these screws, since the self-tapping action of the threads tends to force the sheets apart. The screw size must be small enough that the hole can be drilled to the final size after the screws are removed, as the screws will mar the hole. Washers placed under the heads of the screws keep them from marring or scratching the metal.

Section 19

Metalworking Machines

Without metalworking machines a job would be more difficult and tiresome, and the time required to finish a task would be much longer.

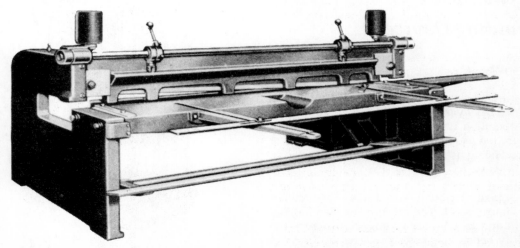

Figure 3-19-1. Gap bed squaring shear

Some of the machines used are discussed here; these include the powered and non-powered metal-cutting machines, such as the various types of saws, powered and non-powered shears, and nibblers. Also included is the forming equipment (both power driven and non-powered), such as brakes and forming rolls, the bar folder, and shrinking and stretching machines.

Squaring Shear

The second most popular shop tool is a squaring shear. These shears consist of a stationary lower blade attached to a bed and a movable upper blade attached to a crosshead (Figure 3-19-1). To make the cut, the upper blade is moved down by placing the foot on the treadle and pushing downward.

The shears are equipped with a spring which raises the blade and treadle when the foot is removed. A scale, graduated in fractions of an inch, is scribed on the bed. Two squaring fences, consisting of thick strips of metal and used for squaring metal sheets, are placed on the bed, one on the right side and one on the left. Each is placed so that it forms a 90° angle with the blades.

Three distinctly different operations can be performed on the squaring shears: Cutting to a line, squaring, and multiple cutting to a specific size. When cutting to a line, the sheet is placed on the bed of the shears in front of the cutting blade with the cutting line directly even with the cutting edge of the bed. The sheet is cut by stepping on the treadle while the sheet is held securely in place by the holddown clamp.

Squaring requires several steps. First, one end of the sheet is squared with an edge (the squaring fence is usually used on the edge). Then the remaining edges are squared by holding one squared end of the sheet against the squaring fence and making the cut, one edge at a time, until all edges have been squared.

When several pieces must be cut to the same dimensions, use the gauge which is on most squaring shears. The supporting rods are graduated in fractions of an inch, and the gauge bar may be set at any point on the rods. Set the gauge at the desired distance from the cutting blade of the shears and push each piece to be cut against the gauge bar. All the pieces can then be cut to the same dimensions without measuring and marking each one separately.

Squaring shears come in several different sizes, measured in both sheet metal capacity and length of cut. One model is called a gap shear.

Figure 3-19-2. Scroll shears

It has the sides open so that a very long cut can be made by sliding the sheet along the bed and extending the cut.

Scroll Shears

Scroll shears (Figure 3-19-2) are used for cutting irregular lines on the inside of a sheet without cutting through to the edge. The upper cutting blade is stationary while the lower blade is movable. The machine is operated by a handle connected to the lower blade.

Throatless Shears

Throatless shears (Figure 3-19-3) are best used to cut 10-gauge mild carbon sheet metal and 12-gauge stainless steel. The shear gets its name from its construction; it actually has no throat.

Figure 3-19-3. Throatless shears

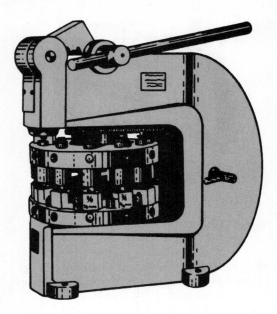

Figure 3-19-4. Rotex bench punch

There are no obstructions during cutting since the frame is throatless. A sheet of any length can be cut, and the metal can be turned in any direction to allow for cutting irregular shapes. The cutting blade (top blade) is operated by a hand lever.

The throatless shear illustrated is named after it's manufacturer and is called a Beverly.

Punches

Bench punches

The Rotex rotary punch (Figure 3-19-4) is used in the airframe repair shop to punch holes in metal parts. This machine can be used for cutting radii in corners, for making washers, and for many other jobs where holes are required. The machine is composed of two cylindrical turrets, one mounted over the other and supported by the frame. Both turrets are synchro-

nized so that they rotate together, and index pins assure correct alignment at all times. The index pins may be released from their locking position by rotating a lever on the right side of the machine. This action withdraws the index pins from the tapered holes and allows an operator to turn the turrets to any size punch desired.

When rotating the turret to change punches, release the index lever when the desired die is within 1 in. of the ram, and continue to rotate the turret slowly until the top of the punch holder slides into the grooved end of the ram. The tapered index locking pins will then seat themselves in the holes provided and, at the same time, release the mechanical locking device, which prevents punching until the turrets are aligned.

To operate the machine, place the metal to be worked between the die and punch. Pull the lever on the top side of the machine toward you. This will actuate the pinion shaft, gear segment, toggle link, and the ram, forcing the punch through the metal. When the lever is returned to its original position, the metal is removed from the punch.

The diameter of the punch is stamped on the front of each die holder. Each punch has a point in its center which is placed in the center punch mark to punch the hole in the correct location.

Several manufacturers make bench and hand punches that only hold one die and punch at a time. In general, these will punch a larger diameter that a Rotex punch. While it takes additional time to change dies and punches, the tooling is normally less expensive and more easily obtained (Figure 3-19-5).

Hand punches

For rivet and bolt sized holes, a hand punch with replaceable tooling is a good investment. They are especially good at punching rivet holes in trailing edges, leaving a clean hole without bending the thin trailing edge and making it wavy.

Chassis punches

Originally designed for punching special shaped holes in radio equipment, chassis punches, Figure 3-19-6, are indispensable. When punching a keyed hole for an electrical switch, nothing else will work. All that is necessary to use a chassis punch is to drill a hole in the center of the area you wish to punch out, install the punch, then tighten the nut.

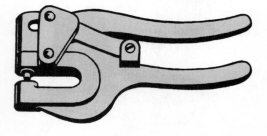

Figure 3-19-5. Roper whitney hand punch

Dies can be purchased for stationary punches that will make the same hole, but they are much more expensive and not as handy. Available in many sizes and shapes, Greenlee brand chassis punches can be ordered from any tool supplier. Their common name is taken from the original manufacturer. They are called Greenlee punches.

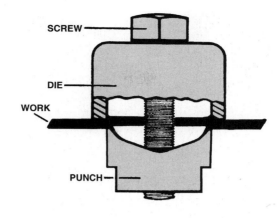

Figure 3-19-6. Greenlee punch

Section 20

Metal-Cutting Powered Tools

Panel Saw

The air operated portable circular-cutting panel saws (Figure 3-20-1) use blades of various diameters. The head of this saw can be turned to any desired angle, and is very handy for removing damaged sections on a stringer. Advantages of a panel saw are:

1. The ability to cut metal up to $3/16$ inches thick.

2. No starting hole is required.

3. A cut can be started anywhere on a sheet of metal.

4. The capability of cutting an inside or outside radius.

To prevent grabbing, keep a firm grip on the saw handle at all times. Before installing a blade, it should be checked carefully for cracks. A cracked blade can fly apart and perhaps result in serious injury. These saws are called a Ketts saw.

Saber Saw

Saber saws are reciprocating saws and can be used for cutting aluminum plate, or for cutting special shapes when the material cannot be taken to a bandsaw. Variable speed saws work the best, because the speed can be adjusted to fit the work thickness. Commercial electrical saws work very well in non-explosive environments. To prevent marring the work, cover it with craft paper. Tape the paper down with masking tape, and cover the shoe of the saw with masking tape as well.

The portable, air powered reciprocating saw has a gun-type shape for balancing and ease of handling and operates most effectively at an air pressure of from 85 to 100 p.s.i. (Figure 3-20-2). The reciprocating saw uses a standard hacksaw blade and can cut a 360° circle or a square or rectangular hole. This saw is easy to handle and safe to use.

A reciprocating saw should be used in such a way that at least two teeth of the saw blade are cutting at all times. Avoid applying too much downward pressure on the saw handle because the blade may break.

Figure 3-20-1. Panel saw
Courtesy of US Industrial Tool and Supply Company

Figure 3-20-2. Air-powered saber saw

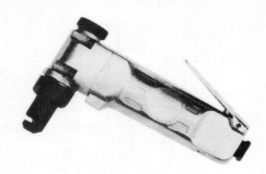

Figure 3-20-3. Portable nibbler
Courtesy of US Industrial Tool and Supply Company

Nibblers

Stationary and portable nibblers, Figure 3-20-3, are used to cut metal by a high-speed blanking action. The cutting or blanking action is caused by the lower die moving up and down and meeting the upper stationary die. The shape of the lower die permits small pieces of metal approximately $1/16$ inch wide to be cut out.

The cutting speed of the nibbler is controlled by the thickness of the metal being cut. Sheets of metal with a maximum thickness of $1/16$ inch can be cut satisfactorily. Too much force applied to the metal during the cutting operation will clog the dies, causing the die to fail or the motor to overheat.

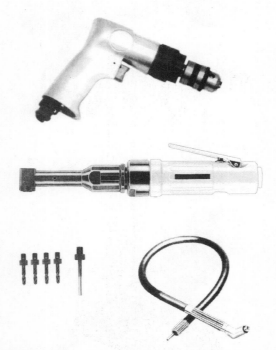

Figure 3-21-1. Various drill motors and attachments
Courtesy of US Industrial Tool and Supply Company

The spring-loaded screw on the base of the lower die should be adjusted to allow the metal to move freely between the dies. This adjustment must be sufficient to hold the material firmly enough to prevent irregular cuts. The dies may be shimmed for special cutting operations.

Section 21
Portable Power Drill

Drill Motors

One of the most common operations in airframe metalwork is that of drilling holes for rivets and bolts. This operation is not difficult, especially on light metal. Once the fundamentals of drills and their uses are learned, a small portable power drill motor is usually the most practical machine to use.

Some hand power drill motors are operated by electricity, batteries, or by compressed air. The order of choice for drill motors is air, electrical, and battery powered, in that order. Most air drill motors will operate at a speed that will provide for a decent feed rate. Some of the smaller electrically powered ones will operate sufficiently fast (2,500 r.p.m. or better), but rarely will a battery powered drill motor operate fast enough to drill efficiently.

Air operated drill motors, by their nature, can be variable speed by restricting the pressure on the trigger. Variable speed on both electrical and battery powered drill motors can be a definite plus in ease of operation. Reversible doesn't hurt.

While battery powered drill motors may be the last choice for drilling sheet metal, they do have a seemingly indispensable position as powered screwdrivers. With the large number of screws to be removed and reinstalled during an inspection or teardown, they are a definite plus.

Drill motors are available in various shapes and sizes to satisfy almost any requirement (Figure 3-21-1). Pneumatic drill motors are recommended for use on projects around flammable materials where sparks from an electric motor might create an explosion hazard.

When access to a place where a hole is to be drilled is difficult or impossible with a straight drill motor, various types of drill extensions and adapters are used. A straight extension can be made from an ordinary piece of drill rod. The twist drill is attached to the drill rod by shrink fit, brazing, or silver soldering. Angle adapters can be attached to either an electric or pneumatic drill motor when the location of the hole is inaccessible to a straight drill. Angle adapters have an extended shank fastened to the chuck of the drill. In use, the drill is held in one hand and the adapter in the other to prevent the adapter from spinning around the drill chuck.

A flexible extension, called a snake drill, can be used for drilling in places which are inaccessible by ordinary means. Its flexibility permits drilling around obstructions with a minimum of effort.

When using the portable power drill, hold it firmly with both hands. Before drilling, be sure to place a backup block of wood under the hole to be drilled to add support to the metal and protect the drill point, as well as yourself.

The twist drill should be inserted in the chuck and tested for trueness or vibration. This may be visibly checked by running the motor freely. A drill that wobbles or is slightly bent should not be used since it will cause enlarged holes.

The drill should always be held at right angles to the work regardless of the position or curvatures. Tilting the drill at any time when drilling into or withdrawing from the material may cause elongation (egg shape) of the hole. In critical locations, there are special fixtures to help stay at 90° to the work surface.

Handheld drill motors can be used to operate hole saws, but should never be used with fly cutters. You can't manually hold everything accurately because of the off-center cutting of a fly cutter. You will damage the work, and stand a good chance of damaging yourself also.

Always wear safety goggles while drilling.

Section 22

Hole Deburring Tools

When drilling through sheet metal, small burrs are formed around the edge of the hole. Burrs must be removed to allow rivets or bolts to fit snugly and to prevent scratching. There are special deburring tools made for the job. Burrs may be removed with a bearing scraper, a countersink, or a twist drill larger than the hole. If a drill or countersink is used, it should be rotated by hand. When using an oversize drill or countersink, remember to remove only the burr. Do not chamfer the edge of the hole.

Section 23

Drill Press

The drill press is a precision machine used for drilling holes that require a high degree of accuracy. It serves as an accurate means of locating and maintaining the direction of a hole that is to be drilled and provides the operator with a feed lever that makes the task of feeding the drill into the work an easy one.

A variety of drill presses are available; the most common type is the upright drill press (Figure 3-23-1).

When using a drill press, the height of the drill press table is adjusted to accommodate the height of the part to be drilled. When the height of the part is greater than the distance between the drill and the table, the table is lowered. When the height of the part is less than the distance between the drill and the table, the table is raised.

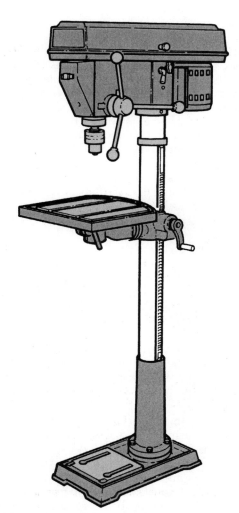

Figure 3-23-1. Upright drill press

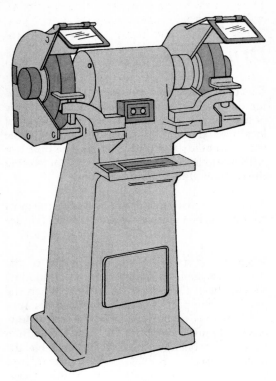

Figure 3-24-1. Bench grinder

After the table is properly adjusted, the part is placed on the table and the drill is brought down to aid in positioning the metal so that the hole to be drilled is directly beneath the point of the drill. The part is then clamped to the drill press table to prevent it from slipping during the drilling operation. Parts not properly clamped may bind on the drill and start spinning, causing the loss of fingers or hands or serious cuts on the operator's arms or body. Always make sure the part to be drilled is properly clamped to the drill press table before starting the drilling operation.

The degree of accuracy that is possible to attain when using the drill press will depend to a certain extent on the condition of the spindle hole, sleeves, and drill shank. Therefore, special care must be exercised to keep these parts clean and free from nicks, dents, or warpage. Always be sure that the sleeve is securely pressed into the spindle hole. Never insert a broken drill in a sleeve or spindle hole. Be careful never to use the sleeve-clamping vise to remove a drill since this may cause the sleeve to warp.

Choose a cutting fluid that is compatible with the material being drilled. Use a coolant if necessary, or if drilling deep holes.

Drill presses are especially good at running fly cutters because of the sensitive feed control and from the material being clamped down securely.

Section 24

Grinders

The term grinder applies to all forms of grinding machines. To be specific, it is a machine having an abrasive wheel which removes excess material while producing a suitable surface. There are many kinds of grinding machines, but only those which are helpful to the airframe technician will be discussed here.

Grinding Wheels

A grinding wheel is a cutting tool with a large number of cutting edges arranged so that when they become dull they break off and new cutting edges take their place.

Silicon carbide and aluminum oxide are the kinds of abrasives used in most grinding wheels. Silicon carbide is the cutting agent for grinding hard, brittle material, such as cast iron. It is also used in grinding aluminum, brass, bronze, and copper. Aluminum oxide is the cutting agent for grinding steel and other metals of high tensile strength.

The size of the abrasive particles used in grinding wheels is indicated by a number which corresponds to the number of meshes per linear inch in the screen through which the particles will pass. As an example, a number 30 abrasive will pass through a screen having 30 holes per linear inch, but will be retained by a smaller screen having more than 30 holes per linear inch.

The bond is the material which holds the abrasive particles together in forming the wheel. The kind and amount of bond used determines the hardness or softness of the wheel. The commonly used bonds are vitrified, silicate, resinoid, rubber, and shellac. Vitrified and silicate are the bonds used most frequently, vitrified bond being used in approximately three-fourths of all grinding wheels made. This bonding material forms a very uniform wheel and is not affected by oils, acids, water, heat, or cold. The silicate bond, however, is best suited for grinding edged tools.

Resinoid bonded wheels are better for heavy-duty grinding. Rubber bonded wheels are used where a high polish is required. Shellac bonded wheels are used for grinding materials where a buffed or burnished surface is needed.

A pedestal or floor type grinder usually has a grinding wheel on each end of a shaft which runs through an electric motor or a pulley operated by a belt. This grinder is used for sharpening tools and other general grinding jobs.

The wet grinder, although similar to the pedestal grinder, differs from it in that the wet grinder has a pump to supply a flow of water on a single grinding wheel. The water reduces the heat produced by material being ground against the wheel. It also washes away any bits of metal or abrasive removed during the grinding operation. The water returns to a tank and can be re-used.

A common type bench grinder found in most metalworking shops is shown in Figure 3-24-1. This grinder can be used to dress mushroomed heads on chisels, and points on chisels, screwdrivers, and drills. It can be used for removing excess metal from work and smoothing metal surfaces.

Bench grinders are generally equipped with one medium-grain and one fine-grain abrasive wheel. The medium-grain wheel is usually used for rough grinding where a considerable quantity of material is to be removed or where a smooth finish is unimportant. The fine-grain wheel is usually used for sharpening tools and grinding to close limits because it removes metal more slowly, gives the work a smooth finish, and does not generate enough heat to anneal the edges of cutting tools. When it is necessary to make a deep cut on work or to remove a large amount of metal, it is usually good practice to grind with the medium-grain wheel first and then finish up with the fine-grain wheel.

The grinding wheels are removable, and the grinders are usually designed so that wire brushes, polishing wheels, or buffing wheels can be substituted for the abrasive wheels.

As a rule, it is not good practice to grind work on the side of an abrasive wheel. When an abrasive wheel becomes worn, its cutting efficiency is reduced because of a decrease in surface speed. When a wheel becomes worn in this manner, it should be discarded and a new one installed.

Before using a bench grinder, make sure the abrasive wheels are firmly held on the spindles by the flange nuts. If an abrasive wheel should come off or become loose, it could seriously injure the operator in addition to ruining the grinder.

Another hazard is loose tool rests. A loose tool rest could cause the tool or piece of work to be grabbed by the abrasive wheel and cause the operator's hand to come in contact with the wheel. If this should happen, severe wounds may result.

Always wear goggles when using a grinder, even if eye shields are attached to the grinder. Goggles should fit firmly against your face and nose and have side protection. This is the only way to protect your eyes from the fine pieces of steel. Goggles that do not fit properly should be exchanged for ones that do fit.

Check the abrasive wheel for cracks before using the grinder. A cracked abrasive wheel is likely to fly apart when turning. Never use a grinder unless it is equipped with wheel guards.

Section 25
Forming Machines

Forming machines can be either hand operated or power driven. Small machines are usually hand operated, whereas the larger ones are power driven. Straight line machines include such equipment as the bar folder, cornice brake, and box and pan brake. Rotary machines include the slip roll former and combination machine. Power-driven machines are those that require a motor of some description for power. These include such equipment as the power-driven slip roll former, and power flanging machine.

Bar Folder

The bar folder (Figure 3-25-1) is designed for use in making bends or folds along edges of sheets. This machine is best suited for folding small hems, flanges, seams, and edges to be wired. Most bar folders have a capacity for metal up to 22 gauge in thickness and 42 inches in length. Invaluable in a tin shop, the aviation uses of a bar folder are limited.

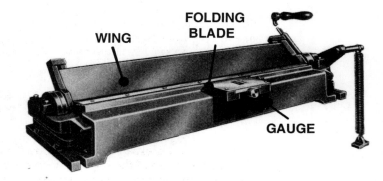

Figure 3-25-1. Bar folder

Figure 3-25-2. Cornice brake

vided and can be adjusted to any degree of bend within the capacity of the machine.

For forming angles of 45° or 90°, the correct stop is moved into place. This will allow the handle to be moved forward to the correct angle. For forming other angles, an adjustable collar is used. This is accomplished by loosening a set screw and setting the stop at the desired angle. After setting the stop, tighten the set screw and complete the bend.

To make the fold, adjust the machine correctly and then insert the metal. The metal goes between the folding blade and the jaw. Hold the metal firmly against the gauge and pull the operating handle toward the body. As the handle is brought forward, the jaw automatically raises and holds the metal until the desired fold is made. When the handle is returned to its original position, the jaw and blade will return to their original positions and release the metal.

Cornice Brake

The cornice brake, or common sheet metal brake, has a much greater range of usefulness than the bar folder (Figure 3-25-2). Any bend formed on a bar folder can be made on the cornice brake. The bar folder can form a bend or edge only as wide as the depth of the jaws. In comparison, the cornice brake allows the sheet that is to be folded or formed to pass through the jaws from front to rear without obstruction. Actual operation of a cornice brake is covered in depth in the chapter on Metal Forming.

In making ordinary bends with the cornice brake, the sheet is placed on the bed with the sight line (mark indicating line of bend) directly under the edge of the clamping bar. The clamping bar is then brought down to hold the sheet firmly in place. The stop at the right side of the brake is set for the proper angle or amount of bend, and the bending leaf is raised until it strikes the stop. If other bends are to be

Before using the bar folder, several adjustments must be made for thickness of material, width of fold, sharpness of fold, and angle of fold.

The adjustment for thickness of material is made by adjusting the screws at each end of the folder. As this adjustment is made, place a piece of metal of the desired thickness in the folder and raise the operating handle until the small roller rests on the cam. Hold the folding blade in this position and adjust the set screws so that the metal is clamped securely and evenly the full length of the folding blade. After the folder has been adjusted, test each end of the machine separately with a small piece of metal by actually folding it.

There are two positive stops on the folder, one for 45° folds or bends and the other for 90° folds or bends. An additional feature (a collar) is pro-

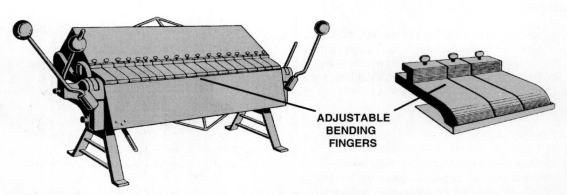

ADJUSTABLE BENDING FINGERS

Figure 3-25-3. A box and pan break

made, the clamping bar is lifted and the sheet is moved to the correct position for bending.

The bending capacity of a cornice brake is determined by the manufacturer. Standard capacities of this machine are from 12- to 22-gauge sheet metal, and bending lengths are from 3 to 12 feet. The bending capacity of the brake is determined by the bending edge thickness of the various bending leaf bars. Most bending should be done with the reinforcing angle iron on the bending leaf attached. If the angle iron is removed, the capacity of the brake must be reduced by at least two gauge numbers.

Most metals have a tendency to return to their normal shape a characteristic known as springback. If the cornice brake is set for a 90° bend, the metal bent will probably form an angle of about 87° to 88°. Therefore, if a bend of 90° is desired, set the cornice brake to bend an angle of about 93° to allow for springback.

Do not exceed the capacity of a cornice brake by trying to bend a material that exceeds the rated capacity. The frame of the brake will be sprung out of alignment and the machine will be of little value afterwards.

Box and Pan Brake

A box and pan break is a modification of a cornice break. The clamping bar is composed of several pieces that are moveable. They can be used singly or in combination to form a specific width. In this way it is possible to form all four sides of a box from a single piece (Figure 3-25-3).

The narrower clamping bars allow the initially bent ends of a box to pass beside them and make the side bends. Using a box break, you can form a nose rib curve, then form the spar attachment flange with a simple straight bend. This couldn't be done with a cornice break. Junction boxes can be formed in one piece, complete with riveting flanges. While layouts can be a bit more complex, the finished part will be much better. Repair parts having two joining flanges can be formed simply and quickly.

The only parts difficult to form are those having joining angles that are less than 90 degrees. However even these can be formed by using annealed material and straightening after forming.

Press Brake

A press brake is best for bending heavier sheet metal used in transport category airplanes. They operate by pressing, or pushing, the material between upper and a lower formed

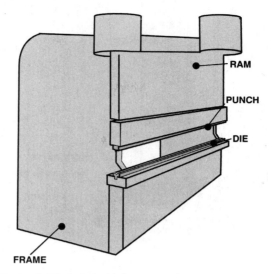

Figure 3-25-4. A typical press brake

dies. The result is a bend that has the form of the dies used. Press brakes come in a variety of sizes also, but the capacities are normally higher that cornice brakes. Figure 3-25-4 illustrates a common type of press brake.

While some smaller press brakes are hand operated, most are hydraulically powered with foot operated controls. This leaves the hands free to control the position of the material being bent. It also means you can get hurt if you put your hands in the wrong place at the wrong time. Be careful!

A variety or upper and lower dies are available for press brakes. Additionally, the method of changing a bend radius by using a pre-formed shoe can also be used, just as with a cornice break (Figure 3-25-5).

Slip Roll Former

The slip roll former is manually operated and consists of three rolls, two housings, a base, and a handle (Figure 3-25-6). The handle turns the two front rolls through a system of gears enclosed in the housing.

The front rolls serve as feeding or gripping rolls. The rear roll gives the proper curvature to the work. The front rolls are adjusted by two front adjusting screws on each end of the machine. The rear roll is adjusted by two screws at the rear of each housing. The front and rear rolls are grooved to permit forming of objects with wired edges. The upper roll is equipped with a release which permits easy removal of the metal after it has been formed.

When using the slip roll former, the lower front roll must be raised or lowered so that the sheet

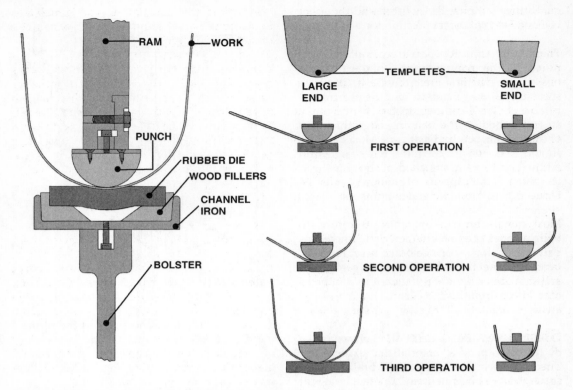

Figure 3-25-5. A typical punch and die arrangement for forming a leading edge

of metal can be inserted. If the object has a folded edge, there must be enough clearance between the rolls to prevent flattening the fold. If a metal requiring special care (such as aluminum) is being formed, the rolls must be clean and free of imperfections.

The rear roll must be adjusted to give the proper curvature to the part being formed. There are no gauges that indicate settings for a specific diameter; therefore, trial-and-error settings must be used to obtain the desired curvature.

The metal should be inserted between the rolls from the front of the machine. Start the metal between the rolls by rotating the operating handle in a clockwise direction.

A starting edge is formed by holding the operating handle firmly with the right hand and raising the metal with the left hand. The bend of the starting edge is determined by the diameter of the part being formed. If the edge of the part is to be flat or nearly flat, a starting edge should not be formed.

Be sure that fingers or loose clothing are clear of the rolls before the actual forming operation is started. Rotate the operating handle until the metal is partly through the rolls and change the left hand from the front edge of the sheet to the upper edge of the sheet. Then roll the remainder of the sheet through the machine.

If the desired curvature is not obtained, return the metal to its starting position by rotating the handle counterclockwise. Raise or lower the rear roll and roll the metal through the rolls again. Repeat this procedure until the desired

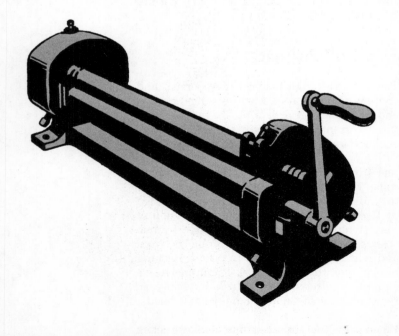

Figure 3-25-6. A slip roll former

curvature is obtained, then release the upper roll and remove the metal.

Frequently, each edge of a piece of material rolled in a slip roll will take a odd set, instead of being smoothly curved. To make the curve smooth end-to-end, sandwich the part between two pieces of like material. This will make a smooth curve clear to the edge. Be careful not to exceed the rolls capacity.

If the part to be formed has a tapered shape, the rear roll should be set so that the rolls are closer together on one end than on the opposite end. The amount of this adjustment will have to be determined by experiment. If the job being formed has a wired edge, the distance between the upper and lower rolls and the distance between the lower front roll and the rear roll should be slightly greater at the wired end than at the opposite end.

Shrinkers and Stretchers

The most common shrinking and stretching machines are foot or hand operated (Figure 3-25-7). While power units are available, their use is limited to very large shops.

Designed for use with material in the annealed condition, these machines operate by first clamping the work in their jaws, then making a small movement either inward or outward, depending on the machine. This movement stretches or shrinks the material a small amount with each stroke.

When used for removing excess material left over from other forming operations, a shrinker will allow you to finish a wrinkled flange easily. Both machines are extremely useful when making cowling, fairings, or other parts having compound curves.

Parts formed by shrinkers and stretchers can be accomplished by hand operations, but the machines make a better looking job, and do it with much less effort. A technician who has not mastered shrinking with a hammer can do good work on the machine.

Flange Forming Machines

Any shop that does extensive forming operations, or many one of a kind projects, could put a flange forming machine to good use. The machines are expensive, but do not place many limits on the parts that can be fabricated.

Because of the quality of the finished work, parts can be fabricated not only for repair, fre-

quently the part can be replaced completely. Replacement always makes a job look better than piecing together a repair.

Wing rib repair parts can be fabricated very accurately. Little, if any, hand forming or straightening will be necessary when using a flange former. Bulkheads and bulkhead repair parts are more accurate than trying to hand form the parts. This is especially important when repairing older airplanes for which major repair parts are no longer available.

Hydropress

Although not specifically a flange forming machine, a hydropress, Figure 3-25-8, can be an invaluable tool for forming repair parts. Principally, a hydropress works by pressing the material to be formed around a die, using a rubber blanket to apply the pressure. Most

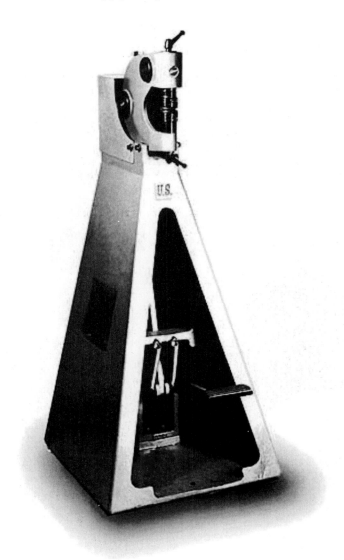

Figure 3-25-7. A typical foot operated shrinker

Courtesy of US Industrial Tool and Supply Company

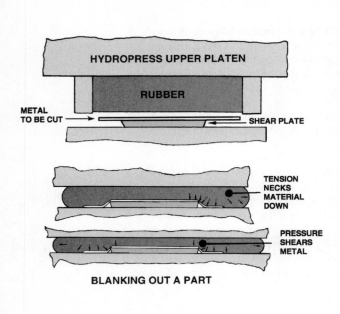

Figure 3-25-8. Hydropress operation

Figure 3-25-9. English wheel forming roller
Courtesy of US Industrial Tool and Supply Company

hydropresses are very large and expensive remnants from some manufacturing operation. When considering tooling cost, operator experience, and production speed, a hydropress can outperform most other forming tools.

Dies, or form blocks, can be made from readily available hardwood, thus reducing tooling costs. It is not unreasonable to make a form block to produce one part. This is one of the best methods of reproducing a nose rib or part of a former. As usual, material should be in the annealed condition for forming.

The English Wheel

Originally developed for forming compound curves for automobiles, the English wheel (Figure 3-25-9) is a forming tool that has found increased use in aviation sheet metal work. It consists of an upper and lower roller between which the sheet metal is pushed back and forth. The metal then takes a curve according to the shape of the lower roller and the amount of pressure between the rollers during each successive pass. By making several passes and increasing the pressure between the rollers with each pass, the amount of the curve can be controlled.

One major advantage of wheel forming is a constant decrease in the thickness of the metal as it is stretched. The prospect of localized stretching from hammer blows is not a problem. With experience, the forming appears flawless.

Stretch Presses

Another forming method in common use is stretch pressing. Used mostly for production because of the cost of set-up, stretch forming is nonetheless an excellent forming method.

Basically it consists of a machine with a hydraulic ram and a clamping arraignment through which the ram can project. The metal to be formed is clamped to the table and the ram, under considerable force, is raised against

it. The result is a piece of metal being formed by taking on the shape of the die that it is forced to stretch around.

Stretch presses also form metal with a fairly constant thickness reduction, and little workhardening. Very large presses can form many of the compound forms found on today's metal airplanes.

Other Tooling

There are many other tools that can be used for forming, but the ones presented above are the most popular. As with most things, it is not so much the operation of the tools, but the workmanship, that really counts.

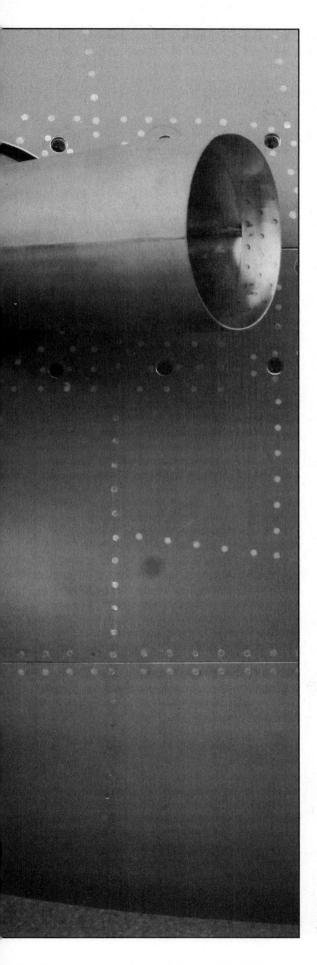

4

Aircraft Riveting

Section 1

Aircraft Rivets and Riveting

More than 150,000 rivets are required in the production of one medium size transport plane and nearly a half million in the production of a larger type.

Each job you are required to do will call for a specific type of rivet. This includes not only the shape of the rivet head but also the kind of metal of which it is made — that is, whether it is made of aluminum or of aluminum alloy, and if an alloy, which one.

Rivets consist of a solid shank capped with a head of various shapes. During the process of riveting you form a head on the end of the shank opposite the manufactured head. This process is known as bucking or upsetting the rivet.

The manufactured heads on AN or MS standard aluminum and aluminum alloy rivets are of five basic shapes. They are identified by the code numbers as shown in Figure 4-1-1.

The Brazier Head rivets (AN455 and AN456) were used extensively for riveting thin sheet (skin) exposed to the slip stream. They are also used in floats and hulls. These rivets will only be found on older airplanes. In general practice they have been replaced with MS20470 Universal head rivets.

Flat head rivets (AN442) are sometimes used on the inside of aircraft structures where increased clearance is necessary. They are also used in the construction of riveted fuel and oil tanks.

Learning Objective

DESCRIBE
- riveting tools
- flush riveting

EXPLAIN
- how to identify a rivet
- rivet heat treatment

APPLY
- properly space rivets
- install and remove rivets
- inspect rivets

Left. Thousands of rivets are used in the construction of a typical aircraft.

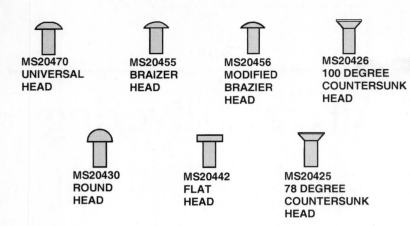

Figure 4-1-1. Rivet identification by head style

head monel, MS20613 Universal head Stainless steel, and MS20427 100° countersunk rivet is made from carbon steel, corrosion-resistant steel, monel, or copper.

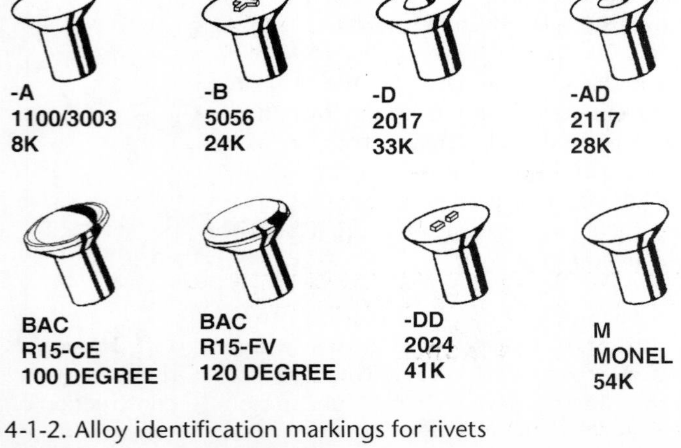

Identification of Rivets

This discussion of rivets so far has dealt with head shapes. When you are selecting a rivet for a specific job, you can distinguish at glance what shape it has. But aircraft rivets are made principally from five kinds of aluminum or aluminum alloy. How do you know which is which? To make their identification easy, AN and MS standards specify a different rivet head marking for each of the five major rivet alloys (Figure 4-1-2.) Any head shape may be any of the five alloy designations. For instance, a universal head rivet could be a type A, D, AD, DD, or B.

Notice that 1100 and 3003 rivets, type A, have a plain head without markings. To distinguish between the two, they are sometimes stamped 2 or 3 on the end of the shank, denoting 1100 or 3003.

The 5056–T rivet, type B, is identified by a raised cross on the head.

The 2017–T rivet, type D, has a bump or raised teat on the center of the head for identification.

The 2117–T rivet, type AD has a dimple in the center of its head.

Boeing Aircraft Company rivets are identified by their special head shapes. They can be made from several different alloys. They have no AN or MS number.

The 2024–T rivet, type DD, is identified by two raised bars, or dashes, on opposite sides of the head.

Special monel and stainless steel rivets have a smooth head with no markings.

NOTE: *There are several special head markings that are not identified here. Uncommon rivets can be identified by their special usage.*

MS and AN Rivet Code

The MS rivet code is the current standard. For practical purposes it is not much different than the AN code. In the MS system all solid rivets are in the 20,000 series of classifications. Thus rivet callouts become MS20xxx, with the x's being replaced by the old AN numbers. Additionally, the Universal head rivet can be

The Round Head rivet (AN430) is used in relatively thick sheets and for inside riveting where strength is required. The size of the head is such that it covers a sufficient area around the hole and at the same time offers considerable resistance to tension.

The Universal head rivet (MS20470) may be used to replace all raised head rivets and is the current standard.

Countersunk rivets (MS20426) are used because they offer the least resistance to air flow. They are therefore used on many airplanes for external riveting of thin sheet metal which is exposed to the slip stream. In order to use this rivet head on thin sheet it is necessary to dimple (sometimes called press countersinking) the sheet. Otherwise the countersunk plate will not be strong enough to support the head of the rivet. Countersunk rivets are also used to rivet thick sheets over which other plates must fit, because they do not protrude.

Special rivets made from different materials have different MS numbers; MS20615 Universal

Figure 4-1-2. Alloy identificaiton markings for rivets

RIVET SHANK DIAMETER	DRILL NUMBER	DRILL DECIMAL
$1/16$	52	0.0635
$3/32$	41	0.0960
$1/8$	30	0.1285
$5/32$	21	0.1590
$3/16$	11	0.1910
$1/4$	#F	0.2570

Table 4-1-1. Drill sizes for rivets

RIVET TYPE	USAGE
A	Parts fabricated from 1100 and 3003 alloys
AD	Parts fabricated from 2117 alloy
D	Parts fabricated from 2024 alloy
DD	Parts fabricated from 2024 alloy and as a substitute for AD and D rivets

Table 4-1-2. Selection of rivets

used to replace all protruding head rivets. Here are both old and new numbers:

- AN426 100° Countersunk head - MS20426 100° Countersunk head
- AN430 Round head - MS20470 Universal head
- AN442 Flat head - MS20470 Universal head
- AN455 Brazier head - MS20470 Universal head
- AN456 Modified Brazier head - MS20470 Universal head

For example, suppose you received instructions to use an MS20470 AD-4-5 rivet to do a specific job. What does it mean?

The letters MS means Military Specifications. The 20470, tells you the head shape of the rivet. The two letters, AD, designate the alloy from which the rivet is made. A set of two dash numbers (in this case, -4-5) tell you the diameter and the length of the rivet. The first dash number indicates the diameter in thirty-seconds of an inch and the second is the length in sixteenths of an inch.

Rivets come in various diameters and lengths. The most common rivet diameters are shown in Table 4-1-1 which also gives the sizes of drills to be used for the various diameters of rivets. A drill from 0.002 to 0.004 inch larger than the rivet should be used for sheet and plate riveting.

There are three things you must remember in selecting the correct rivet for the job: the composition of the rivet, the rivet diameter, and the rivet length.

Selecting the rivet of the correct aluminum alloy is very important because, as you learned earlier, rivets carry shear stress. The full shear strength of a riveted joint depends upon the proper combination of material and rivet. If a hard rivet such as 2017–T is driven into a

soft plate such as 1100–0 or 3003–0, the result would be distortion of the sheet. In addition, you would lose completely the high shear strength value of the 2017–T rivet.

Authorities say that it is poor practice to drive a hard rivet into soft metal. But on the other hand, it may, at times, be advisable to use a soft rivet for hard material, especially if the joint is not subjected to unduly high stress. In general, however, the material in the rivet should possess the same properties as the metal it is to be driven into. Table 4-1-2 is a handy guide for this purpose.

The full strength of a riveted joint depends upon picking a rivet of the correct length and diameter. If a large-diameter rivet were inserted in a thin sheet, the pressure required to drive the rivet would result in bulging the thin metal around the rivet head. The accepted rule is to use a rivet whose diameter is three times the thickness of the thickest section through which the rivet is driven. Round up, not down, to the next thirty-second of an inch (Figure 4-1-3).

In any case, the rivet diameter should not be less than the thickness of the thickest plate through which it is driven. Rivets smaller than $3/32$ inch in diameter should not be used for any structural parts which carry stress. On the other hand, very few rivets are used which are more than $5/16$ inch in diameter.

It is decidedly important that the rivet be of the correct length because a rivet that is too long

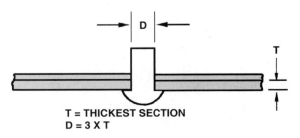

T = THICKEST SECTION
D = 3 X T

Figure 4-1-3. Rivet diameter

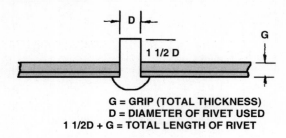

Figure 4-1-4. Rivet length

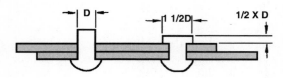

Figure 4-1-5. A properly headed rivet

has a tendency to bend when headed. On the other hand, a too-short rivet will prove too difficult to head and almost impossible to shape properly. The correct length of the rivet should equal the sum of the thickness of the metal plus $1\frac{1}{2}$ times the diameter of the rivet shank, as in Figure 4-1-4.

You also have to know what constitutes a properly headed rivet if you want to pass inspection. In other words, a rivet, to be effective, must be squashed within certain limits. This can only be done if all the conditions mentioned earlier have been strictly followed — particularly the one in regard to the rivet length. In general, the height of the bucktail should equal $\frac{1}{2}$ times the rivet diameter. The minimum width of the bucktail should be $1\frac{1}{2}$ times the rivet diameter. For instance, a properly headed $\frac{1}{8}$ inch rivet should extend a distance of $\frac{1}{16}$ inch above the surface of the metal with the head approximately $\frac{3}{16}$ inch across the flat. Figure 4-1-5 shows a before and after view of the head process.

Rivet Spacing

Rivets should be spaced not less than a distance equal to three times the rivet diameter, and not more than twelve times the rivet diameter.

In practice, the center-to-center distance is usually from 4D to 8D, depending upon the requirements of the job at hand.

Rivets should be spaced in from the edge of the sheet an absolute minimum of twice the rivet diameter. Countersunk rivets this distance must be $2\frac{1}{2}$ times the diameter, as in Figure 4-1-6.

Here are some rules for riveting in general repair work:

- The rivet size should be the same as that of the original rivets as far as possible, or larger.

- The spacing should be kept the same as the spacing of the part being repaired unless closer spacing is necessary.

- Enough rivets must be installed to insure the strength of the parts to be joined.

- When possible, allow an edge distance of 3D. This will allow for the installation of a rivet one size larger during some future repair.

Tips on Aluminum Alloy Rivets

Sometimes a rivet of a certain aluminum alloy can be substituted for a rivet of another alloy. Here are the rules for the selection and use of rivets made of the three common aluminum alloys, 2117–T, 2017–T, and 2024–T:

- **2117-T** — The most widely used aluminum alloy rivet for structural parts. It is used for practically all assembly and repair work to structural parts. This rivet is always heat-treated by the rivet manufacturer and may be driven in the fully heat-treated condition,

- **2017-T** — Not very widely used in aircraft structures, except in highly stressed fittings. These rivets are considered to be icebox rivets, therefore making it difficult for the technician to work with them. 2017–T rivets of $\frac{3}{16}$ inch diameter or less may be replaced with 2117–T rivets providing the replacement rivet is $\frac{1}{32}$ inch larger in diameter, and providing edge distance and rivet spacing is not less than minimum. 2017–T rivets of $\frac{3}{16}$ inch diameter or less may be driven in the heat-treated condition, but those above $\frac{3}{16}$ inch diameter should be kept refrigerated in the as quenched condition or heat-treated just prior to driving.

- **2024-T** — Usually used for highly stressed fittings only. These rivets are definitely considered icebox rivets, making it very difficult to work with them. 2024-T rivets of $\frac{5}{32}$ inch diameter or less may be replaced with 2117–T rivets providing the replacement rivet is $\frac{1}{32}$ inch larger in diameter, and providing edge distance and rivet spacing is not less than the minimum. All 2024-T rivets should be kept refrigerated in the as quenched condition or heat-treated just prior to driving.

In the replacement of rivets in those installations which require rivet heads that match, as in historical restorations, all activities should try to use whichever of rivets, AN430, AN442, AN456, and AN455 that corresponds to the type of rivet removed.

Countersunk head rivets are to be replaced by rivets of the same type and degree of countersunk head, and of a size larger if necessary, as when the rivet hole has become enlarged, deformed, or otherwise damaged. Advisory Circular 43.13-1B states that MS20470 rivets may be used to replace all raised head rivets, and in regular repair work they should be used in place of the old style AN rivets.

Hand Riveting

To do hand riveting you need two tools — a hammer and bucking block. The bucking block is held against the rivet head while you strike the end of the rivet with the face of the hammer.

A medium weight ball-peen hammer or a riveting hammer may be used. Don't try to use too heavy a hammer because it tends to stretch the metal too much, while one that is too light requires you to use too many blows. This means that the rivet will strain-harden rapidly.

The bucking block should have a cup-like depression in the end to take care of the rivet head. The depression should be slightly shallower and also wider than the head of the rivet in order not to distort it. Figure 4-1-7 shows correct and incorrect shapes for this cup-like depression. A rivet set like that used on pneumatic riveters makes a very good bucking bar for hand riveting if you support it in a steel block. Any piece of steel or cast iron is satisfactory. Simply drill a hole in the metal and stick the shank of the set into it, as in Figure 4-1-7.

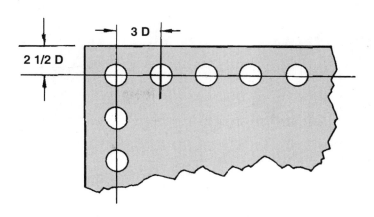

Figure 4-1-6. Rivet spacing

The first step in hand riveting is, of course, to drill a hole for the rivet, The hole must be of the right size. This is important because if the openings are too small, the rivets must be forced through. Forcing leaves tiny grooves on the shanks of rivets which materially affect their strength. There is also a tendency to buckle the metal. On the other hand, large holes are objectionable, because the shanks of the rivets are liable to bend during the heading operations. A series of holes that are too large will permit the sheet to shift out of alignment.

After the holes have been drilled, remove all burrs by using a chip chaser, de-burring tool, reamer, or countersink. A drill slightly larger than the hole is usually used to remove these burrs. Special beburring tools should be purchased, and are well suited for large jobs.

As an extra precaution against marring the heads of rivets, use rivet tape to hold the unbucked rivets in place during heading.

Decide on the diameter and length of the rivet you will use.

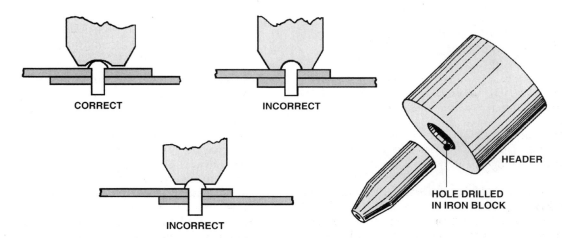

Figure 4-1-7. Hand riveting bucking bars.

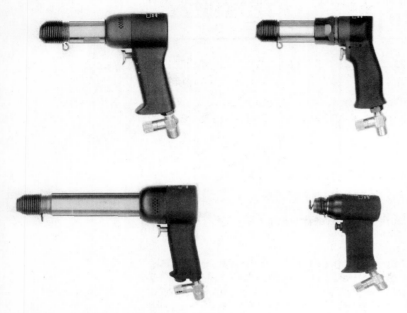

Figure 4-1-8. Pneumatic riveting hammers

Courtesy of US Industrial Tool and Supply Company

Now, place the section of metal to be riveted over the bucking block with the rivet head resting in the cup. If the riveting is to be done on a structural piece, a separate rivet set and bucking bar must be used.

Strike the end of the rivet with the face of the hammer and make sure that each blow hits the rivet shank squarely. After striking the rivet a few times stop and check the bucked end.

Figure 4-1-9. Hand and air operated compression riveters

Courtesy of US Industrial Tool and Supply Company

Pneumatic Riveting

Most riveting is done with a pneumatic riveter. There are four common kinds (Figure 4-1-8). These are the slow hitting, fast hitting, one shot, and compression or squeeze types. Examples of compression riveters are shown in Figure 4-1-9.

Slow hitting riveting hammers have a speed up to approximately 2,500 blows per minute (BPM). The fast hitting hammers range from 2,000 to 5,000 blows per minute. These slow and fast hitting hammers come in various shapes and sizes for the different types of repair work you will have to do.

One shot riveting hammers are generally larger than either slow or fast hitting hammers. As you can guess from the name, the valve mechanism is designed so that each time you pull the trigger a rivet is headed with one blow.

Pneumatic and hand squeeze riveters range in size from the small portable to the large stationary types. They have interchangeable rivet sets so that all sorts of rivets may be driven. When you pull the trigger or press the handles together, the bucking bar (flat set) moves forward on one side and forms the shop head with a direct squeezing action against a rivet set of the proper head type on the other side of the jaw.

These sets can be adjusted so that you can drive different size rivets to the proper heights. One work-saving feature of the squeeze riveter is that after it is set, all of the rivets will be driven in a uniform manner.

How To Choose The Right Gun

You decide upon which gun to use by taking into account the size and the type of alloy of which the rivets are made, and in addition, the accessibility of the place into which the rivets are to be driven.

For instance, if you want to drive medium size, heat-treated rivets which are in accessible places, the slow hitting rivet gun is the one to choose.

For small, soft alloy rivets you should use a fast hitting gun. What would you do if you had to drive medium-size rivets in a corner? Obviously, you couldn't choose a conventional type gun. Instead, you would choose a corner gun, or one having an offset rivet set.

For heavier riveting, use a one shot riveter. While under certain conditions this kind of gun is the fastest means of riveting, you cannot use it on thin metal because it is difficult to control.

A squeeze riveter should be used on the trailing edges, wing root sections, and along those edges where the yoke of this type of gun will fit.

Table 4-1-3 lists the approximate air pressures for rivet guns according to the size of the rivet which is to be driven.

You will usually have no one to blame but yourself if your rivet gun becomes injured. Carelessness is the greatest cause of damage to rivet guns. If you drop it, a number of bad things happen. You may find your gun has a cracked handle, a damaged barrel, or a broken trigger, air inlet, or adjusting sleeve.

As in the case of most tools or machines which have movable parts, you will find that your rivet gun wears out unless you take good care of it. Rivet guns should have a systematic cleaning in a mixture of kerosene and oil at least once a month. They should be regularly oiled.

When guns are in constant use, this procedure for oiling at the cylinder and piston should be followed daily:

1. Invert the gun and inject a small amount of light high grade machine oil into the air inlet.

2. Attach the hose.

3. Allow the gun to operate for about five seconds as you hold the set against a block of soft material (wood).

Never allow a gun to be operated without a set in it and always be sure the set is held against a rivet or a soft solid object such as a block of wood.

Sometimes the handle becomes loose on the barrel. Look out for this and always tighten it to prevent injury both to yourself and to the gun.

Most guns have an adjustable sleeve which regulates their speed and force. Always check this sleeve to see that the pressure is not too great. In no case should the sleeve be loosened so that the adjusting pin sticks out beyond it.

Rivet Sets

When you pull the trigger on a pneumatic riveter, the compressed air forces the piston in the cylinder back and forth with great rapidity. The impact of the piston is passed along to the rivet through the rivet set, or die, which is fitted by means of a retaining spring into the nose of the gun. A selection of rivet sets is shown in Figure 4-1-10.

RIVET SIZE	AIR PRESSURE (p.s.i.)
$^3/_{32}$	25
$^1/_8$	40
$^5/_{32}$	60
$^3/_{16}$	90

Table 4-1-3. Approximate air pressure for rivet guns

The tips of these rivets sets are made to fit the manufactured head of the rivet.

For flush riveting you use a rivet set with a flat face or slightly crowned face.

Keep your sets in good condition — highly polished and free from nicks or scratches. Never test the air pressure of your riveter by putting a rivet set against a steel or solid object. Use instead a soft wood block which is clean and has no dirt or metal particles to mar the rivet set.

Rivet sets are made in a variety of sizes and shapes. In many places where rivets can't be reached with a straight set, you will use an offset, or angular set.

Rivet sets or dies used for the same size rivet are made in several different lengths. The choice of the proper length to use depends upon the driving conditions. When it is possible to get the gun close to the work, use a short straight set since it is most efficient. When structural interference prevents you from getting close to the work, longer sets should be used.

Bucking Bars

When riveting with the pneumatic riveter, you will find it best to work with a partner. The

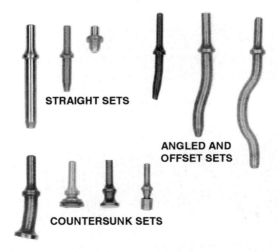

Figure 4-1-10. Rivet sets

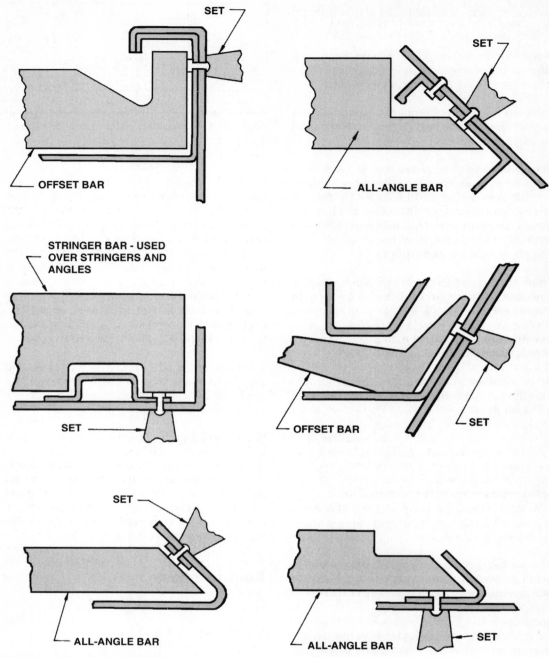

Figure 4-1-11. Using bucking bars.

gunner operates the riveter while the bucker bucks up the rivet by holding a bucking dolly or bucking bar against the rivet shank on the opposite side of the parts to be riveted.

The buckers job is usually more difficult than that of the gunner, since he often has to squirm around in cramped quarters to hold the bucking bar correctly against the rivet.

Bucking bars are usually made of tool steel. They should be heavy enough to buck the rivet solidly, yet light enough to be conveniently handled when bucking. Actually the size, shape and weight of the bar will be

determined by the size, kind, and location of the rivets being bucked. In Figure 4-1-11 are examples of bars used in various locations. Where you run into obstructions, or when you work in places where a plain bucking bar won't do, you may have to make up special bars.

If you follow this procedure carefully, you should do a good job:

1. First select a rivet gun which is right for the job. Be sure that the air line is free from dirt or lint and that it is securely fastened before you open the valve.

2. Then pick a rivet set which has the correct head for the rivet to be used. Check to see that the shank of the rivet set will fit into the gun.

3. Now fit the rivet set into the gun.

WARNING: *Be sure the retaining spring is in place. If it isn't, the set might be thrown from the gun if the trigger is pressed accidentally.*

Even though a modern airplane has hundreds of thousands of rivets, each rivet has an important function and will bear a definite amount of stress. If one rivet fails, there is an added burden on the next one, and on the next, and so forth. A whole line of rivets may start popping and result in structural failure.

Drive every rivet perfectly in order to be sure you have a good, sound structure with uniform strength (Figure 4-1-12).

Butt the rivet set against a block of soft, clean wood and adjust the speed of the gun to suit the job. You will get to know the right speed for different conditions as you gain experience. Try driving a few experimental rivets in some scrap aluminum before you attempt to drive the actual part.

Now you are ready to go. Press the gun set (with the rivet set fitted into it) firmly against the rivet head. Be sure to hold the gun and set at right angles to the material. In this way, you avoid marking the rivet head or leaving a ring or dent (smile) on the surrounding metal.

The bucking bar must also be held in the right angle position. It is placed squarely on the rivet shank. Never operate the rivet gun until your partner with the bucking bar gives you the go sign. And always be sure that the rivet gun is completely through operating before either the gun or bucking bar is taken away. Otherwise, both heads and shanks of the rivet and both sides of the skin may be spoiled.

The bucking bar must be held firmly — no shifting around. Faulty rivets are the result of permitting the bar to wobble.

CAUTION: *Do not hold the bucking bar in such a manner that the force from the air hammer will pass to the wrist or elbow joints. The rapid severe jolting can cause injury.*

If the sheets do not fit together snugly when the rivet is inserted, or the rivet seems a bit too tight to allow the sheets to fit snugly, draw the pieces of metal together before you start riveting. Put the bucking bar against the metal alongside the rivet's shank or use a special drawing bar. Then

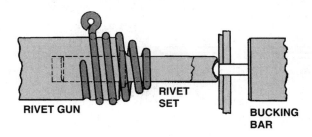

RIVET GUN   RIVET SET   BUCKING BAR

Figure 4-1-12. Driving a rivet

give the bar a short burst from the gun. This trick will draw the two pieces together enough to permit you to drive the rivet. Be careful because done incorrectly, this process will do a lot of damage. Practice a bit before you try to do a draw.

The actual Military Specification for driving solid rivets is MIL-R-47196A(MI) dated 6 September 1977.

Section 2
Rivet Inspection

After driving any solid rivet, you must inspect it to make sure you did it perfectly. practice will allow you to know a good rivet from a bad one just by the sound of the driving process. To judge by sound will allow you to continue the process and then do all of your inspection at one time. Figure 4-2-1 shows some of the more common defects you might produce. These are not all the things you could do, only the most common.

Common Defects

- Normally caused by sliding the bucking bar sideways. An eccentric head can be acceptable if none of the hole is showing.

- Stepped rivet heads are created by having the bar on part of the shank. They may be acceptable if the head meets the height standard.

- A sloped head is caused from a crooked bar. If H1 is not too short and H2 not too long, it may be acceptable.

- Normally caused from using a set one size too small. A marred head may be acceptable if the cut is less than $1/4$ of the head height.

- Not centering the set on the rivet can cause this. See above.

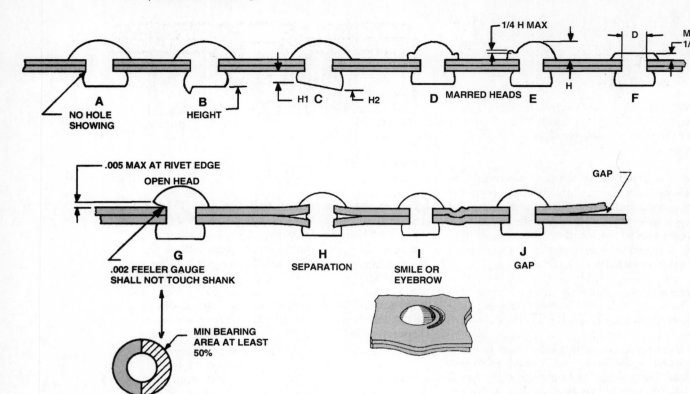

Figure 4-2-1. Protruding head rivet defects

- Flush set on a protruding head rivet. Remaining head height must be at least $^{1}/_{3}$ shank diameter.

- Set at an angle causes this. Obviously not acceptable in fuel tanks or most pressurized areas. If a 0.002 inch feeler gauge cannot be inserted to the rivet shank, 50 percent of the head is tight against the sheet, and the gap is not over 0.005 inch, most standards will let it go.

- Most common cause of separation is a tight fitting rivet and or failure to draw the sheets together before driving. Not cleaning out chips before driving can cause the same problem. Not acceptable.

- Holding the set at an angle and allowing the edge to contact the sheet causes this. Acceptance depends on the degree of damage. Some minor marring may be acceptable, while anything bad enough to cause a stress riser will have to be repaired.

- Edge gaps can be caused from not having enough air pressure on the hammer and driving so much the metal stretches. Also from not having the sheets flat to start with. Gaps are not acceptable in fuel tanks, pressurized areas, or anywhere sealing is required. Depending on company standards, some small gap may be allowed in other areas.

Cracked Bucktails

Some cracking of the upset heads frequently occurs, especially with the higher strength rivet alloys. cracking does not normally appear on a freshly driven rivet, but must be expected anyway. Depending on the severity and direction the cracks propogate, they may be acceptable. They will have to be compared to the manufacturers standards.

Acceptable standards for cracked bucktails do not appear in FAA AC43.13-1B or in MIL-HDBK-5. References do appear in Military Specification MIL-R-47196A(MI). The Mil Spec may or may not be considered approved material by your FAA inspector.

Acceptable Standards

The best place to find acceptable standards is in the manufacturers overhaul manual.

In the case of smaller General Aviation airplanes, standards are most generally referred to FAA AC43.13-1B. Unfortunately, FAA AC43.13-1B refers to MIL-HBDK-5. MIL-HBDK-5 section 8.1.2 ("Solid Rivets"), simply refers to the shear and bearing strengths of individual rivets and rivets in assemblies. In essence, if you can prove that a bad rivet meets shear and bearing standards, it is acceptable.

However, the process is so complicated that it is not practical. The practical process is to simply replace the rivet with one that can pass inspection without question.

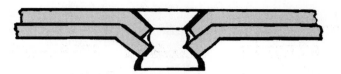

FLUSH RIVET IN A DIMPLED HOLE

Figure 4-3-1. Dimpling dies

Section 3

Flush Riveting

Engineers have overcome drag wherever possible by using flush rivets on exterior surfaces subject to airflow or, in the case of floats, subject to water flow on the bottom. This method of riveting is also used where one part must be fitted over another without the interference of protruding rivet heads.

Flush rivets are more difficult to install than protruding rivets because the parts being riveted must be either dimpled or countersunk, which requires one extra operation following drilling. Since flush rivets are made with angles varying from 82 to 100 degrees, it is necessary to countersink or dimple the metal to the angle of the rivet being used (Figure 4-3-1). Most of your work will be done with the 100-degree angle flush rivet.

All countersinking and dimpling must be done with extreme care to avoid having wrinkles show up in the finished job.

The process you use in preparing the sheet for flush riveting depends upon its thickness. Look at Table 4-3-1. Here you find the general recommendations on which method to use.

Radius Dimpling

Dimpling is done by pressing the metal around the rivet hole to the proper shape by using dies. Since there are different angles of countersunk rivet heads, there must be a special set of dies for each angle as well as for each size of rivet.

The 100-degree countersunk rivet is the universal standard. The old AN425 78-degree rivet has been obsolete for some time and is found today only in repair work on very old equipment. Obviously this means that you will have to redimple or recountersink the hole to take care of the AD rivet. But you must not substitute a machine countersunk hole for a previously dimpled hole.

Boeing uses an 82-degree countersink and an 82/30 degree countersink in some special applications. These applications are of the NACA type and will be spelled out on any applicable

blueprints and/or repair instructions. Do not substitute standard 100-degree angles for the special applications.

Some countersunk head machine screws used today have an 82-degree angle. This is also an angle used for some NACA countersunk rivets on the shop head. In these instances always use the correct cutter to produce the angle; most standard commercial countersinks are 82 degrees.

Dimpling dies are made in sets of two pieces as in Figure 4-3-2. One piece is known as the punch, and the other, the die. The angle cut in the punch and die is 96 degrees for use with the 100-degree head rivet The pin diameters of the punches are as follows.

- $3/32$ in rivets - 0.091 in.
- $1/8$ in. rivets - 0.123 in.
- $5/32$ in. rivets - 0.154 in.
- $3/16$ in. rivets - 0.185 in.

RIVET DIAMETER	TOP SHEET (t)	UNDER SHEET (t)	COUNTERSINK (SEE NOTE)
$3/32$	0.032 or greater	0.052 or greater	A
$3/32$	0.025 or less	0.040 or less	B
$3/32$	0.025 or less		C
$1/8$	0.040 or greater	0.064 or greater	A
$1/8$	0.032 or less	0.051 or less	B
$1/8$	0.032 or less		C
$5/32$	0.051 or greater	0.072 or greater	A
$5/32$	0.040 or less	0.064 or less	B
$5/32$	0.040 or less		C
$3/16$	0.064 or greater	0.091 or greater	A
$3/16$	0.051 or less	0.081 or less	B
$3/16$	0.051 or less		C

NOTE:
A - Machine countersink (cut) top sheet
B - Press countersink (dimple) top sheet and machine countersink under sheet(s)
C - Press countersink (dimple) top and under sheets

Table 4-3-1. Methods for countersinking

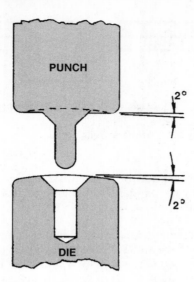

Figure 4-3-2. Dimpling die set

The holes in the corresponding dies are 0.002 inch larger in diameter than the pin of the punch.

Radius dimpling does produce a few difficulties. First, the head does not fit the dimple exactly because the edge of the dimple has a radius; hence it's name, radius dimpling. Even after shaving the rivet there is still a small unfilled groove around the rivet head. On high speed aircraft, this produces skin drag. It also makes finish painting more difficult. Secondly, there is a difference in each sheet as they are nested. Because the metal is stretched around the hole as the dies are forced together, the metal thickness in the dimple itself is not constant. This causes each additional sheet that is nested to require a different angle than the first sheet.

In the illustration of radius dimpling (Figure 4-3-3) on three sheets, it is obvious that three sets of dimple dies will need to be used to make the pieces fit. If the initial 100-degree die was used for all three, there would be serious gaps in the rivet joint and it would be unacceptable.

When you don't have the appropriate tools on hand, you can use a rivet for the punch and a block for the die (Figure 4-3-4). This block should have the correct size hole and, of course, the correct angle of countersinking. Experiment on some scrap metal of the same thickness to make sure the female block is formed correctly.

In dimpling, you predrill the rivet hole smaller than the rivet used, because the hole will be enlarged in the dimpling process.

Dimpling dies for light work can be set up in portable pneumatic or hand squeezers. For repair work, dies can be held by hand. If the dies are used with a squeezer they must be adjusted accurately to the thickness of the sheet being dimpled.

Cut Countersinking

For cut countersinking, predrill the holes to the rivet size and then countersink. The best tool for cut countersinking is a stop type of countersink (Figure 4-3-5). It has the included angle stamped on the cover. The 82-degree and 100-degree angle countersinks are used, naturally, with their respective rivets.

When using a plain cutter instead of a stop countersink, it is very difficult to hold the drill motor at the correct vertical angle. With a plain countersink chatter of the cutting edges can be a problem. Practice on a piece of scrap first. Use a slower speed and a higher pressure than used for drilling.

The most difficult surface to countersink is a curved surface. The greater the curve, the greater the difficulty. Countersinking on a sharper curve will produce an oval countersunk hole instead of a round one. Dimpling should be used instead of cut countersinking to prevent ovals.

Dimpling and Sub-Countersinking

When the lower sheet is thicker, dimpling and sub-countersinking can be used. In this process the thin upper sheet is dimpled and the thicker lower sheet is cut-countersunk, as shown in Figure 4-3-6. This allows the two to be joined quite effectively.

The setup and adjustment of the cut countersink must be carefully done because the sub-countersink will be wider than the initial dimple. The cut countersink must be adjusted

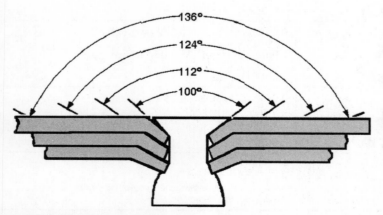

Figure 4-3-3. Dimple cross section

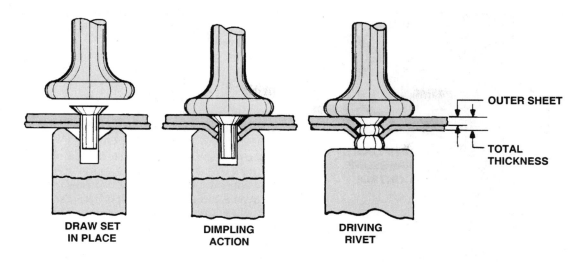

DRAW SET
IN PLACE

DIMPLING
ACTION

DRIVING
RIVET

OUTER SHEET

TOTAL
THICKNESS

Figure 4-3-4. Dimpling by drawing a rivet

using trial setups on scrap material using the final upper sheet thickness.

Press Countersinking (Coin Dimpling)

Coin dimpling could more accurately be called press forging and is accomplished both hot and cold. In coin dimpling the material is actually flowed into the shape of the dies. This leaves all of the sharp corners intact and maintains the size and thickness of the sheet throughout the dimple. The same die can be used for any number of sheets that are nested together. The coining ram, which is the center part of the female die, makes all this possible.

Coining also produces a better fit with a sub-countersunk part. The sub-countersink will be the same size as the initial dimple.

Both stationary (Figure 4-3-7) and portable (Figure 4-3-8) coin dimplers are available, and both can be used with heated dies when necessary. Heated dies are necessary when thicker material and high strength alloys are dimpled; particularly 7075 aluminum alloy. The heaters will spot anneal the material and allow the dies to do their job without cracks forming around the finished dimple. Once spot annealed and formed, the alloy reverts to its' former heat treated condition.

Although the operation of coin dimpling equipment is fairly simple, it's adjustment can be quite complex. Never try to operate or adjust any stationary or portable coin dimpler without proper instruction. If not adjusted correctly, you can severely damage the equipment very quickly.

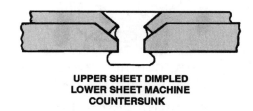

UPPER SHEET DIMPLED
LOWER SHEET MACHINE
COUNTERSUNK

Figure 4-3-6. Sub-countersinking

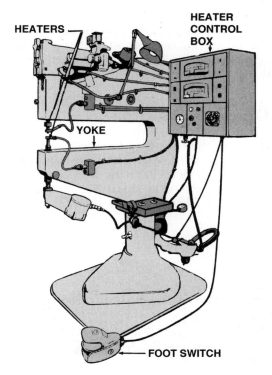

HEATERS

HEATER
CONTROL
BOX

YOKE

FOOT SWITCH

Figure 4-3-7. A large heated coin dimpler

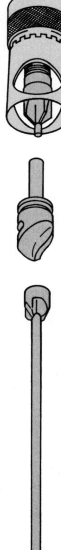

Figure 4-3-5.
Countersink cutters

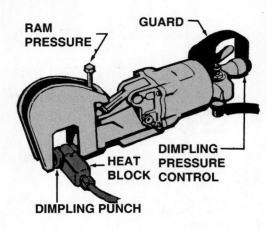

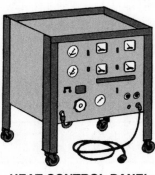

Figure 4-3-8. Portable heated coin dimpler

In both portable and stationary equipment the amount of heat, pressure, and the timing of each are closely controlled. When adjusting the equipment a sample strip the same as the part to be dimpled must be used. Never use the equipment for a real dimple job until everything checks out perfectly.

Dimple Inspection

Naturally the first thing to check is to see if the rivet fits the hole with the correct degree of flushness. The break from the sheet surface and the dimple should be sharp. The dimple also has to be checked for cracks. While any crack-

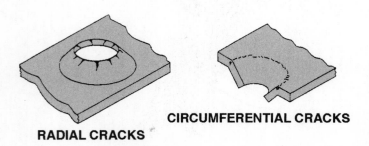

Figure 4-3-9. Coin dimple cracks

ing tendency of the setup should have been found during setup, you still have to check the finished product.

Cracks

Radial cracks

As the metal stretches it can start a radial crack (Figure 4-3-9). It is the most common in 2024-T3 alloy and can be caused by a bad hole or from too deep a dimple. Some inspection standards will allow for some small amount of radial cracking, so be sure and check the published inspection standards.

Circumferential cracks

This type of cracking is always cause for rejection of the part and can be hard to spot. They are the most common on 7075-T6 alloy and can be underneath the clad surface. The cladding being soft pure aluminum, it may simply bend and form to the shape. Circumferential cracking is normally caused from performing the dimpling operation at too low of a temperature. Once again any problems should have been found on the test pieces, but the final part must still be inspected.

Section 4

Countersink Inspection

The countersink should always be equipped with the fiber collar to prevent it from marring the aluminum. Carefully adjust and test your countersink on a piece of scrap metal to be sure that the rivet will fit into the hole with the correct amount (0.001/0.006 inch) of the outer rim extended.

If the job calls for shaving the rivets after driving then the countersink will need to be adjusted differently. A countersunk rivet with the head protruding approximately 0.005 inch before driving will protrude 0.003 inch after driving. This leaves just the correct amount for shaving. As a guide, the outer rim of a countersunk rivet is between 0.004 inch and 0.012 inch, depending on the rivet diameter.

If the under piece of metal is cut countersunk and the outer sheet is dimpled, test the two operations on scrap of the same thickness. The rivets should fit flush and the dimple sheet should fit well into the countersunk sheet.

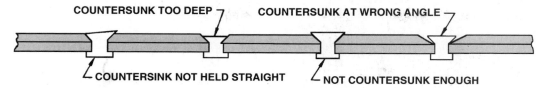

Figure 4-4-1. Incorrect cut countersinking

A stop countersink such as the one just described is operated by a drill motor, which should operate below 2,500 r.p.m. Too high a speed, or a dull cutter, can produce vibration and chatter which result in imperfect holes. Figure 4-4-1 shows some of the things that can happen when you do an incorrect job of countersinking. The shaft of the countersink should be well lubricated with light oil at all times.

outside. In a typical system of team work, the gunner places the gun set on the rivet head. The bucker gives one tap on the rivet shank to indicate that he is ready. The rivet is then upset with one burst by the riveting gun. Then, if an extra short burst is necessary to complete the riveting, the bucker taps once again. Two taps by the bucker indicate that the rivet is satisfactory. Three taps mean take it out and replace the rivet.

Always check the rivets to make certain they are driven to the proper specifications.

Section 5

Driving Flush Rivets

Now that you have learned something about the preparation of holes for flush riveting, you are ready to go ahead and do the riveting. Equipment for flush riveting is the same as any other except that the rivet sets are either flat faced or slightly arched, because, of course, you want to drive a rivet which will not protrude above the surface of the metal. There are two types of such rivet sets: the mushroom and the swivel set. The mushroom set is made in one piece. The swivel has a large face and is made with a ball joint which is surrounded by a rubber sleeve to prevent marring the aluminum and also to prevent the tool from slipping.

You will have to be considerably more careful in driving and bucking flush rivets than ordinary rivets. You and the bucker must in most cases use the signals you have figured out in order to know when the rivet is driven sufficiently.

You and your partner must each regulate the pressure which you apply on the gun and against the buckling bar so that the skin is not stretched. You don't want to produce a bulge in the sheet. Be careful to hold the rivet set flat against the rivet to avoid nicking and marking up the skin. The actual driving of the rivet is similar to that used for ordinary rivets.

You will have to devise and adopt a system of signaling to be used between you and the bucker. This is particularly important when the bucker is inside a structure and the gunner is

Section 6

Rivet Shaving

An increasingly popular method of ensuring flushness is called rivet shaving, or micro shaving. Because of the 0.005 inch rim around the standard MS20427 flush rivet, very good results can be achieved by shaving. When a rivet that has been cut-countersunk is shaved, an exceptional degree of smoothness can be achieved. Micro shaving a radius dimpled rivet does not produce good results. A rivet shaver is shown in Figure 4-6-1.

Figure 4-6-1. An air powered rivet micro shaver
Courtesy of US Industrial Tool and Supply Company

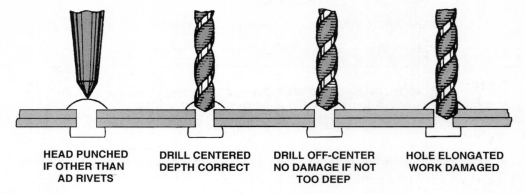

HEAD PUNCHED IF OTHER THAN AD RIVETS   **DRILL CENTERED DEPTH CORRECT**   **DRILL OFF-CENTER NO DAMAGE IF NOT TOO DEEP**   **HOLE ELONGATED WORK DAMAGED**

Figure 4-7-1. Correct and incorrect ways to drill out a rivet

Section 7

Removing Rivets

Drilling Out A Rivet

In repair work, you will be confronted with the job of removing rivets from an aluminum surface. Although the task is really simple, you must take a few precautions to avoid ruining the section. Refer to Figure 4-7-1 while reading the following:

Here's how: Lightly center punch the heads of the rivets. Pick a drill that is the same size as the shank of the rivet. Now, drill through the head of the rivet only. If you run the drill through the entire rivet, you take a chance of cutting into the sheet. Using a pin punch that is the same size as the drill, insert it in the hole and snap the rivet head off with a sideways movement and drive out the shank. Be sure you back

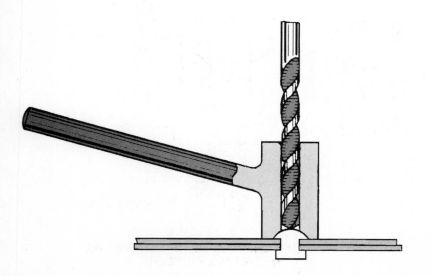

Figure 4-7-2. Drill guide for protruding head rivets

the metal up by placing a buckling bar next to the bucked head or use a wood block with an oversized hole as backup.

If the rivet to be drilled out is an AD rivet, you can use the head dimple as a center point. Any other type will have to be center punched. Use great care in punching. Don't bend the structure or sub-structure by too heavy a blow. Also use a center punch, not a prick punch or anything else. The angle produced by a center punch will more closely approach a drill point angle than any other punch.

Instead of punching each rivet, you can use a drill guide (Figure 4-7-2) to make a starting mark on protruding head rivets. Each diameter of rivet has its' own guide. To protect the guide use it only for starting the hole. Otherwise it may clog with chips and freeze the drill in the guide.

Flush rivets are removed in much the same way, with the exception of the drill and punch sizes. The drill size should be $1/64$ to $1/32$ smaller than the rivet shank and the hole drilled a little deeper. Go past the depth of the material, but do not go through the shop head. Break the rivet head off with a pin punch the same size as the drill. Use a pin punch one size smaller and a backup block to drive the rivet shank out the back. This process will also work for replacing rivets in the fuel tank areas.

After a countersunk rivet is removed, unless it is a gas tight installation, there will always be a small ring of rivet material left between the sheets. This is in the space created by the edges of the countersunk sheets not being straight with the hole. In theory, the excess material will collapse into the hole you drilled. That is why you use a smaller pin punch; to allow room for the rivet wall to collapse. If you don't do it this way, the process of punching the rivet out can severely damage the dimples and may even crack the sheet.

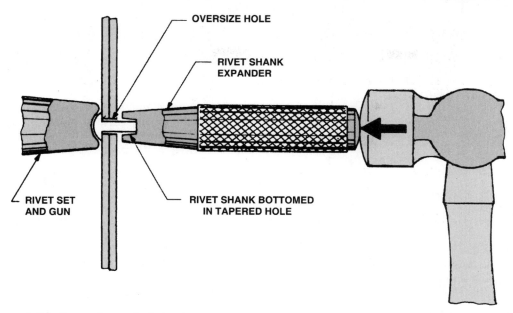

Figure 4-8-1. Expanding a rivet shank

Section 8

Special Procedures and Fixes

No matter how careful you are in preparing your work, problems do arise from time to time. In most cases you can believe that it isn't the first time the problem has surfaced. In some cases there are standard fixes.

Oversized Rivet Holes

Frequently, when removing existing sheet metal for replacement or repair, you end up with an oversized hole. If a hole is seriously oversize, the only repair is to re-drill it to the next rivet size. This is not the most desirable method because it leaves no room for future repairs. But what do you do if it is just a little oversized?

Expanding Rivet Shanks

The best way to expand a rivet shank is with a rivet shank expanding tool. Figure 4-8-1 shows the operation in cutaway. Using the rivet gun and set as a bucking bar, the expander is struck with a hammer. Because it is bucked solid, the rivet head isn't going to move. The shank will absorb the blow. To do this material has to move somewhere. The shank moves out radially and shortens its length by a like amount.

Notice that the expander has a tapered hole for the rivet. This prevents the expanding rivet

from jamming and permits removal of the tool. Now drive the rivet in the normal manner.

Countersink Repair Washers

When a machine countersunk patch needs to be placed over another part that is already countersunk, you have a problem. Somehow the lower countersink needs to be removed, or at least negated. The answer to this dilemma is a countersink repair washer as illustrated in Figure 4-8-2. In essence they are nothing but countersunk rivets with a hole drilled in the head, and no shank. They serve as a spacer to

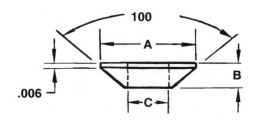

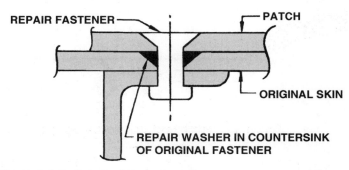

Figure 4-8-2. Countersink repair washers

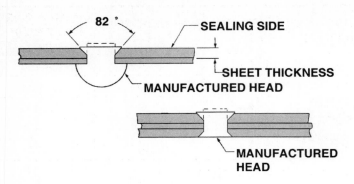

Figure 4-8-3. NACA riveting examples

bring the lower countersunk hole up to level. Normally they are used with sealant on the countersink and the washer.

Salvage Rivets

When a countersink has been oversized and the hole is too big, a salvage rivet with an oversized head may be the answer. The same can hold true when a rivet hole needs to be enlarged and the head size cannot be enlarged. A salvage rivet with a shank of the next larger rivet size can be used. This will maintain the countersink spacing edge distance and still allow the oversized shank to be used.

These rivets must be ordered special and must be kept separate from all standard rivets. Use of salvage rivets should be kept to a minimum. The next person working on the airplane will have no idea what you used. Likewise, you must stay alert to what the person ahead of you used in his repair.

NACA Riveting Method

The National Advisory Commission on Aeronautics (NACA) was an engineering group formed by the CAA (predecessor of the FAA) in the early 1930s. Its purpose was to investigate all matters aviation and establish standards. During the committees existence it produced a large volume of work, a lot of which is the basis

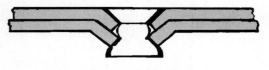

FLUSH RIVET IN A DIMPLED HOLE

Figure 4-8-4. Dimpling dies

for the way we do things today. The standard layout of sheet metal patches, engine cowling basics, and riveting procedures are just a few. NACA riveting is another process developed by them.

NACA riveting refers to countersinking a shop head instead of the manufactured head. Although they are generally driven like any other solid rivet, the process can be reversed; that is, using the gun on the shop head and a hand set for a bucking bar. If desired, the finished product can be shaved.

NACA riveting causes the maximum amount of shank swelling possible with a countersunk head. Originally they were used in places like fastening wing ribs to spar flanges allowing wing skin to fit flush.

Today you will find them used for attaching skin to stringers, rib flanges, access doors, filler necks, and for integral fuel tanks. Because of the improved shank swelling, they work especially good for integral fuel tanks. In some instances the rivets are installed wet. Figure 4-8-3 shows countersunk angles of 82 degrees, but there are many installations using standard 100 degree countersinks.

Wet Rivet Installation

Sometimes a set of instructions will call for rivets to be installed wet. While this may sound funny, it means just what it says. Before driving the rivets they are to be dipped in a liquid material and driven before the liquid dries out; thus wet. The most common dip is Zinc Chromate Primer, but the dip will always be called out in the instructions. Sometimes the dip is for corrosion prevention, sometimes for liquid proof sealing. When used for corrosion prevention the material to use is spelled out in Federal Specification TT-P-1757.

Leakproof Riveting

Integral fuel tanks can be a problem when it comes to repairs. All rivets and joints must be leak proof. Leak proof joints begin with a true rivet hole. New holes should use a drill guide.

During rivet removal you should also use a drill guide in order not to oversize the hole. The drill should be 0.030 inch smaller than the original hole size to ensure that oversize doesn't occur. A pin punch $1/32$ inch smaller than the hole size should be used to drive out the old shank.

New holes are normally drilled one rivet size smaller, then line drilled or reamed to the finish size. This will provide the most accurate finished hole for rivet installation.

As the shop head swells the most during driving, they are normally placed on the fuel side of the structure. NACA riveting is frequently found in fuel tanks. When the sheet is too thin to cut countersink, it can be dimpled. However, the normal dimple forms an air space in the center of the rivet joint as shown in Figure 4-8-4. To overcome this potential leak, dimples are made using a smaller pilot, then line drilled or reamed to the finish size. The end result is a rivet hole with smooth sides and no air spaces. Almost all fuel proof riveted seams will involve either the rivets being driven wet, or some form of sealer will be used.

TYPE OF RIVET	YIELD STRENGTH (p.s.i.)	SHEAR STRENGTH (p.s.i.)	ULTIMATE TENSILE STRENGTH (p.s.i.)
1100-H	21,000	13,000	24,000
3003-H	25,000	16,000	29,000
2117-T	18,500	25,000	38,000
2017-T	32,000	30,000	62,000
2024-T	40,000	35,000	62,000

Table 4-9-1. Comparison of strength of rivets

Section 9

Heat-Treating Rivets

Strength is an all-important factor in the construction of aircraft. And strength is one of the two qualities which heat-treating adds to rivets. Because an airplane is held together principally by rivets, it is absolutely necessary that you know when and where to use heat-treated rivets, or those that do not require heat treatment. And what's more, you have to know how to heat-treat rivets and how to take care of them so that you get the maximum benefit from their particular physical qualities. You can get some idea of the difference in strength between heat-treated and non-heat-treated rivets from Table 4-9-1. Compare the shearing and tensile strength of a 1100–H rivet and a 2024–T rivet.

As you can see from Table 4-9-1, 1100–H rivets (not heat-treated) have a shearing strength of 13,000 pounds per square inch and a tensile strength of 24,000 pounds per square inch. Alloy 2024–T rivets (heat-treated) on the other hand, have almost three times the shearing strength—35,000 pounds. Their tensile strength is 62,000 pounds. 2024–T rivets are almost three times stronger—a very important factor. It's easy to see what would happen to an airplane held together with 1100–H rivets when 2024–T rivets should have been used.

From Figure 4-9-1 it is easy to determine that the shear strength of a $1/4$ inch diameter 2117–T alloy composition rivet is approximately 1,300 pounds.

As you learned earlier, there are two general groups of rivets. Those which can be used without being heat-treated are types A and AD rivets. Those which must be heat-treated before

they can be used are D and DD rivets. In addition to developing maximum strength heat-treatment of 2017 and 2024 alloyed rivets also makes them soft so that they can be driven. Table 4-9-2 shows the single shear strength of different rivet sizes. A complete shear and bearing chart is shown in Table 4-9-3.

The most important thing to remember in getting together the equipment for heat-treating rivets is that the success of your job depends directly upon temperature control. If you overheat the rivets, they begin to disintegrate or break down. If they are not heated enough, you might as well have saved your effort. The treatment has no effect.

Rivets can be heated in either of two ways: in a bath of sodium nitrate or in a hot air furnace.

Salt Baths for Rivets

The design of the sodium nitrate baths for heat-treating rivet should be such that the rivets do not come into contact with the molten salt.

This equipment usually consists of a round tank or pot installed in a vertical electric furnace. The inside of the tank is fitted with a number of liquid-tight, vertical metal tubes, which keep the molten salt out. The clearance between these metal tubes should be at least $1/4$

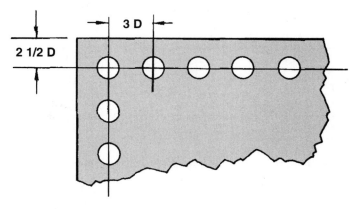

Figure 4-9-1. Rivet spacing

COMPOSITION OF RIVET (ALLOY)	ULTIMATE STRENGTH OF RIVET METAL (P.S.I.)	DIAMETER OF RIVET (INCHES)						
		$1/16$	$3/32$	$1/8$	$5/32$	$3/16$	$1/4$	$5/16$
2117-T	27,000	83	186	331	518	745	1,325	2,071
2017-T	30,000	92	206	368	573	828	1,472	2,300
2024-T	35,000	107	241	429	670	966	1,718	2,684

NOTE:
Double shear strength is found by multiplying the above values by 2.

Table 4-9-2. Single shear strength of aluminum alloy rivets (pounds)

of an inch in order to permit the salt bath to circulate freely around their outside surfaces. These tubes are about 2 inches to $2^{1}/_2$ inches in diameter. They are closed at the bottom but are left open at the top so that you can slip into them the individual rivet containers.

The top of the tank has a cover plate through which the tops of the metal tubes stick out. A close fitting insulated door covers the entire top of the tank and tubes. Thus for all practical purposes this kind of salt bath equipment is simply an air furnace in which the heat is supplied by the molten salt.

In order to make it easy for you to transfer hot rivets from the salt bath to the quenching bath, you will need perforated containers which will fit into the vertical tubes of the tank. These rivet containers should be short enough so that their tops are at least four inches below the surface of the salt bath.

You will also need a pyrometer to eliminate all guess work concerning the temperature of the rivet bath. The pyrometer should be of the automatic controlling and recording type—preferably the potentiometer type. You should also use a thermocouple designed for

THICKNESS OF SKIN (INCHES)	DISTANCE ACROSS CUTOUT IN INCHES							
	$1/8$	$1/4$	$3/8$	$1/2$	$5/8$	$3/4$	$7/8$	1
0.020	188	375	563	751	937	1,125	1,313	1,500
0.025	234	469	706	938	1,172	1,406	1,640	1,875
0.032	300	600	900	1,200	1,500	1,800	2,100	2,400
0.036	338	675	1,012	1,350	1,688	2,025	2,363	2,700
0.040	375	750	1,125	1,500	1,875	2,250	2,625	3,000
0.045	422	843	1,265	1,688	2,199	2,524	2,953	3,375
0.051	478	956	1,434	1,913	2,390	2,870	3,350	3,825
0.064	600	1,200	1,800	2,400	3,000	3,600	4,200	4,800
0.072	675	1,325	2,025	2,700	3,375	4,050	4,725	5,400
0.081	759	1,518	2,277	3,036	3,759	4,554	5,315	6,075
0.091	853	1,706	2,559	3,412	4,265	5,118	5,971	6,825
0.120	956	1,912	2,868	3,824	4,788	5,736	6,692	7,650
0.125	1,172	2,343	3,515	4,687	5,859	7,031	8,203	9,375
0.156	1,463	2,925	4,388	5,851	7,314	8,777	10,240	11,700
0.250	2,344	4,687	7,031	9,375	11,719	14,063	16,407	18,750

NOTES:
- *Total load to be carried by rivets on both sides of break with 60,000 p.s.i. assumed load and 1.25 safety factor used through out the table.*
- *The above values must be divided by the lesser value of the allowable shear or bearing strengths to obtain the number of rivets to be used on each side of the break. These values are based upon the rivet formula: L x T x 60,000 x 1.25/B or S smaller + number of rivets to be used on each side of the break*

Table 4-9-3. Simplified shear and bearing chart for aluminum alloy rivets

salt baths. Insert it into the bath in a suitable protective tube.

Heat Treating Procedure

Put the rivets in the heat furnace and allow them to soak. Soaking means holding the rivets of a given alloy at a certain temperature for a specified length of time to insure an even distribution of heat. The soaking temperature for 2017 rivets should be 925°F to 950°F. Rivets of 2024 alloy should be soaked at a temperature of 910°F to 930°F.

The time you soak them depends on a number of things. It depends upon the type of alloy, the diameter of the rivet and the type of equipment you are using.

In general, you should figure out by experimenting a little what length of time is best to produce the desired results with the equipment you have on hand.

For the salt bath equipment which has just been described, or for air furnaces provided with mechanical recirculation of air, you should not soak the rivets less than 10 minutes This soaking time does not apply, however, to the 2024 rivets.

The soaking time for 2024 rivets should not be less than 30 minutes, leaving out the time it takes the batch of rivets to reach the specified temperature. You can determine this time by placing a thermocouple within or near the bath. Charge is the technical term for the number of rivets heat-treated in any one operation. Use the thermocouple to determine the time for each size and arrangement of charge which you normally use.

After you have soaked the rivets for the specified length of time, remove the rivet container from the furnace and immediately quench the rivets in cold water. Quenching must occur within 10 seconds after removal from the furnace.

If you fail to quench the rivets immediately, they will lose their corrosion resistance, the softened quality which makes them easy to drive, and their ultimate tensile strength. See that you have enough quenching water on hand to avoid any appreciable rise in temperature during quenching.

Storing Heat-Treated Rivets

Heat-treated rivets start to age harden as soon as they are removed from the quenching bath. Age hardening is the automatic return to hardness of the alloy in the rivet following heat treatment. It occurs spontaneously at room temperature and is very rapid during the first 24 hours. Age hardening is considered complete at the end of 4 days.

Therefore, unless you put the rivets in a refrigerator or pack them in dry ice, you must drive them almost immediately. Rivets made of 2017–T alloy must be driven within one hour after quenching unless they are kept at 32°F, in which case they can be driven after one day in such storage. If they are stored in dry ice or a refrigerator below 32°F, they must be driven within one week.

Rivets of 2024–T must be driven within $1/2$ hour, preferably 10 minutes, after they have been quenched. If they are packed in dry ice following quenching, they may be driven within a 24-hour period.

Once you take rivets from a refrigerator, do not return them. Instead, place them in their proper storage place from where they may be reheat-treated. As a general rule, you can heat-treat rivets over and over again as often as you want to providing the heat-treatment is properly and carefully done. An excessive number of reheating will result in the gradual hardening of the rivets. How much is excessive? More than 15 times.

5

Aircraft Hardware

Section 1

Specifications and Standards

When all-metal aircraft were first built, the main purpose of fasteners was to carry shear loads. When additional strength was required to carry higher shear loads, the Hi-Shear rivet was developed. As the aircraft speed and size increased, manufacturers demanded fasteners which would carry shear as well as bearing and/or tensile loads.

As all-metal aircraft designs were improved and greater strength was required, the National Aircraft Standards (NAS) specified an increase in bolthead strengths. This was accomplished by adding a radius fillet between the bolthead and the shank. The fillet removed a stress concentration created by the sharp junction of the head and shank and prevented the possibility of fatigue failure, thereby allowing an increase in the bearing strength of the installed fastener.

When an even greater increase in aircraft structural strength was required, aircraft manufacturers working in conjunction with fastener companies began to develop special (load-carrying) fasteners. These new families of special fasteners were designed to carry additional bearing and shearing loads using newly developed alloys such as titanium, columbium, stainless steel, and monel.

Standard and Special Fasteners

A variety of fasteners is available for the construction of modern aircraft to meet the growing demands of the aerospace industry.

Learning Objective

DESCRIBE
• the types of rivets
• types of threaded fasteners
• control cables

EXPLAIN
• how special rivets and fasteners are installed
• how to select the correct screw
• hole repair hardware
• the use of gaskets and sealers

APPLY
• install bolts
• identify nuts and bolts
• safety wiring

Left. In addition to rivets, many other types of hardware and fasteners are used in aircraft construction.

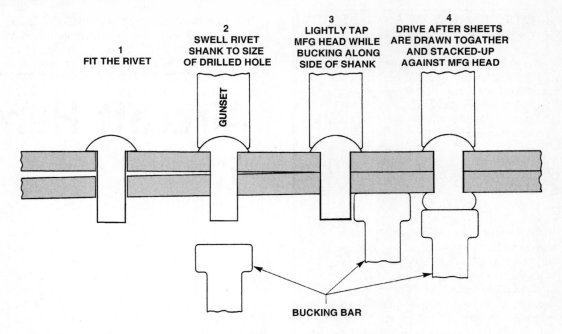

Figure 5-2-1. Driving a solid rivet

The fastening systems to be reviewed are divided according to the order in which they are most commonly used for aircraft construction and repair. The following is a list and description of fasteners most commonly used by structural technicians in the aerospace industry:

1. Standard solid-shank rivets including non-heat-treated and heat-treated types, both aluminum and alloy construction.

2. Special blind fasteners with an emphasis on those which are best used for structural applications.

3. Special structural fasteners, such as straight-pin and tapered-pin styles, which require special hole preparation.

4. Hardware other than bolts and special fasteners.

Different locking devices are used by each fastening system for locking it into place. Some fasteners are locked into place using nuts while others use swaged collars. Each fastening system uses a unique installation method or special tooling to accomplish its purpose.

The strength of a joint using fasteners is determined by the thickness of the metal and the type of fastener being used. As the thickness of the metal increases, so does the strength of the fastener's shank, head, locking collar, nut, or shop head.

One limiting factor which restricts the size of the fastener needed is the alloy from which it

is made. When a fastener is made from a stronger alloy, its diameter and head size can be kept to a minimum without sacrificing strength. Increased bearing and shearing strength will result when fasteners are manufactured from stronger alloys.

The use of stronger alloys, such as titanium, has greatly increased the strength potential in high-stress structural areas of modern turbine aircraft, such as landing gear and engine mounts. Increased strength in these high-stressed areas is the direct result of stronger fasteners, which make it possible to obtain higher strength with smaller hole sizes. The increased use of the high-strength alloys also requires the maintenance technician to become more knowledgeable in the correct application of aircraft hardware.

Section 2
Types of Hardware

Solid Rivets

Solid rivets have been considered conventional hardware ever since all-metal aircraft were first made. As the aircraft industry grew and new aircraft were being developed, the solid rivet changed in head styles and alloy content to meet the challenge. Some of the older types of aircraft rivets are still being used, but only in restoring older aircraft.

Characteristics of Driven Solid Rivets

Take-up is the ability of a fastener to bring two or more layers of material together. The solid rivet does not have the take-up characteristics of the bolt and nut combination, blind rivet, or pull-type special fastener, all of which will be discussed later in this chapter.

When a solid rivet is driven, it cannot normally compress, or take up, two or more sheets of metal. To be able to take up two or more sheets of metal, a solid rivet first needs to be partly swollen just enough to tighten the shank into the hole, then place a bucking bar adjacent to the rivet shank and with a rivet gun lightly tap the rivet until the skins are drawn together, stacking up against the manufactured head, as shown in Figure 5-2-1. The job is finished by driving the rivet to form a bucktail on the end opposite the head.

Four physical changes take place when a solid rivet is driven. The physical size of the head and shank increase, and the amount of both bearing and shearing strength increase. With these changes the rivet is said to be cold worked. The forming of the bucktail causes the rivet shank to expand, as shown in Figure 5-2-2, to the size of its hole. The expanding shank causes the metal to push out against the walls of the hole creating radial and vertical lines of stress.

Rivet Material

1100 Aluminum (A)

Not all rivets are used for structural repair work. The 1100 aluminum rivets are made from (99 percent) pure aluminum and are used for nonstructural applications. Called 1100 and assigned the AN code letter A, the 1100 rivet has no markings on its manufactured head, and for the most part always has a shiny silver finish. The need for soft fasteners to hold nonstructural members together resulted in the manufacturing of the 1100 aluminum rivet. This material is used to rivet other soft aluminum parts such as engine baffles and wing tips of older model aircraft.

2117 Aluminum Alloy (AD)

The rivet made from 2117 aluminum alloy has a shear strength comparable to other rivets of the 2000 series of aluminum alloys. (The 2000 series is alloyed with copper.) Though not the strongest of the aluminum and copper alloyed family, it is the most widely used of all structural rivets. Over 85 percent of the rivets used

in the construction of light aircraft, both internally and externally, are 2117 aluminum alloy. The main advantage of 2117 is that, unlike other types of aluminum alloy, it can be driven without treatment as it is received from the manufacturer. The alloy 2117 has a very high resistance to corrosion and excellent shock-resistant characteristics.

2017 Aluminum Alloy (D)

During the period between the end of the second world war and the start of the jet age, a once highly used rivet alloy, 2017, with AN coding of D, was reworked by the aluminum industry for use in aircraft construction. By reworking the composition of the 2017 alloy, the new form of the 2017 rivet could be driven in the condition received from the manufacturer without further treatment. Note that Table 5-2-1 is a listing of rivets used by the aerospace industry for manufacturing and repairing of aircraft.

2024 Aluminum Alloy (DD)

Older forms of aluminum alloy 2017 in sizes above $3/16$ inch, and all forms of 2024 are too hard to drive in the condition in which they are received from the manufacturer. To make 2024 aluminum alloy rivets soft enough for driving they must be reheated to the temperature of their original heat-treatment.

These rivets are softened by reheating to the proper temperature, soaking until all rivets being treated have reached the same temperature, quenching in ice cold water, then draining and storing them (until ready to use) in a freezer. Because they are stored in a freezer, they are referred to as ice box rivets. Storage at a sub-zero temperature will retard the rivet's return to its natural age hardness. When the storage temperature is cold enough, 2024 aluminum alloy (ice box) rivets can remain soft for periods of two weeks or longer. They may be reheat treated many times before they are finally driven.

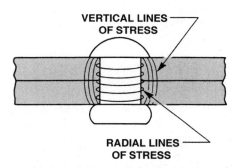
Figure 5-2-2. Lines of stress created by driving

ALLOY AND TEMPER BEFORE DRIVING	MINIMUM UNDRIVEN SHEAR STRENGTH (k.s.i.²)	DRIVING PROCEDURE	TEMPER DESIGNATION AFTER DRIVING	DRIVEN SHEAR STRENGTH (ksi²)
2017-T4	33	Cold, as received	T3	38
2017-T4	33	Cold, immediately after quenching or refrigerated	T31	34
2024-T4	37	Cold, immediately after quenching or refrigerated	T31	41
2117-T4	26	Cold, as received	T3	30
2219-T81	32	Cold, as received	T81	36
5057-H32	24	Cold, as received	H321	28
7050-T73	41	Cold, as received	T73	43

NOTES:
- These designations should be used when ordering rivets.
- Values specified in Military Specification MIL-R-5674D, "Rivets. Structural, Aluminum Alloy, Titanium, Columbium Alloy. General Specifications for," dated 15 December 1981.
- Values published in chapter 8 of MIL-HDBK-5C, "Metallic Materials and Elements for Aerospace Vehicle Structures," dated 1 December 1979. These strengths are used to obtain driven-rivet design allowable loads as defined in MIL-HDBK-5C.

Table 5-2-1. Comparison of aluminum rivets typically used to join aerospace structures

The strongest rivet alloy available for many years was 2024. Its main advantages are the ability to withstand high structural loads and its high shock resistance.

5056 Aluminum Alloy (B)

An example of a specially developed non-heat-treatable alloy, 5056 aluminum alloy gained popularity during the period when magnesium was extensively used in the manufacture of control surfaces. This rivet alloy was developed especially for fastening magnesium skins to the control surfaces of several popular light aircraft. The major alloying ingredient of 5056 is magnesium, thus making it compatible with the magnesium surfaces. Because 5056 aluminum alloy is used to attach skin to control surfaces, it is classified as a structural aluminum alloy.

Corrosion-Resistant Steel (F)

Used in areas where corrosion-resistant steel, more commonly called stainless steel, must be joined by riveting. Firewalls, heat exchangers, and tail cones are examples. This rivet is available in all AN head styles.

Monel (M)

Monel is a corrosion-resistant steel with a higher nickel content. It is softer, easier to drive and has a lower shear strength than a regular corrosion-resistant rivet. Monel is used primarily in high-heat areas.

Head Design

Modern solid rivets are available in two common head styles, universal and countersunk shown in Figure 5-2-3.

The universal head is a combination of all the noncountersunk rivet heads used in the past, such as round, flat, brazier, and modified brazier. Universal head rivets are assigned the MS code numbers 20470. The 100° countersunk rivets used on modern aircraft are assigned the MS code 20426.

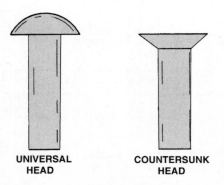

UNIVERSAL HEAD   COUNTERSUNK HEAD

Figure 5-2-3. Rivet head styles

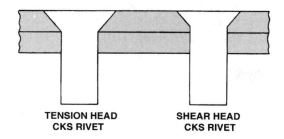

TENSION HEAD CKS RIVET **SHEAR HEAD CKS RIVET**

Figure 5-2-4. Countersunk tension and shear heads

Countersunk rivets have gone through a series of changes as aircraft manufacturers tried to find a head style strong enough yet still provide a smooth aerodynamic airflow. The angle used as the standard for countersunk rivets is 100 degrees. For general use there are two head styles of countersink rivets available; tension and shear heads. Figure 5-2-4 shows the two styles of countersunk rivets with their respective head depth.

Section 3

Special Rivets and Fasteners

One of two groups of special fastening systems, blind fasteners became useful to the aerospace industry when sheetmetal technicians found a need for fasteners which did not require access to forming or installing a locking head.

Friction-Lock Blind Rivets

Friction-lock rivets date back to a time when metal aircraft were first built. These first rivets were an approved replacement for solid-shank rivets. However, they do not have the reliability of a solid-shank rivet. The pulling stem is prone to shaking loose due to vibrations. The result of the pulling stem falling out causes the shear strength of the rivet to be weakened. FAA AC43.13-1B, Acceptable Methods, Techniques and Practices Aircraft Inspection and Repair, states that the diameter of a friction-lock rivet must be increased one size when it replaces a solid-shank rivet.

Two head styles of friction-lock rivets are available, universal and countersunk, as shown in Figure 5-3-1. Countersunk friction-lock rivets

have a head angle of 100 degrees. They are available in standard sizes of $1/8$, $5/32$, and $3/16$ inch.

Friction between the rivet shank and the pulling stem lock the two together. Friction-lock rivets are manufactured by several companies.

Mechanical-Lock Blind Rivets

Mechanical-locking blind rivets were produced next. These rivets have a mechanical lock for retaining the rivet stem in the rivet sleeve after installation. The growth in the number and selection of blind fasteners is the result of competition created by aircraft manufacturers and repair technicians. They made their selection based on the kind of fastener which would do the best job and yet be the most economical. Due to their multiple components and intricate mechanics, blind fasteners are more expensive than most solid-shank rivets and standard bolts. They are sold by the piece rather than the pound, as solid rivets are. They require special installation tools and gauges for proper installation. In order to get the maximum strength from any blind or special fastener, always follow the manufacturers installation recommendation.

CherryMAX®/AllMax® rivets

After installation, the CherryMAX® blind rivet stem is mechanically locked to the rivet sleeve by the patented Safe-Loc® locking collar. The CherryMAX® driving anvil significantly

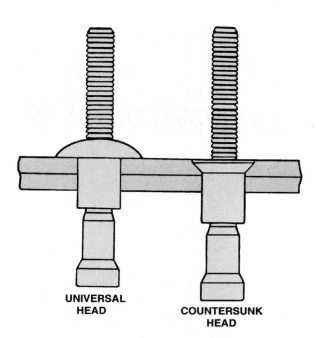

UNIVERSAL HEAD **COUNTERSUNK HEAD**

Figure 5-3-1. Friction-lock blind rivets.

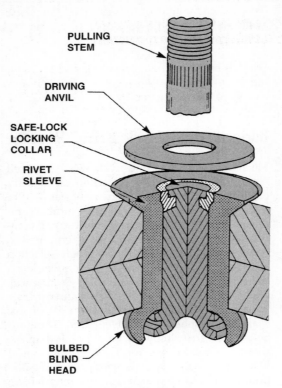

PULLING
STEM

DRIVING
ANVIL

SAFE-LOCK
LOCKING
COLLAR

RIVET
SLEEVE

BULBED
BLIND
HEAD

Figure 5-3-2. CherryMAX® rivet.

reduces wear and replacement of expensive installation tools and provides improved rivet head flushness (Figure 5-3-2). This makes it much different than a friction-lock rivet. When properly installed, CherryMAX® blind rivets have stronger shear strength than an equivalent size solid-shank rivet. CherryMAX® blind

rivets are reliable for replacement of solid-shank rivets when reassembling an aircraft.

Two functional styles of CherryMAX® rivets are available: bulbed and wiredraw. The Bulbed CherryMAX® rivets provide a large bearing surface on the blind side of the structure, giving dependable results for the difficult thin-sheet stack-up applications. Wiredraw CherryMAX® rivets provide increased sheet take-up and hole-fill performance. Wiredrawing fasteners may not be suitable for some thin-sheet application. Both functional styles (Bulbed and Wiredraw) are installed with non-shifting installation tools. These tools are considerably less expensive than older style shifting tools.

Five head styles of CherryMAX® blind rivets are available; Universal, 100° Flush (MS20426), 100 degree Flush (NAS1097), UNISINK, and 120 degree Flush (Figure 5-3-3).

CherryMAX® sizes. CherryMAX® rivets are available in four diameters: $1/8$, $5/32$, $3/16$, and $1/4$ inch. Most CherryMAX® rivet material/head style combinations are available in oversized versions in increments of $1/64$ inch larger than the standard diameter (Figure 5-3-3).

Grip lengths are critical. CherryMAX® rivets are available in grip lengths with increments of $1/16$ inch. CherryMAX® grip gauges are used to find the correct grip length of rivet. If the gauge is not used and the proper grip length is not selected, the joint will not be able to carry the assigned load (Figure 5-3-4).

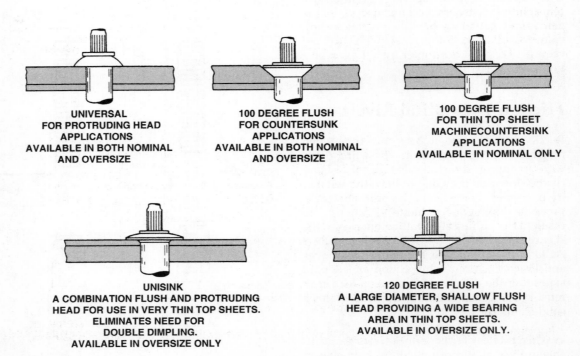

UNIVERSAL
FOR PROTRUDING HEAD
APPLICATIONS
AVAILABLE IN BOTH NOMINAL
AND OVERSIZE

100 DEGREE FLUSH
FOR COUNTERSUNK
APPLICATIONS
AVAILABLE IN BOTH NOMINAL
AND OVERSIZE

100 DEGREE FLUSH
FOR THIN TOP SHEET
MACHINECOUNTERSINK
APPLICATIONS
AVAILABLE IN NOMINAL ONLY

UNISINK
A COMBINATION FLUSH AND PROTRUDING
HEAD FOR USE IN VERY THIN TOP SHEETS.
ELIMINATES NEED FOR
DOUBLE DIMPLING.
AVAILABLE IN OVERSIZE ONLY

120 DEGREE FLUSH
A LARGE DIAMETER, SHALLOW FLUSH
HEAD PROVIDING A WIDE BEARING
AREA IN THIN TOP SHEETS.
AVAILABLE IN OVERSIZE ONLY.

Figure 5-3-3. Various head styles and uses of CherryMAX® rivet.

CHERRYMAX® RIVET SELECTION

DIAMETER

Bulbed CherryMAX® rivets are offered in 1/8" (−4), 5/32" (−5), 3/16" (−6) and 1/4" (−8) shank diameters. They are available in nominal and 1/64" oversize.

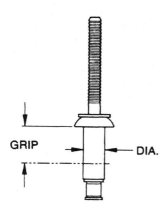

To determine the proper grip rivet to use, measure the material thickness with a Cherry 269C3 selector gage as shown here.
Always read to the next higher number.

GRIP

The grip range of all CherryMAX® rivets is in increments of 1/16", with the last dash number indicating the maximum grip length in 16ths. Example: −4 grip rivet has a grip range of 3/16"(.188) to 1/4"(.250).

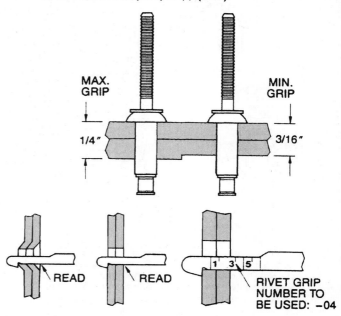

INSTALLATION

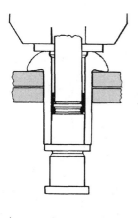

① The CherryMAX® Rivet is inserted into the prepared hole. The pulling head (installation tool) is slipped over the rivet's stem. Applying a firm, steady pressure, which seats the rivet head, the installation tool is then actuated.

② The pulling head holds the rivet sleeve in place as it begins to pull the rivet stem thru the rivet sleeve. This pulling action causes the stem shear ring to upset the rivet sleeve and form the "bulbed" blind head.

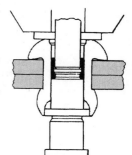

③ The continued pulling action of the installation tool causes the stem shear ring to shear from the main body of the stem as the stem continues to move thru the rivet sleeve. *This action allows the fastener to accommodate a minimum of 1/16" variation in structure thickness.* The Locking Collar then contacts the Driving Anvil. As the stem continues to be pulled by the action of the installation tool, the "Safe-lock" Locking Collar deforms into the rivet sleeve head recess. Formation of the rivet sleeve's "bulbed" blind head is complete.

④ The "Safe-lock" Locking Collar fills the rivet sleeve head recess, locking the stem and rivet sleeve securely together. Continued pulling by the installation tool causes the stem to fracture at the break notch, providing a flush, burr-free, *inspectable* installation.

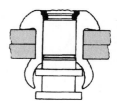

Figure 5-3-4. CherryMAX® rivet selection and installation

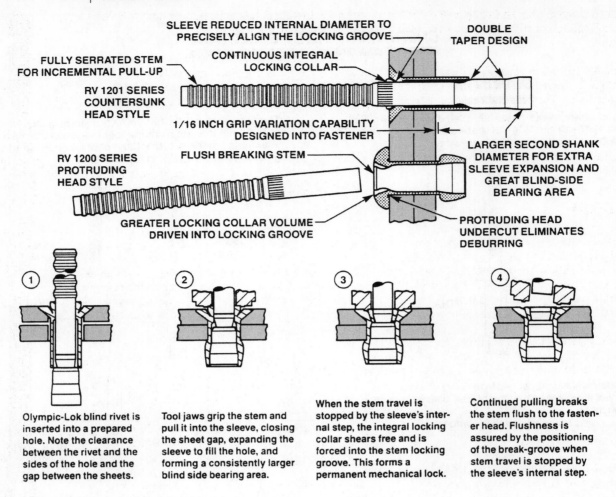

FULLY SERRATED STEM FOR INCREMENTAL PULL-UP

RV 1201 SERIES COUNTERSUNK HEAD STYLE

SLEEVE REDUCED INTERNAL DIAMETER TO PRECISELY ALIGN THE LOCKING GROOVE

CONTINUOUS INTEGRAL LOCKING COLLAR

DOUBLE TAPER DESIGN

1/16 INCH GRIP VARIATION CAPABILITY DESIGNED INTO FASTENER

RV 1200 SERIES PROTRUDING HEAD STYLE

FLUSH BREAKING STEM

LARGER SECOND SHANK DIAMETER FOR EXTRA SLEEVE EXPANSION AND GREAT BLIND-SIDE BEARING AREA

GREATER LOCKING COLLAR VOLUME DRIVEN INTO LOCKING GROOVE

PROTRUDING HEAD UNDERCUT ELIMINATES DEBURRING

① Olympic-Lok blind rivet is inserted into a prepared hole. Note the clearance between the rivet and the sides of the hole and the gap between the sheets.

② Tool jaws grip the stem and pull it into the sleeve, closing the sheet gap, expanding the sleeve to fill the hole, and forming a consistently larger blind side bearing area.

③ When the stem travel is stopped by the sleeve's internal step, the integral locking collar shears free and is forced into the stem locking groove. This forms a permanent mechanical lock.

④ Continued pulling breaks the stem flush to the fastener head. Flushness is assured by the positioning of the break-groove when stem travel is stopped by the sleeve's internal step.

Figure 5-3-5. Allfast®/Olympic-lok blind fasteners

Bulbed CherryMAX® rivet sleeves are made from 5056 aluminum, monel, and INCO 600. Wiredraw CherryMAX® rivet sleeves are made from 2017-T4 aluminum, 5056 aluminum, monel, and A-286 CRES.

CherryLOCK® Rivets

The CherryLOCK® mechanical locking rivet is installed with a shifting tool. The rivet stem is drawn into the rivet sleeve in one motion. The tool then shifts to allow the driving anvil to come forward and set the locking collar. Then, the tool shifts again and pulls the stem until it breaks off flush. CherryLOCK® is available in Bulbed and Wiredraw functional styles.

CherryLOCK® is available in four head styles; Universal, 100° Flush (MS20426), 100 degree Flush (NAS 1097), UNISINK, and 156 Flush.

Wiredraw CherryLOCK® is made for nominal hole diameters of $3/32$, $1/8$, $5/32$, $3/16$, and $1/4$ inch. It is available in rivet sleeve materials of 2017 aluminum, 5056 aluminum, A-286 CRES and monel. The Bulbed version is made for oversized

holes of $1/64$ inch larger than nominal holes. They are made in $1/8$, $5/32$, and $3/16$ inch diameters. Sleeve materials for the Bulbed version are 5056 aluminum, monel, and INCO 600.

CherryMAX® vs. CherryLOCK®

The major difference between the two is the method of installation. The tools used to install CherryMAX® rivets are simple and usually can be done with one tool which fits all diameters. The CherryLOCK® rivet requires more complicated installation tools due to the multiple step installation cycle of the fastener. Separate pulling heads are required for each fastener diameter.

Allfast®/Olympic-Lok

Olympic-lok blind fasteners are light weight, mechanical locked, spindle-type blind rivets. Olympic-loks are equipped with a locking ring which is attached to its head before installation. After installation, the locking ring is made to slip down and lock the center stem in place as shown in Figure 5-3-5. The Olympic-lok blind fastener has its own installation tools.

Olympic-lok rivets are available in three head styles: AN470 universal, AN426 100° flush, and 100° flush shear. They come in three diameters of $1/8$, $5/32$, and $3/16$ inch. These three diameters are available in eight different alloy combinations of 2017-T4, A-286, 5056, and monel. Their pulling stems or spindles are made from the same alloys.

Huck-Lok Rivets

Huck blind fasteners were the first to provide a method of locking the pulling stem into position for added blind-rivet strength. The design of the Huck rivet used today is not much different than it was many years ago, at least in the traditional one shown in Figure 5-3-6.

The locking method is built into the rivet head. The locking ring is part of the manufactured head, and the tool used for installation has a press which forces the ring down into a recess on the pulling stem. The result is a stem positively held into place. Just as with other pull-type fasteners the Huck rivet has excellent take-up characteristics.

Huck rivets are available in two head styles; protruding and flush. They are made in four diameters $1/8$, $5/32$, $3/16$, and $1/4$ inch. Their lengths are measured in $1/16$-inch increments. They are made available in combinations of three different alloys groups.

1. 5056 sleeve and 2024 pin

2. A-286 corrosion-resistant steel sleeve with an A-286 pin.

3. Monel 400 sleeve with an A-286 pin

Hi-Shear Rivets

Hi-Shear rivets and AN bolts have the same strength. In fact, the only difference between the two is the bolt uses a nut and the Hi-Shear rivet uses a collar for holding them in place. The Hi-Shear rivet dates back into the 1940's where the need for fasteners to carry high-shear loads occurred, when large bombers were being built.

The Hi-Shear rivet's major advantage over the standard bolt is that when installed, its shank does not decrease in size due to torque. The Hi-Shear rivet is installed into a tight fitting hole where the side wall clearance is reamed to a specific tolerance. The Hi-Shear rivet, when properly installed, has to be driven into its hole before its collar is swaged on.

Two head styles are available; flat and countersunk. The rivet is designed specially to absorb high-shear loads, thus the reason for its commercial name. The Hi-Shear rivet is made from steel alloy which has the same tensile strength as an equal size AN bolt. The lower portion of its shank has a specially milled groove with a sharp edge for retaining and finishing the collar as it is swaged into the locking position, as shown in Figure 5-3-7.

Other alloy types of Hi-Shear were not produced. The Hi-Shear did, however, make way for its younger generation family of high-strength fasteners called Hi-Lok and High-Tigue. Removal of Hi-Shear rivets during the disassembly of an aircraft will not create a reassembly problem. They can be replaced with standard AN bolts or the easier to install Hi-Loks.

Hi-Lok Rivets

One advantage of the Hi-Lok rivet over a Hi-Shear rivet is that it is manufactured in several different alloys such as titanium, stainless steel, steel, and aluminum. They can be made to withstand bearing and shearing loads.

Available in two head styles, flat and countersunk, the Hi-Lok manufactured head is machine formed to its shank. The shank of the conventional Hi-Lok is straight and a set of

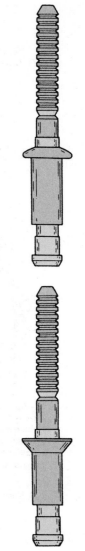

Figure 5-3-6. Huck-lok rivets.

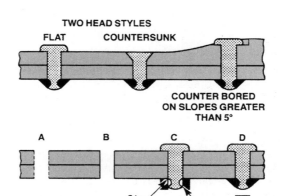

TWO HEAD STYLES
FLAT   COUNTERSUNK

COUNTER BORED
ON SLOPES GREATER
THAN 5°

A   B   C   D

C1—   NIPPERS

EXCESS
RING CUT OFF

A.   HOLE DRILLED APPROXIMATELY .007 UNDERSIZE
B.   HOLE DRILLED + .0005 TO − .001 INTERFERENCE FIT
C.   STUD TAPPED INTO HOLE
C1.   STUD SHOULD BE NO SHORTER OR LONGER THAN 1/32"
D.   INSTALLED HI-SHEAR RIVET

Figure 5-3-7. Hi-shear rivets

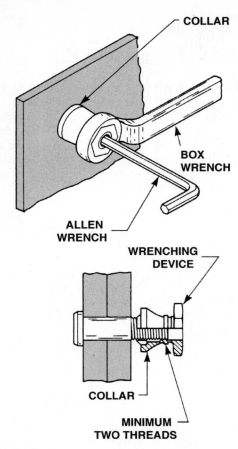

Figure 5-3-8. Hi-lok hand installation tools

standard threads are located at the end of the Hi-Lok shank. The threads are compatible with those of AN bolts of the same size.

Retaining collars can be installed using specially prepared tools or a simple Allen and box-end wrench, as shown in Figure 5-3-8. The preparation of the holes for Hi-Loks are the same as any interference fit fastener. After fitting the Hi-Lok using a special gauge provided by the manufacturer or by using a fastener with a smaller diameter, it is usually driven into the hole.

The Hi-Lok threaded section must extend the prescribed amount as indicated by the manufacturer in Figure 5-3-9. The threads on the lower end of a Hi-Lok shank are not used to torque it into position like the conventional AN bolt, but rather to set its locking collar to its recommended torque. This means when the locking nut is torqued to its maximum, the shear nut fractures away and the shank of the Hi-Lok is not stretched.

Hi-Lite Fastener

Light weight to strength ratio is the main advantage of this product of the Hi-Shear com-

pany. This light weight with strength retention is obtained by making the shank-to-thread transition shorter than the conventional Hi-Lok fastener.

Hi-Lites are available in an assortment of diameters ranging from $3/16$ to $3/8$ inch. They are available in lengths measured in $1/16$-inch increments.

The Hi-Lite is made to be installed either with the same type of locking collar as the standard Hi-Lok, or by a swaged collar like the lockbolt. In either case the shank diameter is not made smaller by torque.

Special Fasteners

The requirements of shear and bearing loads are met by all fastening systems used on modern aircraft. For example Hi-Shear, Hi-Loks, Hi-Tigues, lockbolts, or CherryBUCK® fasteners, Figure 5-3-10, are available for carrying either bearing or shear loads. A fastener which can carry both bearing and shearing loads at the same time is the Taper-Lok fastener

Hi-Shear, Hi-Lok, Hi-Tigue, lockbolts,and CherryBUCKs are classified as straight-pin fasteners. The Taper-Lok are not straight-pin fasteners. Due to the shape of their shanks, they have the ability to preload the holes they are inserted into. The ability to preload a hole increases the strength of the joint.

When installing special straight-pin fasteners, there are several common installation and handling techniques:

- Exact hole dimensions to produce the required strength are specified by most manufacturers. The dimension will have a plus (+) or minus (-) tolerance.

- When fitting straight-pin shanks into the grip length of the metal, it must extend a specified distance beyond the thickness of the metal to obtain correct bearing strength of its locking collar.

- The alloy content of each special fastener being replaced can be different; therefore, they must each be replaced with exactly the same type alloy as the original.

Lockbolts

Lockbolts are manufactured according to military standards. The military standards detail the size of the manufactured head in relationship to the shank diameter, as well as the alloy content of the different types of lockbolts. Lockbolts are made in two configurations, shear and tension,

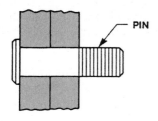

(A) INSERT THE PIN INTO THE PREPARED NON-INTERFERENCE FIT HOLE.

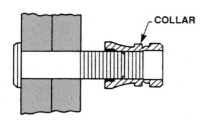

(B) MANUALLY THREAD THE COLLAR ONTO THE PIN.

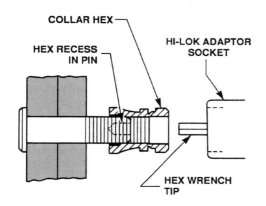

(C) INSERT THE HEX WRENCH TIP OF THE POWER DRIVER INTO THE PIN'S HEX RECESS, AND THE SOCKET OVER THE COLLAR HEX. THIS PREVENTS ROTATION OF THE PIN WHLE THE COLLAR IS BEING INSTALLED.

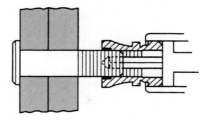

(D) FIRMLY PRESS THE POWER DRIVER AGAINST THE COLLAR, OPERATE THE POWER DRIVER UNTIL THE COLLAR'S WRENCHING DEVICE HAS BEEN TORQUED OFF.

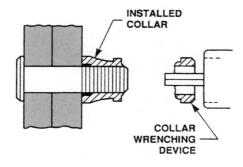

(E) THIS COMPLETES THE INSTALLATION OF THE HI-LOK FASTENER ASSEMBLY.

NOTE:

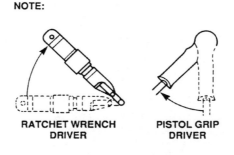

TO EASE THE REMOVAL OF THE DRIVING TOOL'S HEX WRENCH TIP FROM THE HEX RECESS OF THE PIN AFTER THE COLLAR'S WRENCHING DEVICE HAS SHEARED OFF, SIMPLY ROTATE THE ENTIRE DRIVER TOOL IN A SLIGHT CLOCKWISE MOTION.

Figure 5-3-9. Hi-lok rivet installation

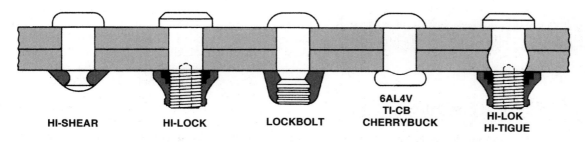

Figure 5-3-10. Special fasteners available for use in either shear or bearing loads

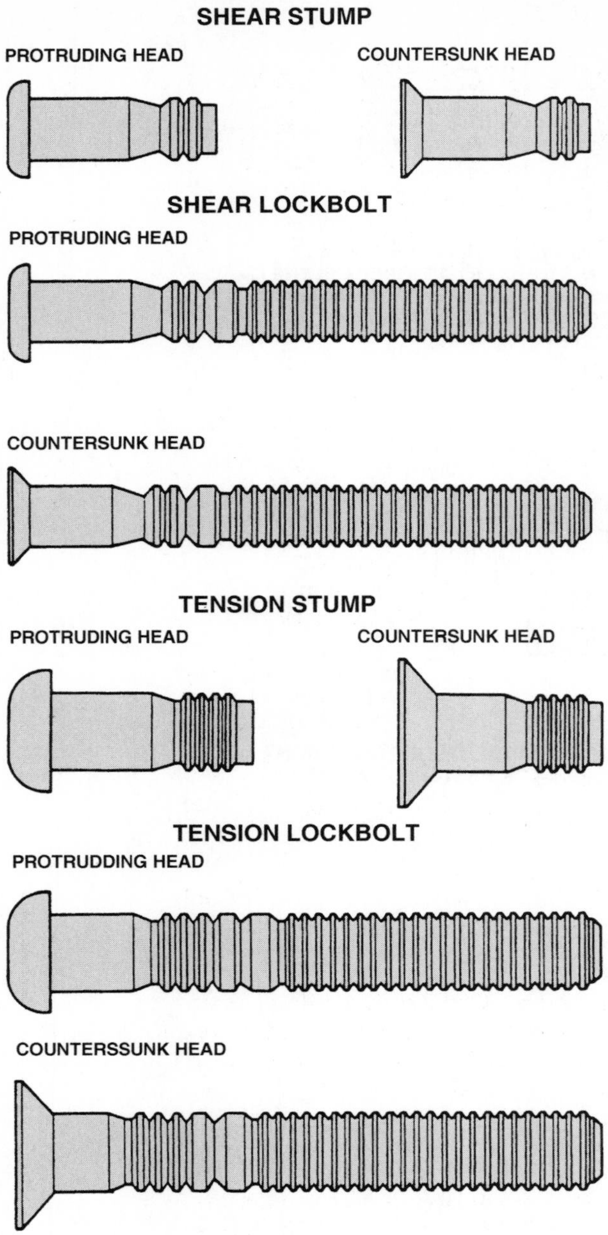

SHEAR STUMP

PROTRUDING HEAD   COUNTERSUNK HEAD

SHEAR LOCKBOLT

PROTRUDING HEAD

COUNTERSUNK HEAD

TENSION STUMP

PROTRUDING HEAD   COUNTERSUNK HEAD

TENSION LOCKBOLT

PROTRUDDING HEAD

COUNTERSSUNK HEAD

Figure 5-3-11. Shear and tension style lockbolts

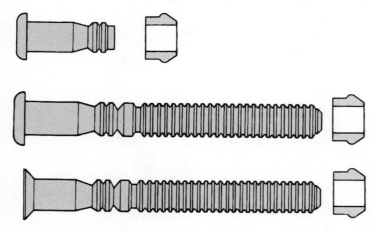

Figure 5-3-12. Lockbolt types

as shown in Figure 5-3-11. Lockbolts are available in three styles, pull, stump, and blind types as shown in Figure 5-3-12.

Lockbolts were among the first special fasteners to be used by the manufacturers of jet transports. Many of the lighter jet aircraft superstructures are presently being fastened together with lockbolts as well as other new types of fasteners. The reason lockbolts and other special fasteners are not used extensively in general aviation is due to the fact that the installation tools for special fasteners are very expensive.

Higher strength was possible with the use of lockbolts, thus allowing the aircraft to carry a larger payload. Lockbolts are used to obtain high strength in areas like landing gears, engine-to-wing spar attachments, and wing-to-fuselage joints. The lockbolt takes over where larger solid-shank rivets and Hi-Lok rivets leave off. There are structural assemblies where lockbolts and Hi-Loks are used next to one another. This is due to the aircraft manufacturer's choice based upon particular strength needs.

CherryBUCK® Fasteners

CherryBUCKs are a one-piece fastener made from two lightweight structural metals, titanium alloy 6AL-4V and Ductile Ti-Cb (titanium and columbium) (Figure 5-3-13). The manufacturer's head and grip portion of the shank are made from titanium alloy, while the bucktail forming end is made from titanium and columbium. It has a driven shear strength of 95 KSI. Like other special fasteners, the CherryBUCK® is installed into an interference fit hole. The CherryBUCK® can be driven just like a regular solid-shank rivet, however, its shank does not expand when driven.

Advantages of the CherryBUCK®: the first is its one-piece feature which, when installed around jet engine intakes, greatly reduces foreign object damage (FOD). FOD sometimes occurs when the locking collar of a multiple-piece fasteners detaches from its locking recess. CherryBUCKs also have an additional advantage over the collar-type fasteners in that it can be used on inclined surfaces up to 10 degrees without using a special locking collar to secure it. Another advantage of the CherryBUCK® is it can be used in small aviation shops because they can be installed just as the solid-shank rivet; this means the installed CherryBUCK® does not need expensive installation tools. One of its main disadvantages is the same as for a solid-shank rivet, that is its ability to take up a multiple stack of sheet metal.

Available in five diameters, CherryBUCKs range from $5/32$ to $3/8$ inch, in increments of $1/32$

inch. They are available in three head styles: MS20426 flush, NAS1079 flush, and protruding. They are lubricated with chlorine-free cetyl alcohol for ease of fitting into their holes.

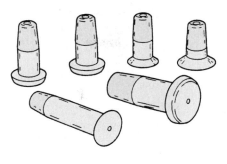

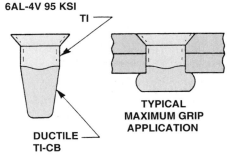

Figure 5-3-13. Typical CherryBUCK® fasteners.

Section 4

Threaded Fasteners

Identification and Coding

Bolts are manufactured in many shapes and varieties. The basic parts of a bolt are the head and the shank. The shank is threaded to accept a nut or to be used with some other type of threaded fitting. Often the shank of a bolt is not threaded all the way up to the head. In this case, the unthreaded portion of the shank is called the grip (Figure 5-4-1).

A clear-cut method of classification is difficult. Bolts can be identified by the shape of the head, method of securing, material used in fabrication, or the expected usage.

As an example, in the bolt part number AN3DD5A, the AN designates that it is an Air Force-Navy Standard bolt, the 3 indicates the diameter in sixteenths of an inch ($^3/_{16}$), the DD indicates the material is 2024 aluminum alloy. (The letter C in place of the DD would indicate corrosion-resistant steel, and the absence of the letters would indicate cadmium-plated steel.) The 5 indicates the length in eighths of an inch ($^5/_8$), and the A indicates that the shank is undrilled. If the letter H preceded the 5 in addition to the A following it, the head would be drilled for safetying.

Close-tolerance NAS bolts are marked with either a raised or recessed triangle on the head of the bolt. The material markings for NAS bolts are the same as for AN bolts, except that they may be either raised or recessed. Bolts inspected magnetically (Magna-flux) or by fluorescent means (Zyglo) are identified by means of colored lacquer, or a head marking of a distinctive type.

Thread Types and Fits

Aircraft bolts, screws, and nuts are threaded in either the American National Coarse (NC) thread series, the American National Fine (NF) thread series, the American Standard Unified Coarse (UNC) thread series, or the American Standard Unified Fine (UNF) thread series. There is one difference between the American National series and the American Standard Unified series that should be pointed out. In the 1-inch diameter size, the NF thread specified 14 threads per inch (1-14NF), while the UNF thread specifies 12 threads per inch (1-12UNF). Both type threads are designated by the number of times the incline (threads) rotates around a 1-inch length of a given diameter bolt or screw. For example, a 4-28 thread indicates that a $^1/_4$-inch diameter bolt has 28 threads in 1 inch of its threaded length.

Threads are also designated by class of fit. The class of a thread indicates the tolerance allowed in manufacturing. Class 1 is a loose fit, class 2 is a free fit, class 3 is a medium fit, and class 4 is a close fit. A class 4 fit requires a wrench to turn the nut onto a bolt, whereas a class 1 fit can easily be turned with the fingers. Aircraft bolts are almost always manufactured in the class 3, medium fit, and aircraft screws are generally manufactured with a class 2 thread fit for ease of assembly.

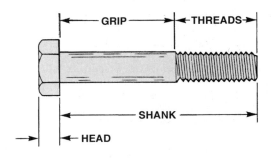

Figure 5-4-1. Bolt identification

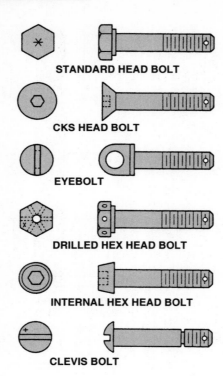

STANDARD HEAD BOLT

CKS HEAD BOLT

EYEBOLT

DRILLED HEX HEAD BOLT

INTERNAL HEX HEAD BOLT

CLEVIS BOLT

Figure 5-4-2. Standard aircraft bolt heads

Standard Aircraft Bolts

AN bolts come in three head styles; hex-head, clevis, and eyebolt (see Figure 5-4-2), while NAS bolts are available in hex-head, internal-wrenching, and countersunk head styles. MS bolts are manufactured in both hex-head, and internal-wrenching styles.

Airframe Bolts

The hex-head aircraft bolt (AN3 through AN20) is an all-purpose structural bolt used for general applications involving tension or shear loads where a light-drive fit is permissible (0.006-inch clearance for a $^5/_8$-inch hole, and other sizes in proportion).

Alloy steel bolts smaller than No. 10-32 and aluminum-alloy bolts smaller than $^1/_4$-inch diameter are not used in primary structures. Aluminum-alloy bolts and nuts are not used where they will be repeatedly removed for purposes of maintenance and inspection. Aluminum-alloy nuts may be used with cadmium-plated steel bolts loaded in shear on land airplanes, but are not used on seaplanes because of the increased possibility of dissimilar-metal corrosion.

The drilled-head bolt is similar to the standard hex-bolt, but has a deeper head which is drilled to receive wire for safetying. The AN3 hex-

head bolt, and the AN73 drilled-head series bolt, are interchangeable, for all practical purposes, from the standpoint of tension and shear strengths.

Close-tolerance bolts are machined more accurately than the general-purpose bolt. Close-tolerance bolts may be hex-headed (AN173 through AN186) or have a 100 degree countersunk head (NAS80 through NAS86). Used in applications where a tight-drive fit is required, tapping with a 12 to 14-ounce hammer is usually necessary (because of the tight fit) to position the grip of the bolt in the bolthole.

Clevis bolts have an oval head are either slotted to receive a common screwdriver or recessed to receive a crosspoint screwdriver. This type of bolt is used only where shear loads occur and never in tension. It is often inserted as a mechanical pin in a control system.

Internal-wrenching bolts, (NAS495 or MS20004 through MS20024) are fabricated from high-strength steel, and are suitable for use in both tension and shear applications. When they are used in steel parts, the bolthole must be slightly countersunk to seat the large corner radius of the shank at the head. The head of the internal-wrenching bolt is recessed to allow the insertion of an internal wrench when installing or removing the bolt. Special high-strength nuts are used on these bolts. When replacing an internal-wrenching bolt, replace it with another internal-wrenching bolt. Standard AN hex-head bolts and washers cannot be substituted for them because they do not have the required strength.

Nuts

Aircraft nuts are made in a variety of shapes and sizes. They are made of cadmium-plated carbon steel, stainless steel, anodized 2024-T aluminum alloy, or brass, and may be obtained with either right- or left-hand threads. While no identifying marking or lettering appears on nuts, they can be identified by their construction and by the characteristic metallic luster or color of aluminum, steel, or brass from which they are made, or by the color or type of insert used when the nut is of the self-locking type.

The two general groups in which aircraft nuts can be divided are non-self-locking and self-locking. Non-self-locking nuts are those that must be safetied by external locking devices, such as cotter pins, safety wire, or locknuts. Self-locking nuts contain a locking feature as an integral part of the nut.

Identification and Coding

Part numbers designate the type of nut. The common types and their respective part numbers are: plain, AN315 and AN335; castle (also called castellated) AN310; plain check, AN316; light hex, AN340 and AN345; and castellated shear, AN320. The patented self-locking types are assigned part numbers ranging from MS20363 through MS20367. Part number AN350 is assigned to the wing nut.

Letters and digits following the part number indicate such items as material, size, threads per inch, and whether the thread is right or left hand. The letter B following the part number indicates the nut material to be brass; a D indicates 2017 aluminum alloy; a DD indicates 2024 aluminum alloy; a C indicates stainless steel; and a dash in place of a letter indicates cadmium-plated carbon steel.

The digit(s) following the dash, or the material code letter, is known as the dash number of the nut, which indicates the size of the shank and threads per inch of the bolt on which the nut will fit. The dash number corresponds to the first figure appearing in the part number coding of general-purpose bolts. A dash and the number 3, for example, indicates that the nut will fit an AN3 bolt (10-32); a dash and the number 4 means it will fit an AN4 bolt ($^1/_4$-28); a dash and the number 5, an AN5 bolt ($^5/_{16}$-24); and so on.

The code numbers for self-locking nuts end in three- or four-digit numbers. The last two digits refer to threads per inch, and the one or two preceding digits stand for the nut size in sixteenths of an inch. Some other common nuts and their code numbers are:

Code Number AN310D5R:

AN310	=	Aircraft castle nut
D	=	2024-T aluminum alloy
5	=	$^5/_{16}$ inch diameter
R	=	Right-hand thread (usually 24 threads per inch)

Code Number AN320-10:

AN320	=	Aircraft castellated shear nut, cadmium-plated carbon steel
10	=	$^5/_8$ inch diameter, 18 threads per inch (this nut is usually right-hand thread)

Code Number AN350B1032:

AN350	=	Aircraft wingnut
B	=	Brass
10	=	Number 10 bolt
32	=	Threads per inch

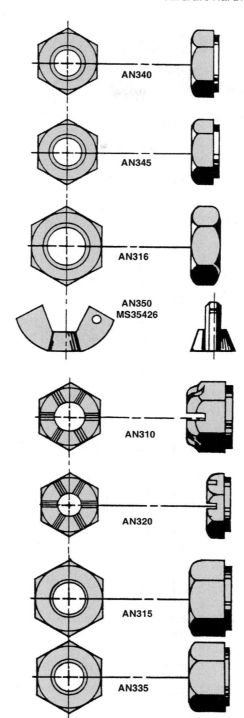

Figure 5-4-3. Non-self-locking nuts

Non-Self-Locking Nuts

Most of the familiar types of nuts, including the plain nut, the castle nut, the castellated shear nut, the plain hex nut, the light hex nut, and the plain check nut are the non-self-locking type (Figure 5-4-3).

The AN310 castle nut is used with drilled-shank AN hex head bolts, clevis bolts, eyebolts, drilled-

 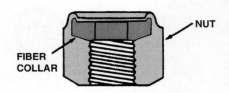 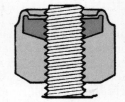

Figure 5-4-4. Elastic stop nut

head bolts, or studs. It is fairly rugged and can withstand large tensional loads. Slots (called castellations) in the nut are designed to accommodate a cotter pin or lock wire for safety.

The AN320 castellated shear nut is designed for use with devices (such as drilled clevis bolts and threaded taper pins) which are normally subjected to shearing stress only. Like the castle nut, it is castellated for safetying. Note, however, that neither the nut nor the castellations are as deep nor as strong as the AN310 castle nut.

The AN315 and AN335 (fine and coarse thread) plain nut is of rugged construction. This makes it suitable for carrying large tensional loads. However, since it requires an auxiliary locking device such as a check nut or lockwasher, its use on aircraft structures is somewhat limited.

The AN316 plain check nut is employed as a locking device for plain nuts, set screws, threaded rod ends, and other devices.

The AN340 course-thread machine screw nut is a much lighter nut than the plain nut and must be locked by an auxiliary device. It is used for miscellaneous light-tension requirements.

The AN345 fine-thread machine screw nut is also a much lighter nut than the plain nut, and likewise requires an auxiliary locking device. Like the AN340, the AN345 is also used for miscellaneous applications requiring light tension.

The AN350 wing nut is intended for use where the desired tightness can be obtained with the fingers and where the assembly is frequently removed.

The AN355 slotted engine nut is designed for use on an aircraft engine and is not approved for airframe use. It is heat-treated and has a class 3 fit in national fine threads and is available in sizes from AN355-3 ($3/16$ inch) to AN355-12 ($3/4$ inch).

The AN360 plain engine nut is similar to the AN355, except that it does not have the slots for a cotter pin and it has a black rustproof finish. It is not approved for airframe use.

Self-Locking Nuts

As their name implies, self-locking nuts need no auxiliary means of safetying, but rather have a safetying feature included as an integral part of their construction. Self-locking nuts are used on aircraft to provide tight connections which will not shake loose under severe vibration. Common applications are:

1. Attachment of antifriction bearings and control pulleys

2. Attachment of accessories, anchor nuts around inspection holes, and small tank installation openings

3. Attachment of rocker-box covers and exhaust stacks. Self-locking nuts are acceptable for use on certificated aircraft subject to the restrictions of the manufacturer.

Low-Temperature Self-Locking Nuts

Elastic stop nut. The elastic stop nut is a standard nut with the height increased to accommodate a fiber-locking collar. This fiber collar is very tough and durable. It is unaffected by immersion in hot or cold water, ordinary solvents such as ether, carbon tetrachloride, oils, and gasoline. It will not damage bolt threads or plating.

The fiber-locking collar is not threaded, as shown in Figure 5-4-4, and its inside diameter is smaller than the largest diameter of the threaded portion, or the outside diameter of a corresponding bolt. When the nut is screwed onto a bolt, it acts as an ordinary nut until the bolt reaches the fiber collar. When the bolt is screwed into the fiber collar, however, friction (or drag) causes the fiber to be pushed upward. This creates a heavy downward pressure on the load-carrying part and automatically throws the load-carrying sides of the nut and bolt threads into positive contact. After the bolt has been forced all the way through the fiber collar, the downward pressure remains constant. This pressure locks and holds the nut securely in place even under severe vibration.

Normally, elastic stop nuts can be used many times with complete safety and without detriment to their locking efficiency. When reusing elastic stop nuts, be sure the fiber has not lost its locking friction or become brittle. If a nut can be turned with the fingers, replace it.

After the nut has been tightened, make sure the rounded or chamfered end of the bolts, studs, or screws extends at least the full round or chamfer through the nut. Flat-end bolts, studs, or screws should extend at least 1/32 inch through the nut. Bolts of 5/16-inch diameter and over with cotter pin holes may be used with self-locking nuts, but only if free from burrs around the holes. Bolts with damaged threads and rough ends are not acceptable. Do not tap the fiber-locking insert. The self-locking action of the elastic stop nut is the result of having the bolt threads impress themselves into the untapped fiber.

Do not install elastic stop nuts in places where the temperature is higher than 250°F, because the effectiveness of the self-locking action is reduced beyond this point. Self-locking nuts may be used on aircraft engines and accessories when their use is specified by the engine manufacturer.

High-temperature self-locking nuts. The stainless steel self-locking nut may be spun on and off with the fingers, as its locking action takes place only when the nut is seated against a solid surface and tightened. The nut consists of two parts; a case with a beveled locking shoulder and key, and a threaded insert with a locking shoulder and slotted keyway.

Until the nut is tightened, it spins on the bolt easily, because the threaded insert is the proper size for the bolt. However, when the nut is seated against a solid surface and tightened, the locking shoulder of the insert is pulled downward and wedged against the locking shoulder of the case. This action compresses the threaded insert and causes it to clench the bolt tightly. The cross-sectional view in Figure 5-4-5 shows how the key of the case fits into the slotted keyway

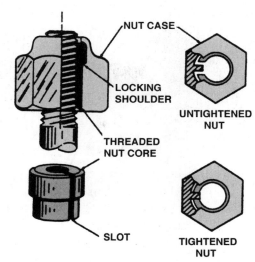

Figure 5-4-5. Stainless steel self-locking nut

of the insert so that when the case is turned, the threaded insert is turned with it. Note that the slot is wider than the key. This permits the slot to be narrowed and the insert to be compressed when the nut is tightened.

Special Forms of Self-Locking Nuts

AN364 Shear, Self-Locking Nuts

Similar to the AN365 self-locking nut, the AN364 is thinner than the AN365, and only approved for shear load applications.

Anchor Nuts

Some installations, such as inspection panels and access doors, are held in position by screws, but are designed in such a manner that the use of a normal nut is not possible. In these cases, anchor nuts, as seen in Figure 5-4-6, are installed to facilitate the use

TWO-LUG ANCHOR NUT

ONE-LUG ANCHOR NUT

CORNER ANCHOR NUT

TWO-LUG FLOATING ANCHOR NUT

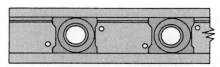

GANGED ANCHOR NUTS (CHANNEL NUTS)

Figure 5-4-6. Anchor nuts

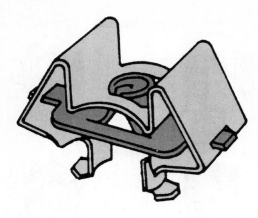

Figure 5-5-1. Instrument mounting nut

of securing screws. Common styles of anchor nuts (commonly called nut plates) include the one-lug, two-lug, and corner anchor nuts. For installations requiring large numbers of securing screws, floating anchor and channel (or ganged) nuts are used to allow enough play to align the installation.

Section 5

Sheet Metal Nuts

Tinnerman nuts are sheet spring steel type nuts. They are used with standard and sheet metal self-tapping screws in nonstructural

Figure 5-5-2. Anchor-type Tinnerman nut

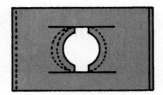

Figure 5-5-3. U-type Tinnerman nut

locations. They are used in supporting conduit and tubing clamps, electrical equipment, access doors, instruments, and are available in types appropriate for their usage.

Instrument Mounting Nuts

Used either in the instrument panel or in the instrument case itself, instrument mounting type Tinnerman nuts are used to hold instruments (such as flight instruments, engine instruments, etc.) in the instrument panel. They consist of a nonmagnetic phosphor bronze cage holding a brass nut in alignment behind the hole through which the screw passes (Figure 5-5-1).

On many light aircraft, anchor-type Tinnerman nuts are used as anchor nuts or nut plates. While they do not possess the strength of regular anchor nuts, they are light-weight, and are used in nonstructural applications where the repeated removal and installation of self-tapping screws would eventually cause nonrepairable damage to the aircraft skin (Figure 5-5-2).

U-Type Tinnerman Nuts

Consisting of a piece of metal bent to form a U shape when viewed from the edge, the U-type Tinnerman nut is designed to be slipped over the edge of an inside or mounting surface, straddling the screw hole. Used in light aircraft cowling installations and for some interior access panels, the cowling or access panel is placed against the mounting surface, a screw is passed through it near the edge and through the underlying U-type Tinnerman nut. Like the anchor-type Tinnerman nut, the U-type prevents nonrepairable damage in an area where self-tapping screws are repeatedly removed and reinstalled. An example of a U-type Tinnerman nut (seen from above and from its edge) is illustrated in Figure 5-5-3.

Aircraft Screws

Screws are the most commonly used threaded fastening devices on aircraft. They differ from bolts in as much as they are generally made of lower strength materials. They can be installed with a loose-fitting thread, and the head shapes are made to engage a screwdriver or wrench. Some screws have a clearly defined grip or unthreaded portion while others are threaded along their entire length.

Several types of structural screws differ from the standard structural bolts only in head style. The material in them is the same, and a definite grip length is provided. The AN525 washer-head screw and the NAS220 through NAS227 series are such screws.

Commonly used screws, shown in Figure 5-5-4, are classified in three groups:

1. Structural screws, which have the same strength as equal size bolts.

2. Machine screws, which include the majority of types used for general repair.

3. Self-tapping screws, which are used for attaching lighter parts.

Identification and Coding

The coding system used to identify screws is similar to that used for bolts. There are AN and NAS screws. NAS screws are structural screws. Part numbers 510, 515, 550, and so on, catalog screws into classes such as roundhead, flathead, washer-head, and so forth. Letters and digits indicate their material composition, length, and thickness. Examples of AN and NAS code numbers are:

Code Number AN501B-416-7:

AN	=	Airforce-Navy standard
501	=	Fillister head, fine thread
B	=	Brass
416	=	$^4/_{16}$ inch diameter
7	=	$^7/_{16}$ inch length

Code Number NAS144DH-22:

NAS	=	National aircraft standard
144	=	Head style, diameter and thread ($^1/_4$ - 28) bolt
DH	=	Drilled head
22	=	Screw length in 16ths of an inch (1 $^3/_8$ inches long)

Material indicators. The letter D in place of the B would indicate that the material is 2017 aluminum alloy. The letter C would designate corrosion-resistant steel. An A placed before the material code letter would indicate that the head is drilled for safetying.

The basic NAS number identifies the part. The suffix letters and dash numbers separate different sizes, plating material, drilling specifications, etc. The dash numbers and suffix letters do not have standard meanings. It is necessary to refer to a specific NAS page in the Standards book for the legend.

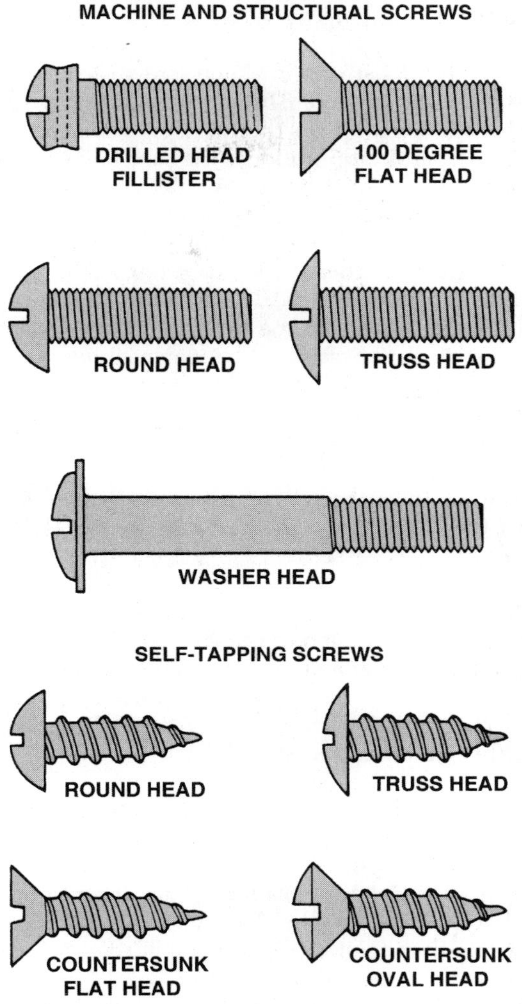

MACHINE AND STRUCTURAL SCREWS

SELF-TAPPING SCREWS

Figure 5-5-4. Commonly used screws

Machine Screws

Machine screws are usually of the flathead (countersunk), roundhead, or washer-head types. These screws are general-purpose screws and are available in low-carbon steel, brass, corrosion-resistant steel, or aluminum alloy.

The AN500 fillister-head screw is a general-purpose screw and is used as a capscrew in light mechanisms. This could include attachments of cast aluminum parts such as gear-box cover plates. Made of low-carbon steel, corrosion-resistant steel, or brass, the AN500 has coarse threads. Screws larger than No. 6 have a hole drilled through the head for safetying purposes.

The AN501 fillister-head screw, like the AN500, is a general-purpose screw and is used as a cap-screw in light mechanisms. Also available in low-carbon steel, corrosion-resistant steel, or brass, the AN501 has fine threads. AN501 screws larger than No. 6 also have a drilled head for safetying purposes.

The AN505 flathead machine screw is countersunk at an angle of 82 degrees, and is coarse-threaded. Except for the fact that it is used in countersunk applications, the AN505 is used basically the same as the AN500, and is available in the same materials.

The AN507 flathead machine screw is countersunk at an angle of 100 degrees, and is available in both coarse and fine threads. Except that it is used in applications requiring a countersink of 100 degrees, the AN507 is used in the same applications and is made of the same materials as the AN500 and AN501.

The AN510 flathead machine screw is the same as the AN505, except that it is fine-threaded rather than coarse.

The AN515 roundhead machine screw is the round-head version of the AN500. It is coarse-threaded, available in the same materials, and is used in applications requiring the use of roundhead screws. The roundhead may be either slotted or recessed.

The AN520 roundhead machine screw is the round-head version of the AN501. It is fine-threaded, available in the same materials, and is used in applications requiring the use of roundhead screws. The AN520 is available with either a slotted or recessed head.

The AN526 truss-head machine screw is similar to the AN515 and AN520 roundhead screws previously described, except that a raised edge causes the rounded portion of the head to terminate slightly above the base of the head. It is available in both fine-thread and coarse-thread versions.

Structural screws are made of alloyed steel, are properly heat-treated, and can be used as structural bolts. These screws are found in the NAS204 through NAS235, AN509, and AN525 series. They have a definite grip and the same shear strength as a bolt of the same size. Shank tolerances are similar to AN hex-head bolts, and the threads are National Fine. Structural screws are available with round, brazier, or countersunk heads. The recessed head screws are driven by either a Phillips or a Reed and Prince screwdriver.

The AN502 fillister-head screw is a fine-threaded screw used as a capscrew where great strength is required.

The AN503 fillister-head screw is a coarse-threaded screw commonly used, because of the softness of the metal, as a capscrew in tapped aluminum-alloy and magnesium castings.

The AN509 100° flathead screw is used in countersunk holes where a flush surface is necessary.

The AN525 washer-head structural screw is used where raised heads are not objectionable. The washer-head screw provides a large contact area.

Self-Tapping Screws

AN504 and AN506 are listed as machine self-tapping screws. The AN504 screw has a roundhead, while the AN506 is 82° countersunk. These screws are used for attaching removable parts, such as name-plates, to castings and parts in which the screw cuts its own threads.

The AN530 and AN531 self-tapping sheetmetal screws are blunt on the end. They are used in the temporary attachment of sheetmetal for riveting, and in the permanent assembly of nonstructural assemblies. Self-tapping screws should not be used to replace standard screws, nuts, bolts, or rivets.

Pins

The four main types of pins used in aircraft structures are the rollpin, flathead pin, cotter pin, and taper pin. Pins are used in shear applications and for safetying.

Rollpins

The rollpin is a pressed-fit pin with chamfered ends. It is tubular in shape and is slotted the full length of the tube. The pin is inserted with hand tools and is compressed as it is driven into place. Pressure exerted by the rollpin against the hole walls keeps it in place, until deliberately removed with a drift punch or pin punch.

Flathead Pin

Commonly called a clevis pin, the flathead pin (MS20392) is used with tie-rod terminals and in secondary controls which are not subject to continuous operation. The pin is customarily installed with the head up so that if the cotter pin, safety wire, or other retention device fails or works out, the pin will remain in place.

Cotter Pin

The AN380 cadmium-plated low-carbon steel cotter pin is used for safetying bolts, screws, nuts, other pins, and in various applications where such safetying is necessary. The AN381 corrosion-resistant steel cotter pin is used in locations where nonmagnetic material is required, or in locations where resistance to corrosion is desired.

Taper Pins

Plain and threaded taper pins (AN385 and AN386) are used in joints which carry shear loads and where absence of play is essential. The plain taper pin is drilled and usually safetied with wire. The threaded taper pin is used with a taper-pin washer (AN975) and shear nut (safetied with cotter pin), or self-locking nut.

Section 6

Aircraft Washers

A washer prevents corrosion and guards against mechanical damage to the material being bolted. Be sure that washers are used under both the heads of bolts and nuts unless their omission is specified. An aluminum-alloy washer should be used under the head and nut of a steel bolt securing aluminum or magnesium alloys. The result is that any corrosion that occurs then attacks the washer rather than alloyed material. Steel washers should be used when joining steel material with steel bolts. Washers used in airframe repair are either plain, lock, or special type washers.

Flat Washers

The AN960 and AN970 plain washers are used under hex nuts. The AN960 is shown in Figure 5-6-1. They provide a smooth bearing surface and act as a shim in obtaining correct grip length for a bolt and nut combination. They are used to adjust the position of castellated nuts with respect to drilled cotter pin holes in bolts. Plain washers should be used under lockwashers to prevent damage to the surface material.

Aluminum-alloy washers may be used under boltheads or nuts on aluminum alloy or magnesium structures where corrosion caused by dissimilar metals is a factor. When used in this manner, electric current flow will be between the washer and the steel bolt, and not between the bolt and the structure. However, it is common practice to use a cadmium-plated steel washer under a nut bearing directly against

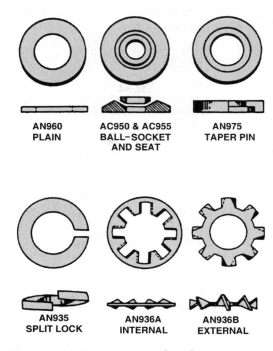

AN960 PLAIN AC950 & AC955 BALL-SOCKET AND SEAT AN975 TAPER PIN

AN935 SPLIT LOCK AN936A INTERNAL AN936B EXTERNAL

Figure 5-6-1. Various types of washers

a structure because this type of washer will resist the cutting action of a nut better than an aluminum-alloy washer.

The AN970 steel washer provides a greater bearing area than the AN960 washer, and is used on wooden structures under both the head and the nut of a bolt to prevent crushing the surface.

Lockwashers

AN935 and AN936 lockwashers are used with machine screws or bolts where the use of self-locking or castellated type nuts is not appropriate. The spring action of the AN935 washer provides enough friction, to prevent loosening of the nut from vibration. The AN936 washer prevents loosening of the nut by the gripping action of the tangs of the washer. These washers are shown in Figure 5-6-1.

Lockwashers should never be used under the following conditions:

1. With fasteners to primary or secondary structures.

2. With fasteners where failure might result in damage or danger to the aircraft or personnel.

3. Where failure would permit the opening of a joint to the airflow.

4. Where the screw is subject to frequent removal.

5. Where the washers are exposed to the air-flow.

6. Where the washers are subject to corrosive conditions.

7. Where the washer is against soft material without a plain washer underneath to prevent gouging the surface.

Shakeproof Lockwashers

Shakeproof lockwashers are round washers designed with tabs or lips that are bent upward across the sides of a hex nut or bolt to lock the nut in place. There are various methods of securing the lockwasher to prevent it from turning, such as an external tab bent downward 90 degrees into a small hole in the face of the unit, or an internal tab which fits a keyed bolt.

Able to withstand higher heat than other methods of safetying, shakeproof lockwashers can safely be used under high-vibration conditions. Most shakeproof lockwashers should be used only once because the tabs tend to break when bent a second time. However, some are manufactured with multiple tabs or tangs to facilitate reuse one time per tang.

Special Washers

The AC950 and AC955 ball-socket and seat washers are special washers used where a bolt is installed at an angle to a surface, or where perfect alignment with a surface is required. These washers are used together. They are shown in Figure 5-6-1.

NAS144 through NAS158 series internal wrenching bolts require the use of NAS143 and MS20002 washers. This washer is either plain or countersunk. The countersunk washer (designated as NAS143C and MS20002C) is used to seat the bolt-head shank radius, and the plain washer is used under the nut.

Section 7

Hole Repair Hardware

While damaged threads on bolts or nuts can be remedied by replacement of the defective bolt or nut, if internal threads are damaged, two alternatives are available. Either the entire part may be replaced, or the threads can be either repaired or replaced. Correction of the thread problem is usually less expensive and more convenient. Two methods of repairing are by installation of Heli-Coils or Acres sleeves.

Heli-Coil® Inserts

Heli-Coil Inserts (Reg. U.S. Pat. Off.-Heli-Coil, and Black & Decker Co.) are precision formed screw thread coils of 18-8 stainless-steel wire having a diamond shaped cross-section (Figure 5-7-1. They form Unified Coarse or Unified Fine thread classes 2-B and 3-B when assembled into (Heli-Coil) threaded holes. The assembled insert accommodates UNJ (controlled radius root) male threaded members. Each insert has a driving tang with a notch to facilitate removal of the tang after the insert is screwed into a Heli-Coil tapped hole.

Used as screw thread bushings, in addition to being used to restore damaged threads, Heli-Coil inserts are used in the original design of missiles, aircraft engines, and various types of mechanical equipment and accessories. Heli-Coil inserts are included in original designs to protect and strengthen tapped threads in light materials, metals, or plastics. This is particularly important in locations which require frequent assembly, disassembly, and/or where a screw-locking action is desired.

Heli-Coil installation (Figure 5-7-2) is a five or six step operation. In some applications, the sixth step may not be used. The following steps are for informational purposes only, and are not necessarily those of every insert manufacturer. The manufacturer's instructions should always be followed during installation.

1. Determine what threads are damaged.

2. Hole preparation.

   a. No Heli-Coil insert previously installed. Drill out damaged threads to minimum depth specified.

   b. Previously installed Heli-Coil insert. Using proper size extracting tool, place edge of blade 90° in from the edge of the insert. Tap with hammer to seat tool. Turn to left, applying pressure, until insert backs out. Threads are not damaged if insert is properly removed.

3. Tap. Use a tap of required nominal thread size. The tapping procedure is the same as standard thread tapping. Tap length must be equal to or exceed the requirement.

4. Gauge. Threads may be checked with a Screw Thread Insert (STI) thread gauge.

5. Insert assembly. Using the proper tool, install insert to a depth that puts end of

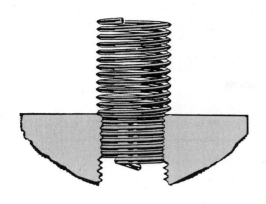

Figure 5-7-1. Heli-coil® insert

top coil one-fourth to one-half turn below the top surface of the tapped hole.

6. Tang break-off. Select proper break-off tool. Tangs should be removed from all drilled through holes. In blind holes, the tangs may be left in place if desired. If removal is necessary, the tang may be removed if enough hole depth is left below the tang of the installed insert to facilitate the use of the break-off tool.

NOTE: *Again, these instructions are general in nature and are not to be considered instructions for a specific Heli-Coil installation. The manufacturer's instructions must be followed when performing Heli-Coil installations.*

Acres Sleeves

Acres fastener sleeves are thin-wall, tubular, elements with a flared end. The sleeves are installed in holes to accept standard bolts and rivet type fasteners. The existing fastener holes are drilled $1/64$-inch oversize for installation of the sleeves. The sleeves are manu-factured in 1-inch increments. Along their length, grooves provide a place to break or cut off excess length to match fastener grip range. The grooves also provide a place to hold adhesive or sealing agents when bonding sleeve into the hole.

Advantages and Limitations

The sleeves are used in holes which must be drilled $1/64$-inch oversize to clean up corrosion or other damage. The oversize hole, with the sleeve installed, allows the use of the original diameter fastener in the repaired hole. The sleeves can be used in areas of high galvanic corrosion where the corrosion must be confined to a readily replaceable part. Oversizing of holes reduces the net cross-sectional area of a part and should not be done unless absolutely required. The manufacturer of the aircraft, aircraft engine, or aircraft component should be consulted prior to repair of damaged holes with Acres sleeves.

Identification

The sleeve is identified by a standard code number (Figure 5-7-3A) which represents the type and style of sleeve, a material code, the fastener shank diameter, surface finish code letter, and grip tang for the sleeve. The type and material of the sleeve is represented by the basic code number. The first dash number represents the diameter of the sleeve for the fastener installed, and the second dash represents the grip length of the sleeve. The required length of the sleeve is determined on installation, and the excess is broken off of the sleeve. A JK5512A-05N-10 is a 100° low-profile head sleeve of aluminum alloy. The diameter is for a $5/32$-inch fastener with no surface finish and is $5/8$-inch in length.

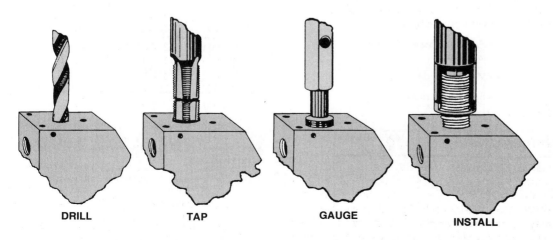

DRILL   **TAP**   **GAUGE**   **INSTALL**

Figure 5-7-2. Heli-coil® installation

ACRES SLEEVE	TYPE	Basic Part Number
	100° 509 Tension Head Plus Flange	JK5610
	Protruding Head (Shear)	JK5511
	100° Low Profile Head	JK5512
	100° Standard Profile Head (509 Type)	JK5516
	Protruding Head (Tension)	JK5517
	100° Oversize Tension Head (1/64 Oversize Bolt)	JK5533

SLEEVE PART NO.	BOLT SIZE	SLEEVE LENGTH [2]
JK5511( )04 ( )( ) JK5512( )04 ( )( ) JK5516( )04 ( )( ) JK5517( )04 ( )( )	1/8	8
JK5511( )45 ( )( ) JK5512 JK5516( )45 ( )( ) JK5517( )45 ( )( )	#6	8
JK5511( )05 ( )( ) JK5512( )05 ( )( ) JK5516( )05 ( )( ) JK5517( )05 ( )( )	5/32	10
JK5511( )55 ( )( ) JK5512( )55 ( )( ) JK5516( )55 ( )( ) JK5517( )55 ( )( ) JK5610( )55 ( )( )	#8	10
JK5511( )06 ( )( ) JK5512( )06 ( )( ) JK5516( )06 ( )( ) JK5517( )06 ( )( ) JK5610( )06 ( )( )	#10	12
JK5511( )08 ( )( ) JK5512( )08 ( )( ) JK5516( )08 ( )( ) JK5517( )08 ( )( ) JK5610( )08 ( )( )	1/4	16
JK5511( )10 ( )( ) JK5512( )10 ( )( ) JK5516( )10 ( )( ) JK5517( )10 ( )( ) JK5610( )10 ( )( )	5/16	16
JK5511( )12 ( )( ) JK5512( )12 ( )( ) JK5516( )12 ( )( ) JK5517( )12 ( )( ) JK5610( )12 ( )( )	3/8	16

PART NUMBER BREAKDOWN

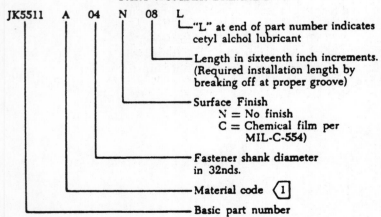

JK5511 A 04 N 08 L

- "L" at end of part number indicates cetyl alchol lubricant
- Length in sixteenth inch increments. (Required installation length by breaking off at proper groove)
- Surface Finish
N = No finish
C = Chemical film per MIL-C-554)
- Fastener shank diameter in 32nds.
- Material code [1]
- Basic part number

MATERIAL	MATERIAL CODE
5052 Aluminum alloy (1/2 hard)	A
6061 Aluminum alloy (T6 condition)	B
A286 Stainless steel (passivate)	C

ACRES SLEEVE FOR 1/64 OVERSIZE BOLT

SLEEVE PART NO. [1]	BOLT SIZE	SLEEVE LENGTH [2]
JK5533( )06 ( )( )	13/64	12
JK5533( )08 ( )( )	17/64	16
JK5533( )10 ( )( )	21/64	16
JK5533( )12 ( )( )	25/24	16

NOTES

[1] Acres sleeve, JK5533 1/64 oversize available in A286 steel only.

[2] Acres sleeve length in sixteenth inch increments.

Figure 5-7-3A. Acres sleeve identification

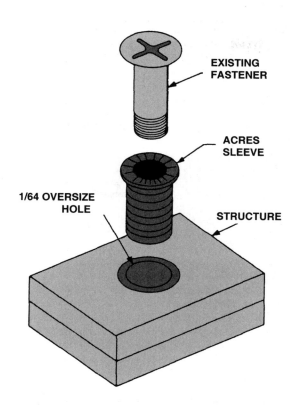

EXISTING FASTENER

ACRES SLEEVE

1/64 OVERSIZE HOLE

STRUCTURE

HOLE PREPARATION FOR $^{1}/_{64}$ OVERSIZE BOLT		
BOLT SIZE	DRILL NUMBER	DRILL DIAMETER
$^{13}/_{64}$	$^{7}/_{32}$	0.2187
$^{17}/_{64}$	$^{9}/_{32}$	0.2812
$^{21}/_{64}$	$^{11}/_{32}$	0.3437
$^{25}/_{64}$	$^{13}/_{32}$	0.4062

HOLE PREPARATION				
BOLT SIZE	STANDARD FIT		CLOSE FIT	
	DRILL NUMBER	DRILL DIAMETER	DRILL NUMBER	DRILL DIAMETER
$^{1}/_{8}$	$^{9}/_{64}$	0.1406	28	0.1405
#6	23	0.1540	24	0.1520
$^{5}/_{32}$	$^{11}/_{64}$	0.1719	18	0.1695
#8	15	0.1800	16	0.1770
#10	5	0.2055	6	0.2040
$^{1}/_{4}$	14	0.2660	$^{17}/_{64}$	0.2656
$^{5}/_{16}$	$^{21}/_{64}$	0.3281	-	-
$^{3}/_{8}$	$^{25}/_{64}$	0.3908	-	-

INSTALLATION PROCEDURE

1. Drill out corrosion or damage to existing hole to $^{1}/_{64}$ oversize

2. Select proper type and length acres sleeve for existing structure

3. Bond sleeve in structure hole MIL-S-8802 class A $^{1}/_{2}$ sealant

Figure 5-7-3B. Acres sleeve identification

Before hole preparation see Figure 5-31B for drill number for standard or close fit holes. Inspect hole after drilling to assure all corrosion is removed before installing the sleeve. The hole must also be the correct shape and free from burrs. The countersink must be enlarged to receive the flare of the sleeve so the sleeve is flush with the surrounding surface.

Installation

After the correct type and diameter sleeve has been selected, use the 6501 sleeve breakoff tool for final installation length (Figure 5-7-3B for the sleeve breakoff procedure. The sleeve may be installed with, or without, being bonded in the hole. When bonding the sleeve in a hole, use MIL-S-8802A1/2 sealant. Reinstall original size fastener and torque as required.

Sleeve Removal

Sleeves not bonded in the hole may be removed by either driving them out with a drift pin of the same diameter as the outside diameter of the sleeve, or they may be deformed and removed with a pointed tool. Bonded sleeves may be removed by this method, but care should be used not to damage the structure hole. If this method cannot be used, drill the sleeves out with a drill 0.004-inch to 0.008-inch smaller than the installation drill size. The remaining portion of the sleeve, after drilling, can be removed using a pointed tool and applying an adhesive solvent to the sealant.

Section 8

Cowling Fasteners

Used to secure inspection plates, doors, or other removable panels on aircraft, cowling fasteners are manufactured and supplied by a number of manufacturers under various trade names. Some of the most commonly used are the Dzus, Camloc, and Airloc. The most desirable feature of these fasteners is that they permit quick and easy removal of access panels for inspection and servicing purposes.

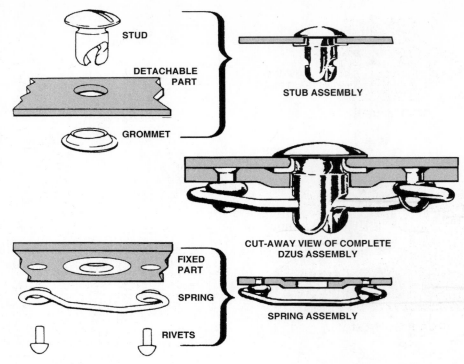

Figure 5-8-1. Dzus fastener

Dzus Fasteners

Consisting of a grommet, spring, and stud, an installed Dzus fastener and its various parts are illustrated in Figure 5-8-1.

The grommet is made of aluminum or aluminum-alloy material. It acts as a holding device for the stud. Grommets can be fabricated from 1100 aluminum tubing, if none are available from normal sources.

The spring is made of steel, cadmium plated to prevent corrosion. The spring supplies the force that locks or secures the stud in place when two assemblies are joined.

The stud is fabricated from steel, is cadmium plated, and is available in three head styles; wing, flush, and oval. Body diameter, length, and head type may be identified or determined by the markings found on the head of the stud (Figure 5-8-2). The diameter is always measured in sixteenths of an inch, and stud length

(the distance from the head of the stud to the bottom of the spring hole) is measured in hundredths of an inch.

A Dzus key, or a specially ground screwdriver, locks or unlocks the fastener. A quarter of a turn of the stud (clockwise) locks the fastener. The fastener may be unlocked only by turning the stud counterclockwise one quarter turn.

Airloc Fasteners

Airloc fasteners, like that shown in Figure 5-8-3, consist of three parts; a stud, a cross pin, and a stud receptacle.

The studs are manufactured from steel and case hardened to prevent excessive wear. The stud hole is reamed for a press fit of the cross pin. The total amount of material thickness to be secured with the Airloc fastener must be known before the correct length of stud can be selected for installation. The total thickness of material that each stud will satisfactorily lock together is stamped on the head of the stud in thousandths of an inch (0.040, 0.070, 0.190, etc.). Studs are manufactured in three head styles: flush, oval, and wing.

The cross pin (Figure 5-8-3) is manufactured from chrome-vanadium steel and heat-treated to provide maximum strength, wear, and holding power. It should never be used the second time; once removed from the stud, it should be replaced with a new pin.

F = FLUSH HEAD

6 1/2 = BODY DIAMETER 1N 1/16THS OF AN INCH

.50 = LENGTH (50/100THS OF AN INCH)

Figure 5-8-2. Dzus identification

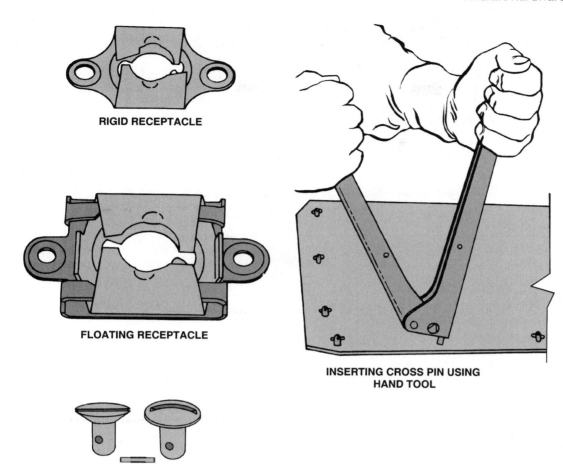

RIGID RECEPTACLE

FLOATING RECEPTACLE

INSERTING CROSS PIN USING
HAND TOOL

STUDS AND PIN

Figure 5-8-3. Airloc fastener

Receptacles for Airloc fasteners are manufactured in two types, rigid and floating. Sizes
are classified by number: No. 2, No. 5, and
No. 7. They are also classified by the center-
to-center distance between the rivet holes of
the receptacle: No. 2, $^3/_4$ inch; No. 5, 1 inch;
and No. 7, 1 $^3/_8$ inch. Receptacles are fabricated from high-carbon, heat-treated steel.
An upper wing assures ejection of the stud
when unlocked and enables the cross pin
to be held in a locked position between the
upper wing, cam, stop, and wing detent,
regardless of the tension to which the receptacle is subjected.

Camloc Fasteners

Camloc fasteners are used to secure aircraft
cowlings and fairings. Although Camloc
fasteners are made in a variety of styles and
designs, they consist of three basic parts; a
stud assembly, a grommet, and a receptacle.
Two types of receptacles are available; the
rigid type, and the floating type. An example
of the Camloc fastener can be seen in Figure
5-8-4.

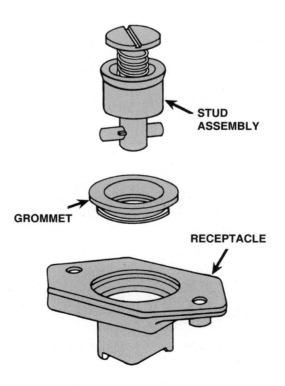

STUD
ASSEMBLY

GROMMET

RECEPTACLE

Figure 5-8-4. Camloc fastener

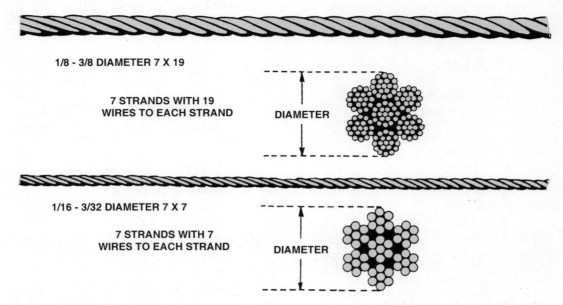

1/8 - 3/8 DIAMETER 7 X 19

7 STRANDS WITH 19 WIRES TO EACH STRAND

DIAMETER

1/16 - 3/32 DIAMETER 7 X 7

7 STRANDS WITH 7 WIRES TO EACH STRAND

DIAMETER

Figure 5-9-1. Cable cross sections

The stud and grommet are installed in the removable portion; the receptacle is riveted to the structure of the aircraft. The stud and grommet are installed in either a plain, dimpled, countersunk, or counterbored hole, depending on the location and thickness of the material involved.

A quarter turn (clockwise) of the stud locks the fastener. The fastener can be unlocked only by turning the stud counterclockwise.

Section 9

Control Cables and Terminals

While cables are the most widely used linkage in primary flight-control systems, they are also used in engine controls, emergency extension systems for the landing gear, and various other systems throughout the aircraft.

Cable has several advantages over the other types of linkages. It is strong and light in weight, and its flexibility makes it easy to route through the aircraft. An aircraft cable has a high mechanical efficiency and can be rigged to eliminate backlash or looseness within a control system, which is very important for precise control.

Cable linkage also has some disadvantages. The most common problem with cable is that tension must be adjusted frequently due to stretching and temperature changes. Caution must be observed to prevent kinking of the cable, and it must be protected from corrosion. Cables exposed to the elements have been known to have inner strands corrode, making detection nearly impossible.

Steel Control Cable

Aircraft control cables are fabricated from carbon-steel or stainless-steel wire. The diameter of the wire determines the total diameter of the cable. Aircraft control cables vary in diameter, ranging from $1/16$ to $3/8$ inch. The diameter is measured as shown in Figure 5-9-1. A number of wires are preformed into a helical or spiral shape and then formed into a strand. These preformed strands are laid around a straight center strand to form a cable. Cable designations are based on the number of strands and the number of wires in each strand.

Nonflexible Cable

Normally made from 1x7 (one strand made up of 7 wires) or from 1x19 (one strand made up of 19 wires), nonflexible cable is normally used in applications where short cables are used that do not pass over any pulleys and require little or no flexing. Nonflexible cable may be found on some engine controls, vent controls, or heater controls.

Flexible Cable

The 7x7 cable consists of seven strands of seven wires each. Six of these strands are laid around the center strand (Figure 5-9-1). This is a cable of medium flexibility and is used for trim tab controls, engine controls, or indicator controls.

Extra-Flexible Cable

The 7x19 cable is made up of seven strands of 19 wires each. Six of these strands are laid around the center strand (see Figure 5-9-1). This cable is extra flexible and is used in primary control systems, or in other places where operation over pulleys is frequent.

Woven Splices

Prior to the advent of mechanical means of splicing, cables were spliced by weaving the wires of the cable. Not only were two cables spliced in this way, but a cable could also be turned back and woven to itself creating an eye terminal. The problem with the woven-type splice is that it is laborious, time consuming, and that the resultant splice is not as strong as the cable from which it is made.

Swaged Terminals

Using a hand or power swaging tool, swaged fittings are pressed onto the cable. The result is a fitting as strong or stronger than the cable itself. A before and after go/no-go gauge is used to determine that the fitting is properly swaged onto the cable.

Swaged terminal fittings are generally available in the threaded end, fork end, eye end, single-shank ball end, and double-shank ball end. The threaded-end, fork-end, or eye-end terminals are used to connect the cable to a turnbuckle, bellcrank, or other linkage in the system. The ball-end terminals are used for attaching cables to quadrants or special connections where space is limited. Figure 5-9-2 illustrates the various types of terminal fittings.

Nicopress Oval Sleeves

Found in many light aircraft, Nicopress oval sleeves are copper sleeves that are slipped over the ends of cables and compressed. Like the swaged terminals, Nicopress oval sleeves are tested with a go/no-go gauge to determine that the fitting has been properly installed. And when properly installed the fitting will have a strength at least equal to that of the cable.

For splices, the ends of each cable are inserted through the sleeve and the sleeve is compressed

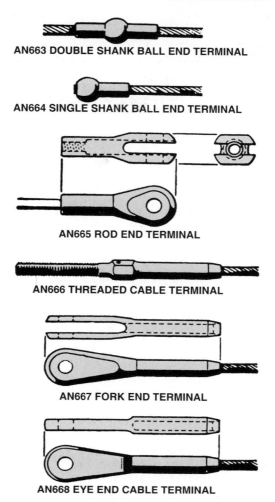

AN663 DOUBLE SHANK BALL END TERMINAL

AN664 SINGLE SHANK BALL END TERMINAL

AN665 ROD END TERMINAL

AN666 THREADED CABLE TERMINAL

AN667 FORK END TERMINAL

AN668 EYE END CABLE TERMINAL

Figure 5-9-2. Types of terminal fittings

with a Nicopress tool. For terminals requiring an eye-end fitting, one side of the sleeve is slid down the cable and the end of the cable is bent back and inserted into the other side of the sleeve. The size of the eye is determined by the distance of the sleeve from the end of the loop created in the cable. When the proper size eye is formed, the sleeve is compressed. Cables may be equipped with several different types of fittings such as terminals, thimbles, bushings, or shackles (Figure 5-9-3).

Turnbuckles

A turnbuckle assembly is a mechanical screw device consisting of two threaded terminals and a threaded barrel. A typical turnbuckle assembly can be seen in Figure 5-9-4.

Turnbuckles are fitted in the cable assembly for the purpose of making minor adjustments in cable length and for adjusting cable tension. One of the terminals has right-hand threads and the other has left-hand threads. The barrel has matching right- and left-hand internal

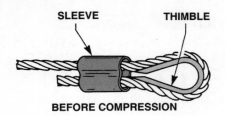

SLEEVE   THIMBLE

BEFORE COMPRESSION

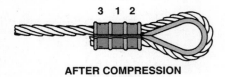

3 1 2

AFTER COMPRESSION

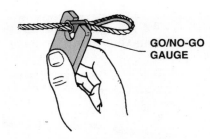

GO/NO-GO
GAUGE

Figure 5-9-3. A typical nicopress oval sleeve installation

threads. The end of the barrel with the left-hand threads can usually be identified by a groove or knurl around that end of the barrel.

When installing a turnbuckle in a control system, it is necessary to screw both of the terminals an equal number of turns into the barrel. It is also essential that all turnbuckle terminals be screwed into the barrel until not more than three threads are exposed on either side of the turnbuckle barrel. After a turnbuckle is properly adjusted, it must be safetied. The methods of safetying turnbuckles are discussed later in this chapter.

Section 10

Methods of Safetying

The Safety Process

Safetying is the process of securing all aircraft bolts, nuts, screws, pins, and other fasteners so that they do not work loose because of vibration, shock, airflow, or flexing of the airframe or component. A familiarity with the various methods and means of safetying equipment on an aircraft is necessary in order to perform maintenance and inspection.

There are various methods of safetying aircraft parts. The most widely used methods are safety wire, cotter pins, lockwashers, snaprings, and special nuts, such as self-locking nuts, pal nuts, and jamnuts. Some of these nuts and washers have been previously described in this chapter.

Safety Wire

The use of safety wire is the most positive and satisfactory method of safetying capscrews, studs, nuts, boltheads, and turnbuckle barrels which cannot be safetied by any other practical means. It is a method of wiring together two or more units in such a manner that any tendency of one to loosen is counteracted by the tightening of the wire.

The size of the safety wire used is determined by the size of the safety wire hole; approximately 75 percent of the hole should be filled by the wire. Zinc-coated, soft steel wire is used for general safetying purposes. Where nonmagnetic and heat resisting qualities are desired, corrosion-resistant wire is used. These wires are most commonly found in sizes of 0.020 inch, 0.032 inch, and 0.041 inch. Copper wire with a maximum diameter of 0.020 inch is used for safetying devices that require a break-away ability in an emergency, such as fire extinguisher pins, door- or window-hinge pin releases, etc.

Safety wire is generally twisted. This twisting may be accomplished by hand, except for the final few twists. These are made with pliers in order to apply torsion and to secure the ends of the wire properly. Safety wire pliers can be used to twist safety wire, however caution must be exercised to prevent crimping of the wire by the teeth of the pliers, causing a weak point in the wire. Extreme care must be used when twisting the wires together to ensure that they are tight but not overstressed to the point where breakage will occur under slight loads or vibrations.

Safety Wire Methods

The two methods of using safety wire are the double-twist method, and the single-wire method.

The double-twist method is the most common method of securing with safety wire. Examples of this method can be seen in Figure 5-10-1, numbers one through seven. Generally the loose ends of the wire are held so that they form, approximately, a 90° angle at the point where they meet. During twisting, tension should be maintained to give a smooth and even twist, preventing loose or kinked twists. Ideally there should be between 6 and

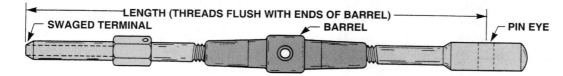

Figure 5-9-4. Typical turnbuckle

12 twists per inch, depending on the size of the wire. Small diameter wire (0.020 inch) provides its best safety at 12 twists per inch, and large diameter wire (0.041 inch) is best at about 6 twists per inch. Standard 0.032-inch safety wire provides the best safety without being overstressed at about eight twists per inch. The following general rules apply when using the double-twist method:

1. Use 0.020-inch safety wire on parts having a hole diameter of less than 0.045-inch diameter.

2. On parts having a hole diameter of more than 0.045 inch, use a safety wire of at least 0.032-inch in diameter.

3. Install safety wire in drilled head bolts, screws, or other parts which are grouped together, in series rather than individually.

   a. When installing safety wire to widely spaced bolts by the double-twist method, a group of three should be the maximum within a series.

   b. When installing safety wire to closely spaced bolts, the number of bolts that can be secured by a 24-inch length of wire should be the maximum number of bolts in that series.

   c. The term, widely spaced groups, means that the bolts, or other items being safetied, are from 4 to 6 inches

apart. Safety wire should not be used when distances are greater than 6 inches, unless tie points are provided on adjacent parts to shorten the span of the twisted safety wire to 6 inches or less.

The single-wire safety method is used with closely spaced small screws, in a closely spaced closed geometrical patterns (triangle, square, rectangle, circle), on parts installed in electrical systems, or in places that are difficult to reach. The largest size wire which the hole will accommodate may be used. For purposes of the single-wire safety method, closely spaced means a maximum of 2 inches between centers. An example of the single-wire safety method can be seen in part 8 of Figure 5-10-1.

Termination of the single-wire safety is a twisted pigtail of the same dimensions (6 to 12 twists per inch) as with the double-twist method. The pigtail is described later in this section.

Typical Single-Wire Locations

Screws that meet the requirements of the single-wire safety method which are used to secure hydraulic or air seals that hold hydraulic pressure, or are used in critical areas of clutch mechanisms and superchargers, should use the double-twist, rather than the single-wire method of safety wiring.

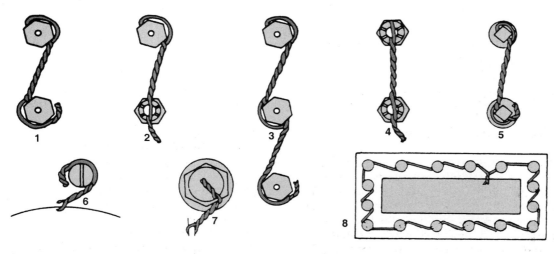

Figure 5-10-1. Safety wiring methods

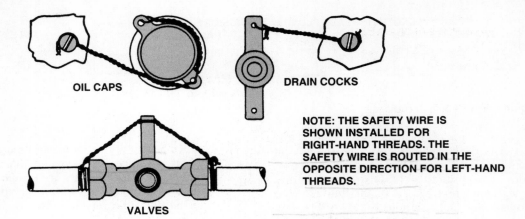

OIL CAPS

DRAIN COCKS

NOTE: THE SAFETY WIRE IS
SHOWN INSTALLED FOR
RIGHT-HAND THREADS. THE
SAFETY WIRE IS ROUTED IN THE
OPPOSITE DIRECTION FOR LEFT-HAND
THREADS.

VALVES

Figure 5-10-2. Safety wiring oil caps, drain cocks, and valves

General Safety Wiring Rules

When using the safety wire, the following general rules should be followed (unless otherwise noted, the word bolt is used for simplicity, and means bolts, nuts, or any other type of device that is safetied with wire).

Whether single wire or double twist, always terminate a wire safety with a pigtail. After completing the safety, continue twisting for a distance of between $1/2$ and 1 inch. Trim the excess wire so that $1/4$ to $1/2$ inch (three to six twists) remains at the end of the wire. This excess wire is then bent back or under to form the pigtail. Forming a pigtail prevents the end of the safety from stabbing, cutting, or snagging.

The safety wire must be new for each application. Never reuse safety wire.

Parts being safety wired should be torqued to recommended values and the holes aligned before attempting the safetying operation. Never over torque or loosen a torqued nut to align safety wire holes. When castellated nuts are to be secured with safety wire, tighten the nut to the low side of the selected torque range, unless otherwise specified, and if necessary, continue tightening until a slot aligns with the hole.

All wire safeties must be tight after installation, but not under such tension that normal handling or vibration will break the wire.

Positive Safety

Safety wire must be applied so that all pull exerted by the wire will tend to tighten the bolt. This is known as a positive safety. If tension applied to the wire would loosen the bolt, the safety is said to be a negative safety. If the safety wire hole is aligned with the lay of the safety wire so that the safety is neither positive nor negative, the safety is said to be neutral. Negative safeties are to be avoided at all cost. However, a neutral safety may be permitted within a series, provided that the first and last bolt in the series is positive, and that the bolts on either side of the neutral safety have a positive safety.

Twists should be tight and even, and the wire between the bolts as taut as possible without overtwisting.

Loops Around Screwheads and Bolt Threads

Safety wire should always be installed and twisted so that the loop around the head stays down and does not tend to come up over the bolthead, causing a slack loop.

Special Safety Wire Methods

Oil Caps, Drain Cocks, and Valves

These items are safety wired as shown in Figure 5-10-2. In the case of the oil cap, the wire is anchored to an adjacent fillister-head screw. This method applies to any other item which must be safety wired individually. Ordinarily, anchorage lips are conveniently located near these individual parts. When such provisions are not made, the safety wire is fastened to some adjacent part of the assembly.

Electrical Connectors

Under conditions of severe vibration, or under moderate vibration for long durations, the coupling nut of an electrical connector may

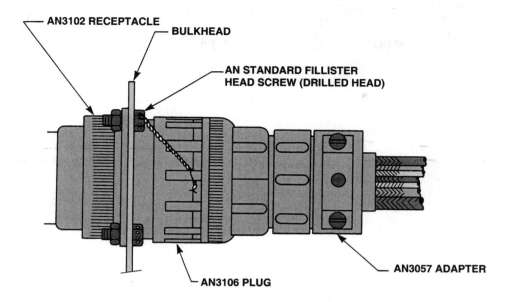

Figure 5-10-3. Safety wiring attachment for plug connectors

vibrate loose or may even come apart. When this occurs, that circuit can no longer function. To prevent this from occurring, the connector should be safety wired as is shown in Figure 5-10-3. The safety wire should be as short as practicable, and must be installed in such a manner that the pull on the wire is in the direction which would tighten the nut on the plug (i.e., a positive safety).

Turnbuckles

After a turnbuckle has been properly adjusted, it must be safetied. While there are several methods of safetying turnbuckles, the two methods most often used are the old double-wrap safety wire method and the newer clip-locking method. These methods are illustrated in Figure 5-10-4.

The double-wrap safety wire method requires the use of two separate lengths of the proper wire as shown in Table 5-10-1.

1. Run one end of the wire through the hole in the barrel of the turnbuckle and bend the ends of the wire towards opposite ends of the turnbuckle. Pass the second length of the wire through the hole in the barrel, and bend the ends along the barrel on the sides opposite that of the first wire. Then pass the wires at each end of the turnbuckle through the holes in the turnbuckle eyes, or between the jaws, of the turnbuckle fork, as applicable. Bend the wires so that they lay along the shank. Wrap one wire around the shank, and all three wires laying against the

shank at least four turns, at a point just below the eye or fork. Trim the excess wire. At a point between those wraps and the turnbuckle, wrap the remaining wire around the shank, and the two wires laying against the shank at least four turns. Again, trim the excess. Having completed the double wraps on one side of the turnbuckle, move to the other side and repeat the procedure, remembering to keep tension on the wires for a smooth safety.

   a. When a swaged terminal is being safetied, pass the ends of both wires, if possible, through the hole provided in the terminal for this purpose and wrap both ends around the shank as described previously.

   b. If the hole is not large enough to allow passage of both wires, pass the wire through the hole and loop it over the free end of the other wire, and then wrap both ends around the shank as described.

2. The correct diameter of the safety wire in turnbuckle assemblies depends on the diameter of the cable. If the hole size of the terminal is insufficient to accommodate the specified safety wire diameter, a smaller diameter may be used. Great care must be taken, particularly where corrosion is a factor, since the smaller wire sizes tend to crack when sharp bends are encountered in the installation. Table 5-10-1 shows preferred and acceptable safety wire diameters for various cable diameters.

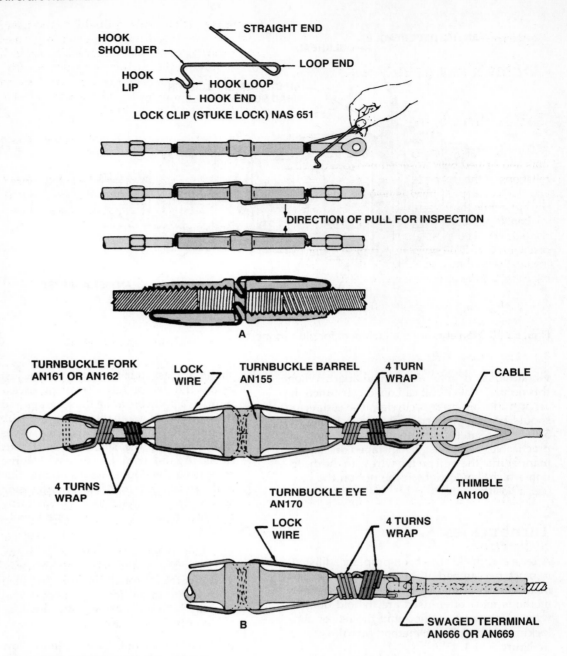

Figure 5-10-4. Safetying turnbuckles

CABLE SIZE (INCHES)	TYPE OF WRAP	DIAMETER OF SAFETY WIRE (INCHES)	MATERIAL (ANNEALED CONDITION)
$1/16$	Single	0.020	Stainless Steel
$3/32$	Single	0.040	Copper, Brass*
$1/8$	Single	0.040	Stainless Steel
$1/8$	Double	0.040	Copper, Brass*
$1/8$	Single	0.057 (minimum)	Copper, Brass*
$5/32$ and greater	Single	0.057	Stainless Steel

NOTE:
*Galvanized or tinned steel or soft iron wires are also acceptable.

Table 5-10-1. Turnbuckle safetying guide

The Clip-Locking Method

For the clip-locking method of turnbuckle safetying (Stuke Lock) to be used, both shanks of the turnbuckle must be grooved to accept the clip. Once the turnbuckle is adjusted, a clip is inserted into each of the grooves. The grooves must be spaced so they are on opposite sides of the barrel (in other words 180° apart). When the clip is inserted into the barrel, the V end of the clip is inserted into the hole in the center of the barrel. With one clip on each side of the barrel, the V ends are inserted from opposite directions, and are inter-locked inside the barrel.

Section 11

Cotter Pins and Snaprings

Cotter Pin Safetying

Cotter pins are generally used with castellated nuts and drilled bolts. Inserted between the castellations of the nut and through the hole in the bolt, the cotter pin's head is held on one side of the nut, while the ends (prongs) of the cotter pin are bent in a manner designed to retain the pin in the hole. The cotter pin should fit neatly into the hole with very little sideplay. A typical cotter pin installation is shown in Figure 5-11-1. The following general rules apply to cotter pin safetying:

1. The prong bent over the bolt end should not extend beyond the bolt diameter. Cut it off if necessary.

2. The prong bent down should not rest against the surface of the washer. Cut it off if necessary.

3. If the optional wraparound method is used, the prongs should not extend outward from the sides of the nut.

4. All prongs should be bent over a reasonable radius. Sharp-angled bends invite breakage. Tapping lightly with a mallet is the best method of bending the prongs.

Snaprings

A snapring is a ring of metal, either round or flat in cross section, which is tempered to have springlike action. This springlike action will hold the snapring firmly seated in a groove. The external types are designed to fit in a groove around the outside of a shaft or cylinder. The internal types fit in a groove inside a cylinder. A special type of pliers is designed to install each type of snapring.

Snaprings can be reused as long as they retain their shape and springlike action.

External-type snaprings may be safety wired, but internal types are never safetied. Safety wiring of an external type snapring is shown in Figure 5-11-2.

Section 12

Shock Absorber Cord

Shock absorber cord is made from natural rubber strands encased in a braided cover of woven cotton cords treated to resist oxidation and wear. Great tension and elongation are obtained by weaving the jacket upon the bundle of rubber strands while they are stretched about three times their original length.

There are two types of elastic shock-absorbing cord. Type I is a straight cord, and Type II is a continuous ring, known as a bungee. The advantages of the Type II cords are that they are easily and quickly replaced, and do not have to be secured by stretching and whipping. Shock cord is available in standard diameters from $1/4$ inch to $13/16$ inch.

OPTIONAL

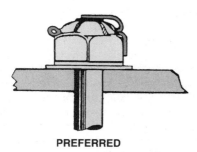

PREFERRED

Figure 5-11-1. Cotter pin installations

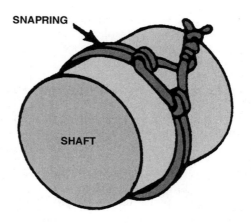

SINGLE WIRE METHOD

Figure 5-11-2. External type snapring with safety wire installed

The cord is color-coded to indicate when it was manufactured and to determine the life of the shock cord. According to MIL-C-5651A, the color code for the year of manufacture is repeated in cycles of 5 years.

The color coding is composed of threads interwoven in the cotton sheath that holds the strands of rubber cord together. Two spiral threads are used for the year coding and one thread is used for the quarter of the year sheath, e.g. yellow and blue would indicate that the cord was manufactured in 1994 during April, May, or June.

The listing below shows the color of the code thread for each year and quarter year.

Years Ending With...	Color	Quarter	Color
0 or 5	Black	1st	Red
1 or 6	Green	2nd	Blue
2 or 7	Red	3rd	Green

Section 13

Gaskets and Sealing Compounds

Used as static (stationary) seals between two flat surfaces, common gasket materials include asbestos, copper, cork, and rubber.

High temperature material is used wherever a heat-resistant gasket is needed. It is used extensively for exhaust system gaskets. Most exhaust gaskets have a thin sheet of copper edging to prolong their life.

A solid copper washer is used for spark plug gaskets, and some hydraulic fittings, where it is essential to have a noncompressible yet semi-soft gasket.

Cork gaskets can be used as an oil seal between the engine crankcase and accessories, and where a gasket is required that is capable of occupying an uneven, or varying, space caused by a rough surface or expansion and contraction.

Rubber sheeting can be used where there is a need for a compressible gasket. It should not be used in any place where it may come in contact with gasoline or oil because the rubber will deteriorate very rapidly when exposed to these substances.

Gaskets are used in fluid systems around the end caps of actuating cylinders, valves, and other units. The gasket generally used for this purpose is in the shape of an O-ring, similar to O-ring packings.

Section 14

Sealing Compounds

Certain areas of all aircraft are sealed to withstand pressurization by air, to prevent leakage of fuel, to prevent passage of fumes, or to prevent corrosion by sealing against the weather. Most sealants consist of two or more ingredients properly proportioned and compounded to obtain the best results. Some materials are ready for use as packaged, but others will require mixing before application.

One-Part Sealant

One-part sealants are prepared by the manufacturer and are ready for application as packaged. However, the consistency of some of these compounds may be altered to satisfy a particular method of application. If thinning is desired, the thinner recommended by the sealant manufacturer should be used.

Two-Part Sealant

Two-part sealants are compounds requiring separate packaging to prevent curing prior to application. The two parts are identified as the base sealing compound and the accelerator. Any alteration of the prescribed ratios will reduce the quality of the material. Generally two-part sealants are mixed by combining equal portions (by weight) of the base compound and the accelerator.

All sealant material should be carefully weighed in accordance with the sealant manufacturer's recommendations. Sealant material is usually weighed with a balance scale equipped with weights specially prepared for various quantities of sealant and accelerator.

Before weighing the sealant materials, both the base sealant compound and the accelerator should be thoroughly stirred. Accelerator which is dried out, lumpy, or flaky should not be used. Pre-weighed sealant kits do not require weighing of the sealant and accelerator before mixing when the entire quantity is to be mixed.

After the proper amount of base sealant compound and accelerator has been determined, add the accelerator to the base sealant compound. Immediately after adding the accelerator, thoroughly mix the two parts by stirring or folding, depending on the consistency of the material.

The material should be mixed carefully to prevent entrapment of air in the mixture. Too rapid or prolonged stirring must be avoided as it will shorten the normal application time (working life) of the mixed sealant.

To ensure a well-mixed compound, it may be tested by smearing a small portion on a clean, flat metal or glass surface. If flecks or lumps are found, continue mixing. If the flecks or lumps cannot be eliminated, the batch should be rejected.

The working life of mixed sealant is from $^1/_2$ hour to 4 hours, depending on the class of sealant. Therefore, mixed sealant should be applied as soon as possible or placed in refrigerated storage.

Curing

The curing rate of mixed sealants varies with changes in temperature and humidity. Curing of sealants will be extremely slow if the temperature is below 60°F. A temperature of 77°F with 50 percent relative humidity is the ideal condition for curing most sealants.

Curing may be accelerated by increasing the temperature. However, the temperature should never be allowed to exceed 120°F at any time in the curing cycle. Heat may be applied by using infrared lamps or heated air. If heated air is used, it must be properly filtered to remove moisture and dirt.

Heat should not be applied to any faying surface sealant installation until all work is completed. Faying surface applications must have all attachments, permanent or temporary, completed within the application limitations of the sealant.

Sealant must be cured to a tack-free condition before applying brush top coatings. (Tack-free consistency is the point at which a sheet of cellophane pressed onto the sealant will no longer adhere.)

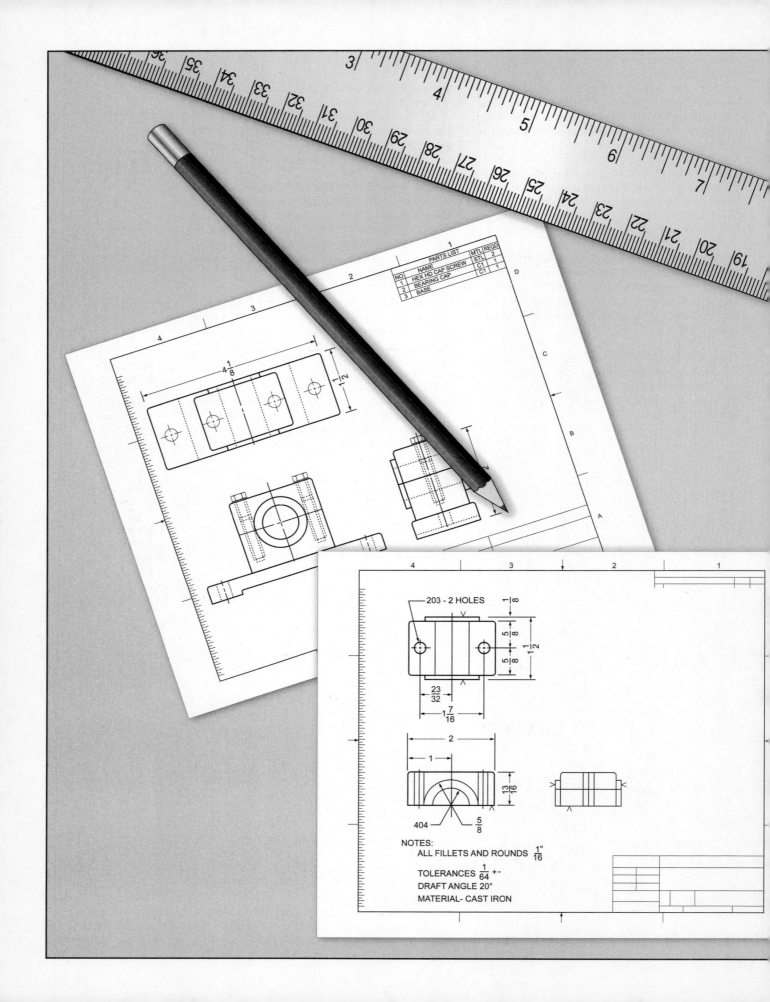

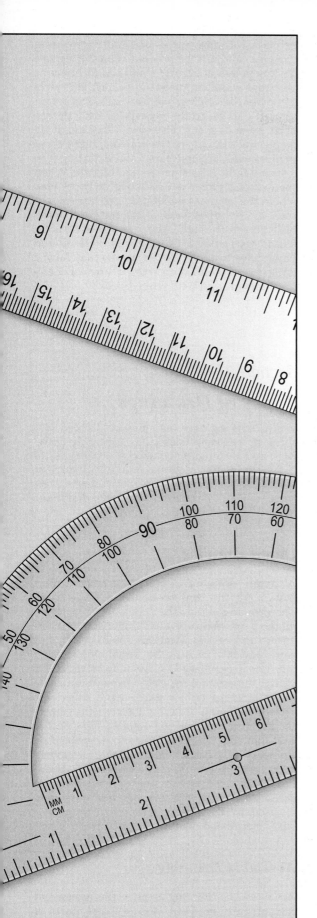

6

Aircraft Drawings

Section 1

Purpose and Function of Aircraft Drawings

The exchange of ideas is essential to everyone, regardless of their vocation or position. Usually, this exchange is carried on by the oral or written word; but under some conditions the use of these alone is impractical. Industry discovered that it could not depend entirely upon written or spoken words for the exchange of ideas because misunderstanding and misinterpretation arose frequently.

Pictures were the earliest form of language used to communicate information and ideas. These pictures were drawn with lines and symbols. Drawing has since evolved along two different lines, artistic and technical. Artistic drawings use lines and forms in the creative expression of cultural things, whereas technical drawings use lines and symbols to express technical ideas and thoughts.

To express in written terms the information required to construct even a simple item would end in disaster. In the design and construction of complex items, drawings are the most accurate way to communicate the information. Each engineering field has made use of drawings. Each field uses standards in the production of drawings, but each has also evolved different symbols.

Drafting is the drawing of an engineering picture of an object. The drawing is a graphic presentation of a real thing. These pictures can be understood by anyone who knows the language of drafting. For this reason drafting is referred to as the universal language (See

Left. Technical drawings contain the information required to properly repair aircraft structures.

"Lines and Their Meanings" later in this chapter).

Aircraft drawings originate in the drafting section of the engineering office. These drawings are referred to as engineering drawings. There are many types of engineering drawings. Some of these types of drawings are discussed in the following paragraphs.

Prints are copies of the original engineering drawing, and are the link between the aircraft designers, manufacturers, and the technicians who repair and maintain the aircraft. A print is a copy of the original working drawing for an aircraft part or group of parts, or for a design of a system or group of systems. They are made by placing a tracing of the drawing over a sheet of chemically treated paper and exposing it to a strong light for a short period of time. When the exposed paper is developed, it turns blue where the light has penetrated the transparent tracing. The inked lines of the tracing, having blocked out the light, show as white lines on a blue background. Other types of sensitized paper have been developed; prints may have a white background with colored lines or a colored background with white lines.

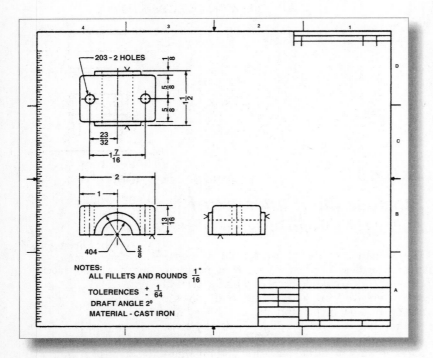

Figure 6-2-1. Detail Drawing

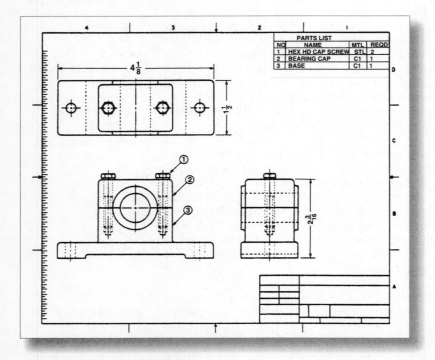

Figure 6-2-2. Assembly Drawing

Section 2

Types of Drawings

While working drawings may be divided into three classes; detail drawings, assembly drawings, and installation drawings; other types of drawings include sectional drawings, exploded views, block diagrams, logic flow charts, electrical wiring diagrams, schematic diagrams, and pictorial electrical diagrams.

Detail Drawing

A detail drawing supplies complete information for the construction of a single part. The drawing shows the size, shape, material, method of manufacture, dimensions, tolerances, and/or specifications for material, finishes, and heat treating. Sectional views, auxiliary views, or enlarged views may be added for clearer understanding. Detail drawings may be either single-detail or multi-detail drawings. The single-detail drawing, Figure 6-2-1, shows the part and perhaps one detailed view of that part that emphasizes or helps to describe size, shape, or any of the other details previously mentioned. The multi-detail drawing is essentially the same as the single detail drawing except that more than one detailed view may be used to describe or emphasize the previously mentioned details.

Assembly Drawing

An assembly drawing depicts the assembled relationships between two or more parts, a combination of parts, or a group of assemblies to form a larger assembly. Assembly drawings vary in the amount and type of information given depending on what the drawing depicts. The function of an assembly drawing is to show an item in its completed shape, to indicate relationships between parts or components, and to show the part number for the parts. Assembly drawings may also show overall dimensions capacities, information for assembly, and operating instructions (Figure 6-2-2).

Installation Drawing

An installation drawing shows the general arrangement of the part(s) or its/their position and the information to install the item(s). The information shown on an installation drawing is that needed to complete the installation. Depending on the type of installation, either electrical or mechanical, the information may vary. Generally, the information will give mounting directions, location and dimensions, and attaching hardware.

Sectional Drawings

Sectional drawings are usually referred to as sectional views and are used to show internal detail more clearly than is possible in any other type of drawing. There are several types of view drawings available depending on what is to be shown. A cutting plane line is used to indicate what surface and where the surface is cut. The portion that is cut is indicated by the use of section lines. A viewing plane line is used to indicate what surface is being viewed and the direction from which it will be viewed.

Full section. A full section view indicates the object is cut or viewed as if it were cut in half (Figure 6-2-3). The cutting plane line passes completely through the object. The viewing plane line does not pass through the object.

Half section. In a half section, the cutting plane extends only halfway across the object, leaving the other half of the object as an exterior view. Half sections are used to advantage with symmetrical objects to show both the interior and exterior.

Exploded Views

This type of drawing shows the relationship of parts and can be helpful in assembling components (Figure 6-2-4).

Block Diagrams

Block diagrams are used to show the relationship and function of each item in the diagram.

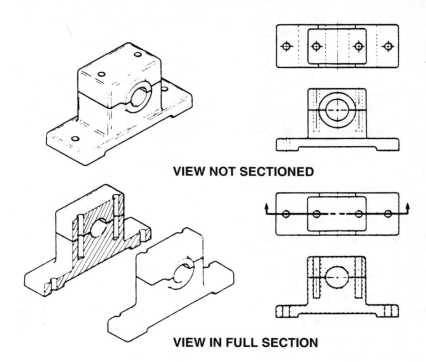

VIEW NOT SECTIONED

VIEW IN FULL SECTION

Figure 6-2-3. Full-Section View

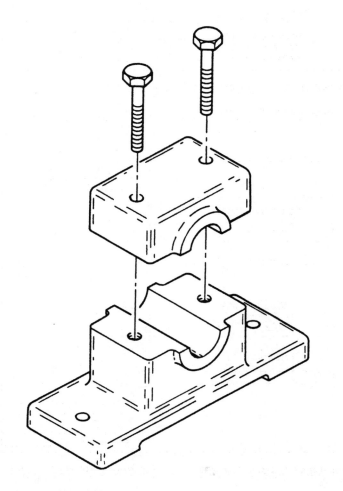

Figure 6-2-4. Exploded View

This type of diagram can be used in electrical, electronic, or mechanical applications. An electrical or electronic block diagram does not show electrical connections (Figure 6-2-5). Block diagrams are so called because each unit is identified by a block or square. Other types of symbols may also be used in block diagrams.

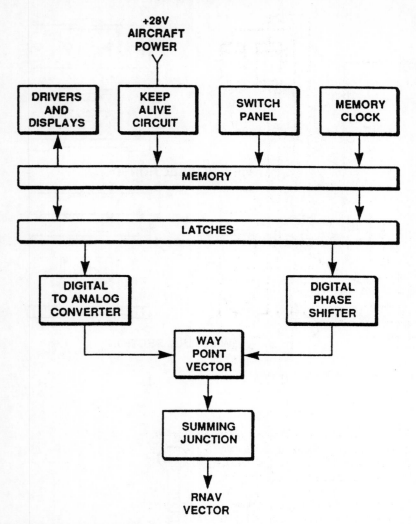

Figure 6-2-5. Block Diagram

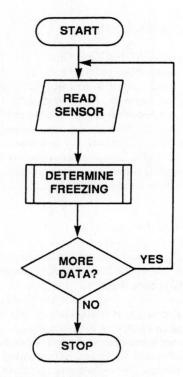

Figure 6-2-6. Logic Diagram

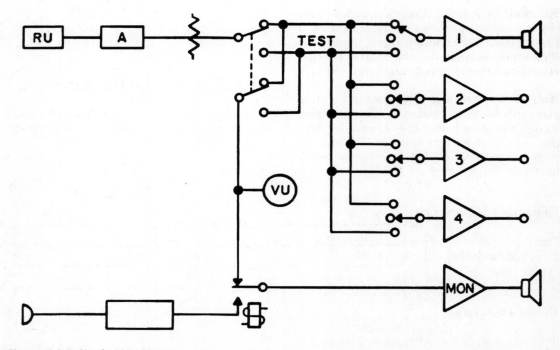

Figure 6-2-7. Single-Line Diagram

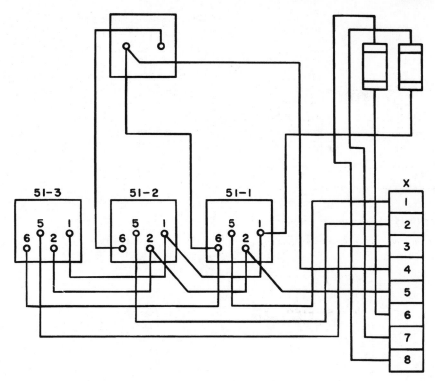

Figure 6-2-8. Connection Diagram

Logic Flow Charts

The logic flow chart represents the mechanical, electrical, or electronic action without necessarily expressing the construction or engineering information. An understanding of logic symbols is needed to interpret logic flow charts. Figure 6-2-6 shows a logic flow chart.

Electrical Wiring Diagram

Electrical wiring diagrams are divided into four types: single-line, schematic or elementary, connection or wiring, and interconnect.

A single-line diagram shows the path of an electrical circuit or system and components using graphic symbols as shown in Figure 6-2-7.

The connection or wiring diagram shows the general arrangement of parts and other information needed to trace or make internal or external connections (Figure 6-2-8).

The interconnect diagram shows only external connections between units (Figure 6-2-9).

Schematic Diagram

Schematic diagrams, like installation diagrams, are used extensively in aircraft manuals.

Pictorial Electrical Diagrams

A pictorial electrical wiring diagram shows pictorial sketches of the parts and the electrical

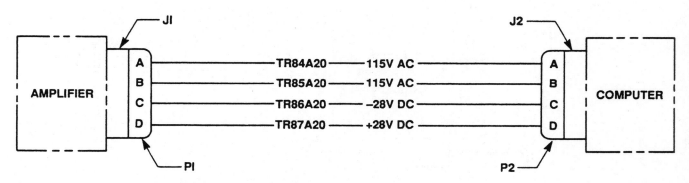

Figure 6-2-9. Interconnection Diagram

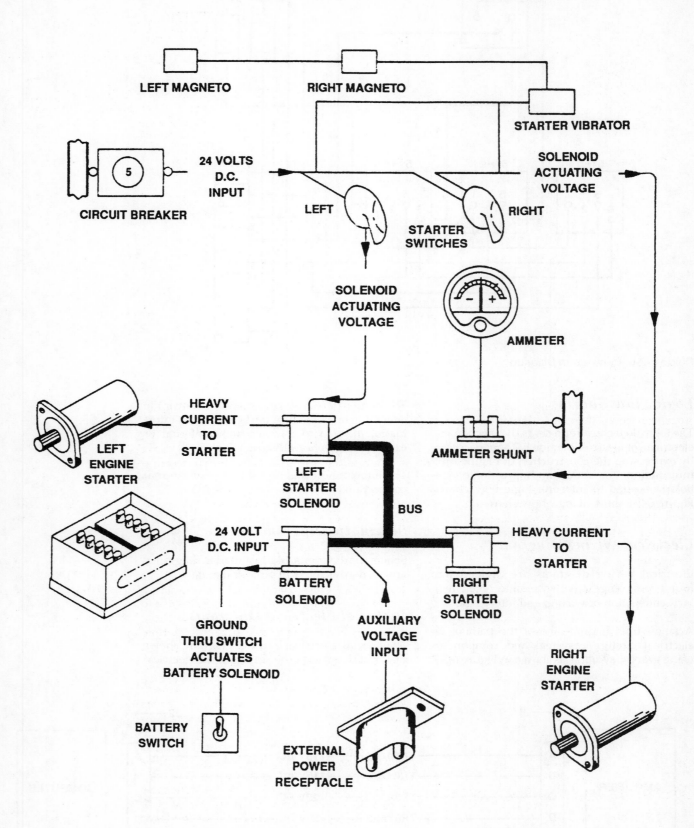

LEFT MAGNETO

RIGHT MAGNETO

STARTER VIBRATOR

CIRCUIT BREAKER

24 VOLTS D.C. INPUT

LEFT

RIGHT

STARTER SWITCHES

SOLENOID ACTUATING VOLTAGE

SOLENOID ACTUATING VOLTAGE

AMMETER

HEAVY CURRENT TO STARTER

LEFT ENGINE STARTER

LEFT STARTER SOLENOID

AMMETER SHUNT

BUS

24 VOLT D.C. INPUT

BATTERY SOLENOID

AUXILIARY VOLTAGE INPUT

RIGHT STARTER SOLENOID

HEAVY CURRENT TO STARTER

RIGHT ENGINE STARTER

GROUND THRU SWITCH ACTUATES BATTERY SOLENOID

BATTERY SWITCH

EXTERNAL POWER RECEPTACLE

Figure 6-2-10. Pictorial Wiring Diagram

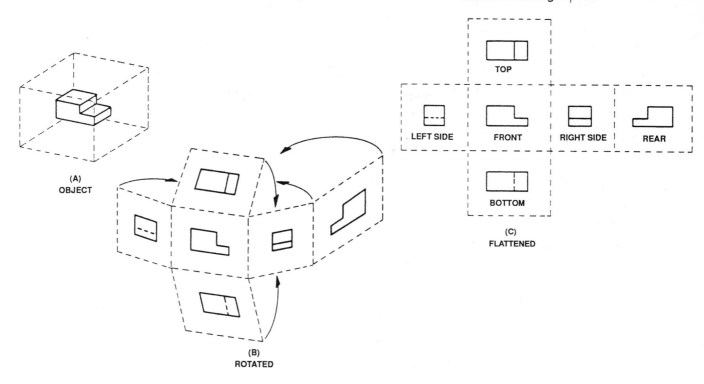

Figure 6-3-1. Orthographic Projection

connections between them. This type of diagram can be used for learning system operation and troubleshooting. It does not show location of equipment. See Figure 6-2-10.

An electrical or electronic elementary schematic diagram indicates the electrical connection and function of electrical or electronic circuits. This type of diagram aids in the tracing, function, and troubleshooting of the circuit without regard to size, shape, or location of the components.

A mechanical schematic diagram depicts the relationship of parts, components, or flow of fluids in a system. For ease of reading and tracing the flow, each component is identified by name, and its location within the system can be ascertained by noting the lines that lead into and out of the unit.

Section 3

Methods of Illustrating Objects

The method used to illustrate an object depends on what is to be shown. Each type of drawing has advantages and disadvantages in presenting the desired information about the object.

Orthographic Projection Drawings

In order to show the exact size and shape of all the parts of complex objects, a number of views are necessary. This is the system used in orthographic projection.

In orthographic projection, there are six possible views of an object because all objects have six sides, front, top, bottom, rear, right side, and left side. Figure 6-3-1, view A, shows an object placed in a transparent box, hinged at the edges. The projections on the sides of the box are the views as seen looking straight at the object through each side. If the outlines of the object are drawn on each surface and the box opened as shown in Figure 6-3-1B, then laid flat as shown in Figure 6-3-1C, the result is a six-view orthographic projection.

It is seldom necessary to show all six views to portray an object clearly; therefore, only those views necessary to illustrate the required characteristics of the object are drawn. One-view, two-view, and three-view drawings are the most common. Regardless of the number of views used, the arrangement is generally as shown in Figure 6-3-1, with the front view being the principal one. If the right-side view is shown, it will be to the right of the front view. If the left-side view is shown, it will be to the left of the front view. The top and bottom views, if included, will be shown in their respective positions relative to the front view. Should a rear view be necessary, it is

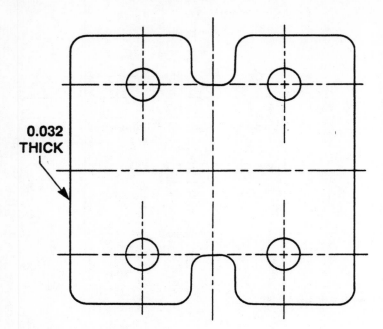

0.032 THICK

Figure 6-3-2. One-view Drawing

Aircraft drawings seldom show more than two principle, or complete, views of an object. Instead, generally there will be one complete view and one or more detail views or sectional views.

Isometric Drawings

In an isometric drawing, all the lines that are parallel on the part being drawn are parallel on the drawing. Vertical lines on the part are shown vertical on the drawing, but horizontal lines are drawn at a 30° angle to the horizontal (Figure 6-3-4). This type of drawing cannot be used to express complex parts. It may be used to clarify orthographic drawings.

Unlike orthographic projection drawings which present three-dimensional objects on a flat plane with a number of views, isometric drawings present a three-dimensional object on a flat plane approximately the same way the eye views it (Figure 6-3-4). The three dimensions shown on an isometric drawing are height, width, and depth. They are also the three isometric axes and their point of intersection is called the point of origin. The angle between these axes is 120°, as shown in Figure 6-3-4. Isometric drawings show external features only.

customary to place it to the left of the left-hand view.

One-view drawings are commonly used for objects of uniform thickness, such as gaskets, shims, and plates. A dimensional note gives the thickness as shown in Figure 6-3-2. One-view drawings are also commonly used for cylindrical, spherical, or square parts, if all the necessary dimensions can be properly shown in one view.

When space is limited and two views must be shown, symmetrical objects are often represented by half views, as illustrated in Figure 6-3-3.

Oblique Drawings

The front face of an oblique drawing is shown in true size and shape as if it were an orthographic drawing. The horizontal lines may be drawn at 30, 45, or 60° angles to the horizontal. The oblique sides are drawn to any scale to give a realistic depth.

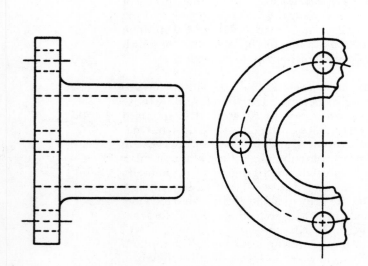

Figure 6-3-3. Symmetrical object with exterior half view

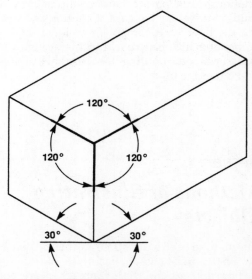

Figure 6-3-4. Isometric drawing

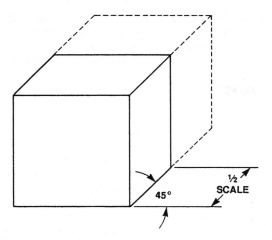

Figure 6-3-5. Cabinet drawing of a cube

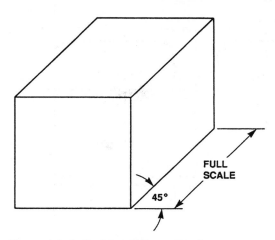

Figure 6-3-6. Cavalier oblique drawing

Cabinet Drawings

A cabinet drawing is a type of oblique drawing. It gets its name from drawings used for cabinet work. Cabinet drawings are drawn with the oblique side at a 30 or 45° angle to the horizontal and use $1/2$ scale of the front view (Figure 6-3-5).

Cavalier Drawings

The cavalier drawing uses the same scale of the front view on the oblique side lines. These lines are set at a 45° angle to the horizontal and create a distorted picture of the object's true proportions (Figure 6-3-6).

Perspective Drawing

The perspective drawing is the most true representation of an object. This method of drawing allows objects to appear proportionally smaller the further the distance, just as they do when viewed.

A perspective drawing is not used in the manufacture or repair of aircraft. This type of drawing may be used effectively for technical illustrations (Figure 6-3-7).

Lines and Their Meanings

Every drawing is composed of lines. Lines mark the boundaries, edges, and intersections of surfaces. Lines are used to show dimensions and hidden surfaces, and to indicate centers. Obviously, if the same kind of line is used to show all of these things, a drawing becomes a meaningless collection of lines. For this reason, various kinds of standardized lines are used on aircraft drawings.

Lines. Most drawings use three widths or intensities of lines; thin, medium, or thick. These lines vary somewhat on different drawings, but there will always be a noticeable difference between a thin and thick line, with the width of the medium line somewhere between the two.

Visible Lines

The visible line is used for all lines on the drawing representing visible lines on the object (Figure 6-3-8A).

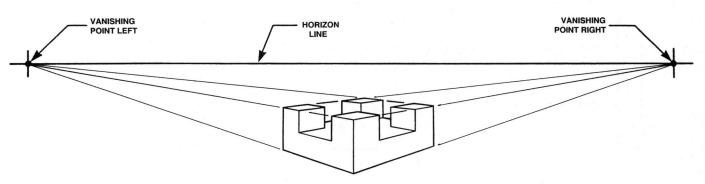

Figure 6-3-7. Perspective drawing

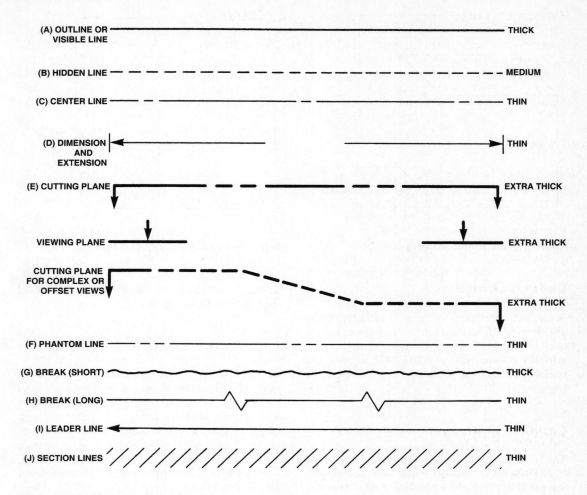

Figure 6-3-8. The meaning of lines

Hidden Lines

Hidden lines indicate invisible edges or contours. Hidden lines consist of short, evenly spaced dashes and are frequently referred to as dash lines (Figure 6-3-8B).

Center Lines

Center lines are made up of alternate long and short dashes. They indicate the center of an object or part of an object. Where center lines cross, the short dashes intersect symmetrically. In the case of very small circles, the center lines may be shown unbroken (Figure 6-3-8C). Center lines may also be used to indicate the travel of a center or used as extension lines.

Dimension Lines

A dimension line is a light solid line, broken at the midpoint for insertion of measurement indications, and having opposite pointing arrowheads at each end to show origin and termination of a measurement. Dimension lines are generally parallel to the line for which the dimension is given, and are usually placed outside the outline of the object and between views if more than one view is shown. Dimension lines should not contact the outline of the object (Figure 6-3-8D).

Extension Lines

Extension lines are thin lines used to move the dimension from the surface of the object to a point where the dimension will not interfere with the other lines. Extension lines should not touch the outline of the object, but may cross object lines. They should not begin or end on object lines (Figure 6-3-9).

Cutting Plane Lines

Cutting plane lines indicate the plane in which a sectional view of the object is taken. In Figure 6-3-9, plane line A-A indicates the plane in which section A-A is taken (Figure 6-3-8E).

Phantom Lines

Phantom lines indicate the alternate position of parts of the object or the relative position of a missing part. Phantom lines are composed of one long and two short evenly spaced dashes (Figure 6-3-8F).

Break Lines

Break lines indicate that a portion of the object is not shown on the drawing. Short breaks are made by solid, freehand lines (Figure 6-3-8G). For long breaks, solid ruled lines with zigzags are used (Figure 6-3-8H). Shafts, rods, tubes, and other such parts, which have a portion of their length broken out, have the ends of the break drawn as indicated in Figure 6-3-9.

Leader Lines

Leaders are solid lines with one arrowhead and indicate a part or portion to which a note, number, or other reference applies (Figure 6-3-8I).

Sectioning Lines

Sectioning lines are generally thin lines, and are sometimes referred to as cross-hatching. Section lines serve two purposes. The lines indicate the surface of an object that has been cut to make it stand out from the rest of the object. Section lines also indicate the type of material from which the object is made. Examples are shown in Figure 6-3-9.

Lettering

Good lettering gives a sketch a professional look. Sloppy lettering will make a good sketch look bad. Good lettering is essential for easy reading; therefore, it is important that you develop skill in lettering. Lettering is drawn, not written, so the standard forms and strokes can be learned through PRACTICE. Fancy, ornate lettering does not belong on a technical sketch.

The proportion of one letter to another in lettering, and the order in which the strokes are drawn are as important as the shape of the individual letters. The proportion of the letters gives them style and character, and the order in which the strokes are drawn will affect the ease and rapidity of lettering.

Numbers

The legibility of numbers and fractions on technical sketches is important. If the numbers on the sketch are hard to read, the wrong information may be communicated and time and material could be wasted.

Fractions

Fractions are always drawn with horizontal division lines. This will lessen the chance of misinterpretation with other numbers. Each figure is two-thirds the height of a whole number. To prevent the figures of a fraction from blending with the horizontal line when drawing fractions, leave space above and below the line. Lightly draw in the guide lines and erase them when you complete each set.

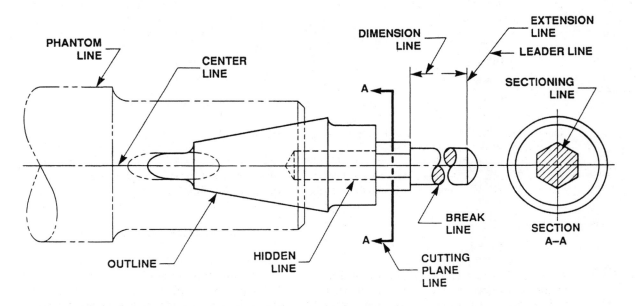

Figure 6-3-9. Correct uses of lines

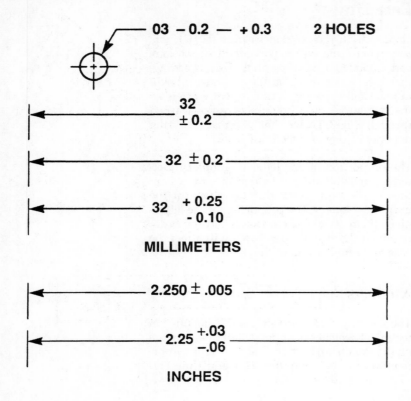

Figure 6-4-1. In limit dimensioning, bilateral tolerancing

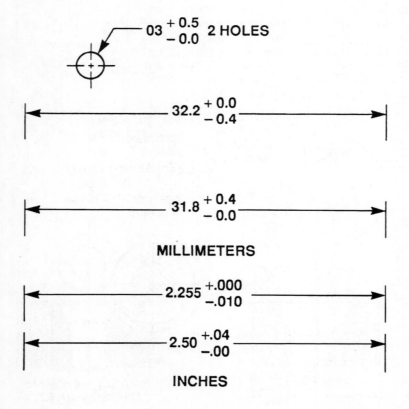

Figure 6-4-2. Plus and minus dimensioning, unilateral tolerancing

Section 4

Dimensioning

Tolerance

Tolerance is the acceptable variation from the specific dimension given on a print or drawing. A tolerance is usually given in three decimals (0.010). The tolerance may be shown by one of the following ways:

1. As a specific tolerance for a specified dimension.

2. As a general tolerance note that indicates the tolerance for all dimensions not covered by specific tolerances. (This tolerance is usually found in the title block.)

Types of tolerances. Tolerances are shown on prints or drawings in two ways; either by limit dimensioning or plus and minus dimensioning.

In limit dimensioning, Figure 6-4-1, the higher limit is placed above the lower limit. If the tolerance is expressed on a single line, the lower limit is expressed first, followed by the higher limit. A dash will separate the two limits.

Plus and minus dimensioning indicates the specific size dimension followed by the plus (high limit) and the minus (low limit). The plus limit is shown above the minus limit as shown in Figure 6-4-2. Plus and minus tolerancing may be expressed as either bilateral or unilateral tolerances. In bilateral tolerancing, the plus and minus limits are generally equal, but designs may dictate unequal values as shown in Figure 6-4-1. Unilateral tolerancing is used when only a high or low limit of a tolerance is used, Figure 6-4-2.

Dimensioning

Dimensioning on a drawing or print is indicated by the use of extension lines, leader lines, dimension lines, figures, notes, or symbols. Dimensions on a drawing indicate length, angles, diameters, radius, or locations. See Figure 6-4-3.

In dimensioning distances between holes in an object, dimensions are usually given from center to center rather than from outside to outside of the holes. When a number of holes of various sizes are shown, the desired diameters are given on a leader followed by notes indicating the machining operations for each hole. If a part is to have three holes of equal size, equally spaced, this information is given. For precision work, sizes are given in decimals. Diameters and depths are given for counterbored holes. For countersunk holes, the angle of countersinking and the diameters are given. Study the examples shown in Figure 6-4-4.

The dimensions given for fits signify the amount of clearance allowed between moving parts. A positive allowance is indicated for a part that is to slide or revolve upon another part. A negative allowance is one given for a force fit. Whenever possible, the tolerance and allowances for desired fits conform to those set up in the American Standard for Tolerances, Allowances, and Gauges for Metal Fits. The classes of fits specified in the standard may be indicated on assembly drawings.

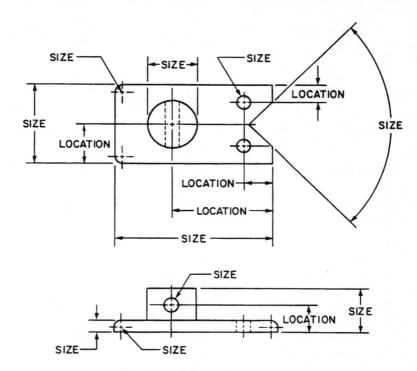

Figure 6-4-3. Size and location of dimension

Section 5

Aircraft Production Drawings

From the manufacturing design of an aircraft or part to the assembly, installation, and repair will require several types of engineering drawings. The engineering drawing is a document that pictorially shows the physical shape, function, or other information the designer wants to present.

To show all these requirements, it will normally take a number of different types of engineering drawings. As a rule, the combination of detail, assembly, installation, and diagrammatic drawings will provide the necessary information for a technician to complete the job. Diagrammatic is the description for usage of various diagrams. It is plural and refers to no specific diagram, but any diagrams that may be required (used). The format for engineering drawings is shown in Figure 6-5-1.

Title Blocks

Every print must have some means of identification. This is provided by a title block. See Figure 6-5-2. The title block consists of a drawing number and certain other data concerning the drawing and the object it represents. This information is grouped in a prominent place on the print, usually in the lower right-hand corner. Sometimes the title block is in the form of a strip extending almost the entire distance across the bottom of the sheet.

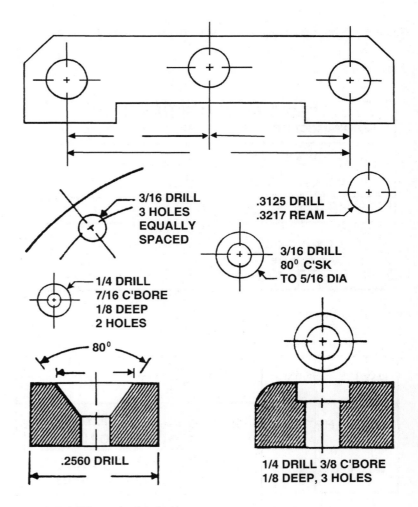

Figure 6-4-4. Dimensioning holes

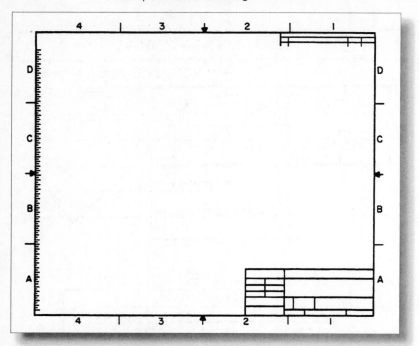

Figure 6-5-1. Engineering drawing format

1. A drawing number to identify the print for filing purposes and to prevent confusing it with any other print.

2. The name of the part or assembly.

3. The scale to which it is drawn.

4. The date.

5. The name of the firm.

6. The name of the draftsperson, the checker, and the person approving the drawing.

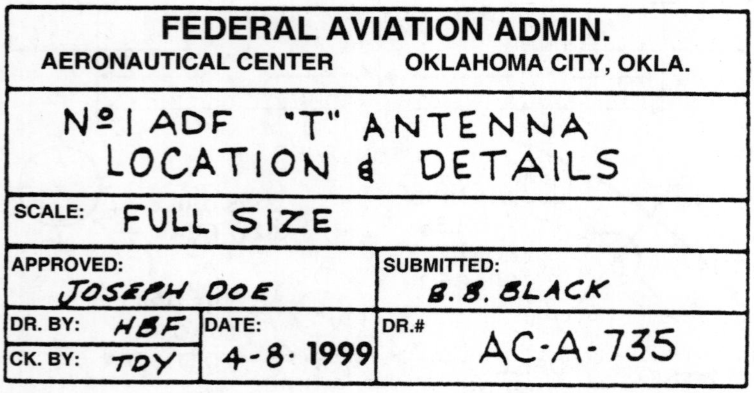

Size

Numbering system

The universal numbering system provides a means of identifying standard drawing sizes. In the universal numbering system, each drawing number consists of six or seven digits. The first digit is always 1, 2, 4, or 5 (Figure 6-5-3), and indicates the size of the drawing. The remaining digits identify the drawing.

Many firms have modified this basic system to conform to their particular needs. Letters may be used instead of numbers. The letter or number depicting the standard drawing size may be prefixed to the number, separated from it by a dash. Other numbering systems provide a separate box preceding the drawing number for the drawing size identifier. In other modifications of this system, the part number of the depicted assembly is assigned as the drawing number.

Drawing numbers. All prints are identified by a number which appears in a number block in the lower right-hand corner of the title block. It may also be shown in other places, such as near the top border line in the upper right-hand corner or on the reverse side of the print at both ends, so that the number will show when the print is folded or rolled. The purpose of the number is for quick identification of a print. If a print has more than one sheet and each sheet has the same number, this information is included in the number block, indicating the sheet number and the number of sheets in the series.

Although title blocks do not follow a standard form insofar as layout is concerned, all of them will present essentially the following information:

Reference numbers that appear in the title block refer a person to the numbers of other prints. When more than one detail is shown on a drawing, dash numbers are used. Both parts would have the same drawing number plus an individual number, such as 40267-1 and 40267-2.

FEDERAL AVIATION ADMIN.	
AERONAUTICAL CENTER OKLAHOMA CITY, OKLA.	
N°1 ADF "T" ANTENNA LOCATION & DETAILS	
SCALE: FULL SIZE	
APPROVED: JOSEPH DOE	SUBMITTED: B. B. BLACK
DR. BY: HBF DATE: 4-8-1999	DR.# AC-A-735
CK. BY: TDY	

Figure 6-5-2. Title block

In addition to appearing in the title block, dash numbers may appear on the face of the drawing near the parts they identify. Dash numbers are also used to identify right-hand and left-hand parts.

SIZE	1	2	4	5
LENGTH	11"	17"	22"	INDEFINITE (ROLL)
WIDTH	8-1/2"	11"	17"	17, 22, 25.50, 34, and 36 inches

Figure 6-5-3. Standard blueprint paper sizes

In aircraft, many parts on the left side are like the corresponding parts on the right side but in reverse. The left-hand part is always shown in the drawing. The right-hand part is called for in the title block. Above the title block will be found a notation such as: 470204-1LH shown; 470204-2RH opposite. Both parts carry the same number, but the part called for is distinguished by a dash number. Some prints have odd numbers for left-hand parts and even numbers for right-hand parts.

Scale

The scale that is printed on the blueprint indicates the size of the part on the drawing as compared to the size of the actual part.

A scale may be indicated as 1 inch equals 2 inches; 1 inch equals 12 inches; $3/8$ inch equals 1 foot, or full size, one-half size, or one-quarter size. The scale 1 inch = 2 inches indicates that a 1-inch line on the drawing is actually 2 inches on the object. When the scale is shown as 3 inches = 1 inch, the line on the drawing is 3 inches long and the line on the object is 1 inch long. This type of scale would be used when drawing a very small object.

Never measure a drawing and use that dimension because the drawing may have been enlarged or reduced.

Page. The title block contains a place to number the pages of a drawing. If a drawing has more than one page, it will be indicated by 1 of 3 on the first page, 2 of 3 on the second page, and 3 of 3 on the third page. When drawings are in book form, this number may be used to indicate the page number of the book.

Responsibility. Within the title block is a space for the date and initials or signatures of the designer, draftsperson, checker, and supervisor. Each drawing may not have all of these positions, but each drawing will indicate the responsibility for the drawing.

Standards

There are standards by which all drawings are made. The purpose of these standards is for the uniformity of drawings among the manufacturers. The standards deal with all aspects of the drawing. These standards are set by organizations with an interest in producing uniform meaning of the information presented on the drawings.

Some of the organizations that set standards for drawings are the Department of Defense (DOD), Society of Automotive Engineers

BILL OF MATERIAL			
ITEM	PART NO.	REQUIRED	SOURCE
CONNECTOR	UG-21 D/U	2	STOCK

Figure 6-5-4. A typical bill of materials

(SAE), American Welding Society (AWS), and the American National Standards Institute (ANSI).

Bill of Material

A list of the materials and parts necessary for the fabrication or assembly of a component or system is often included on the drawing. The list usually will be in ruled columns in which are listed the part number, name of the part, material from which the part is to be constructed, the quantity required, and the source of the part or material. A typical bill of material is shown in Figure 6-5-4. On drawings that do not have a bill of material, the data may be indicated directly on the drawing.

On assembly drawings, each item is identified by a number in a circle or square. An arrow connecting the number with the item assists in locating it in the bill of material.

Revision Block

Revisions to a drawing are necessitated by changes in dimensions, design, or materials. The changes are usually listed in ruled columns either adjacent to the title block or at one corner of the drawing. All changes to approved drawings must be carefully noted on all existing prints of the drawing.

2	CHANGED PART NO. 5	E.O. 1	02/03/00	B. K.
1	REVISED DIMENSIONS	J. L. M.	07/01/98	E. K. P.
NO.	REVISION	AUTH.	DATE	SIGN.

Figure 6-5-5. Revision block

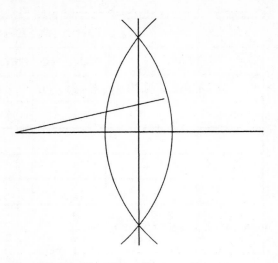

Figure 6-6-1. Bisecting a line

When drawings contain such corrections, attention is directed to the changes by lettering or numbering them and listing those changes against the symbol in a revision block (Figure 6-5-5). The revision block contains the identification symbol, the date, the nature of the revision, the authority for the change, and the name of the draftsperson who made the change.

To distinguish the corrected drawing from its previous version, many firms are including, as part of the title block, a space for entering the appropriate symbol to designate that the drawing has been changed or revised.

Zone Numbers

Zone numbers on drawings are similar to the numbers and letters printed on the borders of a map. They are there to help locate a particular point. To find a point, mentally draw horizontal and vertical lines from the letters and

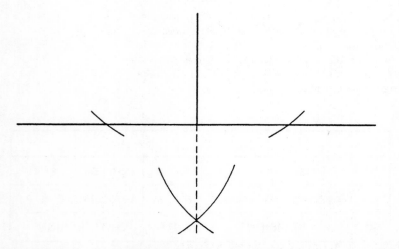

Figure 6-6-2. Drawing a line perpendicular to the baseline

numerals specified; the point where these lines would intersect is the area sought.

Use the same method to locate parts, sections, or views on large drawings, particularly assembly drawings. Parts numbered in the title block can be located on the drawing by finding the numbers in squares along the lower border. Zone numbers read from right to left.

Station Numbers

A numbering system is used in the design and manufacture of aircraft in order to identify any given point within the aircraft to within 1 cubic inch. This system utilizes fuselage stations, waterlines, buttock lines (commonly called butt lines), and wing stations. While each is described in detail in the following paragraphs, each one consists of a set of imaginary lines placed 1 inch apart, parallel to each other, and measured from a 0, or reference datum line. In addition to using this station numbering system on drawings and in the design and manufacture of aircraft, once produced, the weight and balance of the aircraft is determined by utilizing these imaginary lines.

Fuselage Stations

Fuselage stations (FS) are indicated in inches from the datum as set by the engineer. The datum can be at the nose of the aircraft, in front of the aircraft, aft of the nose of the aircraft, or any place the engineer designates. If the datum is aft of the nose of the aircraft, any station towards the nose of the aircraft will be a negative fuselage station. This will be indicated by a minus sign in front of the fuselage station number. For example, FS 15 indicates the station is 15 inches in front of the fuselage datum. When no sign precedes a number, it is positive and indicates that the fuselage station is between the fuselage datum and the tail of the aircraft.

Waterline Stations

Waterline stations (WL) indicate, in inches, the vertical distance from the waterline datum to a location on the aircraft. The waterline datum has no set location. This datum may be a point above the ground, the ground itself, or below the ground. If the location of the datum allows any part of the aircraft to fall below the datum, those waterline stations will be negative.

Buttock Line Stations

Buttock line (BL) stations are measured in inches from the centerline of the aircraft. This is the only datum that is the same on all aircraft. Buttock line stations are measured to the left and right of the datum. This is indicated by right buttock line (RBL) and left buttock line (LBL). The right buttock line is given a positive value from 0 (zero) and the left buttock line is given a negative value from 0 (zero).

Some manufacturers use buttock line stations to indicate positions on the wings. Other manufacturers use wing stations.

Wing Stations

Wing stations (WS) are measured in inches from the datum, which is the centerline of the aircraft. The wing stations are indicated by left or right. LWS indicates a **left-wing station** and RWS would indicate a **right-wing station**. When wing stations and buttock stations are used together, be careful not to confuse the numbers. Wing stations indicate positions on the wing structure only, not positions on the fuselage.

Section 6

Applied Geometry

To sketch an object or an idea, it may become necessary to draw geometric shapes, parallel lines, arcs, angles, or to bisect or divide lines into equal sections in order to communicate the needed information.

Find The Center of a Line

To bisect a straight line, Figure 6-6-1, set the pencil compass to a radius that is greater than half the line's length. Lightly swing an arc from both ends of the line. Connect the points where the arcs cross. The line will intersect the original line at 90° and divide the line in half. Erase the light lines.

Draw a Line Perpendicular to a Baseline

To draw a line perpendicular from a point to a baseline, open the compass to a greater length than from the point to the baseline, then swing an arc across the baseline. Using the two points where the arc crosses the baseline at pivot points, swing an arc from each point on the opposite side of the baseline from the point where the perpendicular line is to start. Connect the point where these two arcs cross

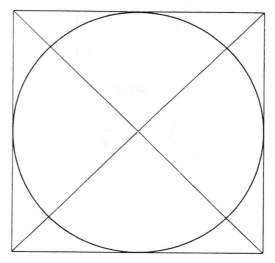

Figure 6-6-3. Finding the center of a circle (square method)

and the point where the perpendicular line is to start and draw a line from that point to the baseline (Figure 6-6-2).

Find The Center of a Circle

One method of finding the center of a circle is to draw a square around the circle. Then draw diagonal lines from the corners. Where the diagonal lines cross is the center of the circle (Figure 6-6-3).

Another method is to draw two lines from one point on the circle to opposite sides of the circle, then bisect each line. Extend the bisecting if necessary for the lines to cross. Where they cross is the center of the circle (Figure 6-6-4).

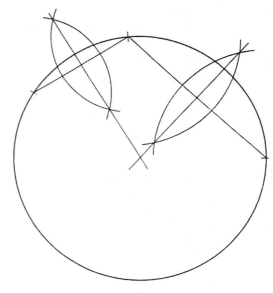

Figure 6-6-4. Finding the center of a circle (bisection method)

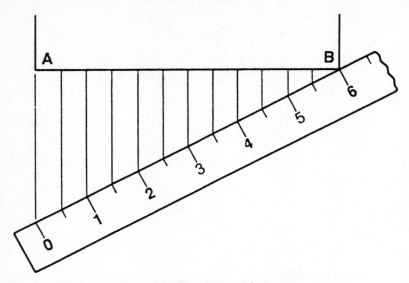

Figure 6-6-5. Dividing a straight line into equal segments

Divide a Line Into an Equal Number of Parts

Divide a straight line into equal sections, Figure 6-6-5, by using a ruler, that has the correct divisions of measurement. Lightly draw a line perpendicular below the line to be divided. With the high numbered end at the right side of the line, rotate the other end until the zero or one crosses the perpendicular line. Then mark the divisions on the paper and draw parallel vertical lines to the line being divided. The line will be divided into equal segments.

Bisect an Angle

To bisect an angle, Figure 6-6-6, set the pencil compass to a radius at least half the length of one of the lines that form the angle. Swing a light arc that crosses both line AB and BC. Then set the compass on points D and E and then swing short arcs from both points toward the opening of the angle. Connect point B where the arcs cross. The angle is bisected.

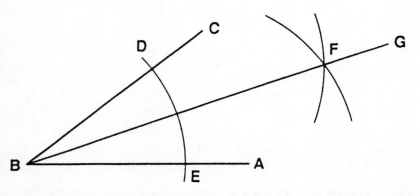

Figure 6-6-6. Bisecting an angle

Section 7
Sketching

The aviation maintenance technician should possess the ability to communicate in the form of technical drawings. The technician should be able to pass on ideas, information, and major repair information in the form of technical drawings. This does not mean that maintenance technicians should be able to produce sets of finished blueprints, but they should be able to present clear, concise, factual, and accurate information on the drawing.

The individual style or method of drawing is not important. The choice of presentation is up to the technician. The only requirement is that the drawing shows what the technician needs and wants to show, as accurately as possible.

Being an artist, or having special talents is not necessary to produce good technical sketches. Through practice and use of the basic skills, anyone can develop their drawing skills to an acceptable level.

Basic Sketching

Sketching Techniques

To produce accurate and usable drawings, there are a few basic techniques that have to be learned, mastered, and practiced.

Try to find a well lighted area with enough room to place the drawing paper and drawing equipment and to support your arms while working. The proper support for the arms is needed to help with the free and easy movement of wrists and fingers. Do not hold the pencil so tightly that your fingers become cramped.

When drawing lines, use short strokes. This allows for control of the pencil's movement, and provides for better control of the pencil point pressure on the paper. Make the pencil marks light while drawing. When the outline is finished, darken only the lines needed to show the object, and erase the rest. Lightly drawn lines are easily erased.

Lines, Arcs, and Circles

To make clear, accurate drawings, the sketcher must be able to sketch lines, circles, and arcs that will intersect lines. These types of lines are done best with drawing tools. Because these tools may not be available when a drawing needs to be made, it is important to be able to sketch freehand.

Freehand Lines

When drawing freehand lines, it is a good practice to place dots lightly on the paper as guides, with one at the beginning and one at the end of the line. If the line is long, a few intermediate dots may be used. Before drawing the line, swing the drawing arm along the dots to relax the arm and to get the feel for the length of the line. With a well sharpened, soft lead pencil, use a light touch and short strokes. The short strokes will help make the line straighter, and the light touch will make erasure easier if it is needed. After drawing a line, examine it for straightness and neatness. Additional practice may be needed, but vertical and slanted lines are drawn in the same way as horizontal lines.

Freehand Arcs and Circles

Drawing a freehand arc or circle requires no more skill than straight lines, but it does require a bit more practice. With the pencil held as shown in Figure 6-7-1, the first or second finger (based on the size desired) is used as a pivot point for the arc. A circle is drawn as a series of connected arcs. As with straight lines, use a light touch and short strokes.

Repair Sketches

When the completion of a repair requires a sketch of the repair, the sketch must be drawn clearly and contain enough information so someone could duplicate the repair. The sketch must show the type of material used, types of fasteners, location of the repair, and any additional information necessary to duplicate the repair.

Section 8

Graphic Presentation of Information

Some of the technical information used in maintaining aircraft can best be understood by presenting the information in the form of charts or graphs.

Charts or graphs can be divided into those that present technical relationships or mathemati-

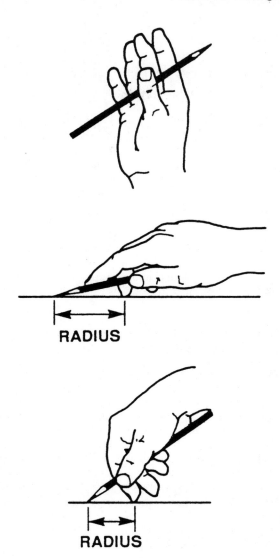

Figure 6-7-1 . Freehand arcs and circles

cal relationships and those used to express nontechnical data.

The type of chart or graph used depends on what information is to be presented. Care must be taken to select the right type of chart or graph, or the information presented could be misinterpreted.

A nomograph is used to show specific relationships between three variables. When the value of the two variables are known, set a ruler between the two and the third variable can be found.

A rectilinear graph shows the relationship between variables. One variable is shown on the vertical and the other is on the horizontal.

Circular charts and bar charts are used to give a visual presentation of the parts to the whole.

Section 9

Microfilm, Microfiche and Computers

Everyone in aviation has a space problem. Space is needed to hangar aircraft, to perform maintenance, for offices and storage, and the need for space goes on and on. The aviation technician who can honestly say that they don't need additional space is rare indeed.

One of the objects that traditionally takes up extraordinary amounts of space is the paperwork necessary to conduct the business of aircraft maintenance. This paperwork includes regulations, instructions, drawings, and other records.

While regulations and records are addressed in greater detail in other chapters of this book, it is necessary to mention them at this time since they too, along with drawings and instructions, have been reduced to microfilm, microfiche, and stored in computer data banks in order to alleviate storage and space problems encountered by everyone in aircraft maintenance.

Microfilm

The practice of recording drawings, parts catalogs, and maintenance and overhaul manuals on microfilm was introduced in recent years. Microfilm is regular 16-mm or 35-mm film. Since 35-mm film is larger, it provides a better reproduction of drawings.

Depending on the size of the drawing to be reproduced, a varying number of drawings can be photographed on one reel of 35-mm film. To view or read drawings or manuals on a reel of film, you need either a portable 35 mm film projector or a microfilm reader or viewer.

The advantage of microfilm is that several reels, which represent perhaps hundreds of drawings, require only a small amount of storage space. A person working on an aircraft may also need to refer to a specific dimension. They can place the reel of microfilm in a projector, locate the drawing or desired information, and read the dimension. If they need to study a detail of the drawing or work with the drawing for a long period of time, an enlarged photographic reproduction can be made, using the microfilm as a negative.

Microfilm of drawings has many other uses and advantages. However, microfilm is not intended to replace the need for original drawings, especially where the originals are modified and kept current over a long period of time.

When drawings are filmed on continuous reels, corrections can be made by cutting out superseded drawings and splicing in the revised ones. When these corrections become numerous, the procedure becomes impractical and is discarded in favor of again filming all the related drawings.

A method that allows corrections to be made easily is to photograph the drawings and then cut up the film into individual slides. This has one disadvantage; it requires considerable time to convert the film into slides, insert them into transparent protective envelopes, and arrange them in sequence so that desired drawings can be located quickly.

A 70 mm microfilm has been developed to replace the older and less versatile 16 mm and 35 mm films. With it, larger size drawings can be reproduced as individual frames or slides, and these can be inserted in regular paper envelopes and kept in an ordinary file. When held to the light, this large microfilm can be read with the naked eye.

Microfiche

A variation of microfilm is microfiche, which uses a sheet of film, typically 4 by 6 inches, on which the information is recorded. Literally thousands of pages of written material can be kept in one three-ring binder or in a small file box designed for microfiche.

The microfiche is divided into grids which are used to identify and locate information in much the same way that grid lines are used to find locations on a road map. The size of the grids is based on the size of the document being reproduced onto the microfiche. As an example, if standard 8-1/2 x 11 inch paper is reproduced on microfiche, most microfiche will accommodate 24 grids across and 12 or 13 grids down.

Microfiche is read on a reader which consists of a plate to hold the film, a light source which illuminates the film, a lens which enlarges the image and allows for focusing, a mirror to deflect the image to the viewing screen, and the viewing screen. Some microfiche readers have the capability to copy the selected image onto paper, which allows the user to have a hard copy of the information or drawing.

NOTE: *Hard copies should be destroyed immediately after use to avoid using material that has changed or been superseded since the hard copy was made.*

Section 10

Use of Computers

While the computer is by no means new, many ways of using them are. Today the computer is utilized by the aircraft maintenance technician to assist in the design and maintenance of aircraft parts, and components.

Computer Assisted Design (CAD)

Most modern aircraft are at least partially designed by engineers and designers using computers to assist them. In addition to assistance in solving complex design formulas, computers can be used to draw the designer's idea or concept on the screen, and transfer it to paper via a printer. By formulating the design on a computer screen, mirror images, corrections, and adjustments are simple key strokes, as compared to manual design which requires extensive erasure or redrawing.

Computer Assisted Maintenance (CAM)

Through the use of the computer, today's aircraft technician can record performed maintenance, find repair procedures, locate illustrations, track equipment performance, account for time, order parts, and much more. Programs and software available to the technician allow access to more information in less time, with more accuracy and less error than ever before. As technology improves the computer and its software, and because computers are becoming ever more affordable and easy to use, the future of CAM is basically unlimited.

Left. Sheet metal is often formed into complex shapes and curves to meet the aerodynamic requirements of the aircraft's designer.

7

Forming Processes

Handwritten notes:

$D \times 6 = .75$

$D \times 7 = .875$

$D \times 8 = 1$

$6 - 8 \times D$ spacing

$5 D \quad ED = .625$

#4 rivets

6×6

$2.25 \pi = 7.065$

3.5

2.25

3.5

Section 1

Importance of Metal Forming

Learning Objective

DESCRIBE
• hand forming procedures
• how to duplicate a part

EXPLAIN
• forming terminology
• the difference between working with aluminum and stainless steel

APPLY
• calculate bend allowance and setback
• lay out metal for forming
• form flanges

Forming is a process of major concern to the sheet metal worker and requires the best of his knowledge and skill. This is especially true since forming usually involves the use of extremely light-gauge alloys. A formed part may seem outwardly perfect, yet a wrong step in the forming procedure may leave the part in a strained condition. Such a defect may hasten fatigue or may cause sudden structural failure.

Since aircraft are constructed chiefly of aluminum and aluminum alloys, this chapter deals with forming that type of metal.

Of all the aircraft metals, pure aluminum (1100) is the most easily formed. In the other alloys, ease of forming varies with the temper condition. Most parts can be formed without annealing the metal, but if extensive forming operations, such as deep draws (large folds) and complex curves, are contemplated, the metal should be in the dead soft or the annealed condition. During the forming of some complex parts, operations may have to be stopped and the metal annealed before the process can be continued or completed. Alloys 2024 and 2024 Alclad and can be formed into almost any shape by any of the common forming operations, but must be heat-treated afterward. Forming in the heat treated condition can produce cracks in the bend radius (Figure 7-1-1).

When forming, use hammers and mallets as sparingly as possible and make straight bends on bar folders and cornice brakes. Use rotary machines if at all possible. If a part fits poorly

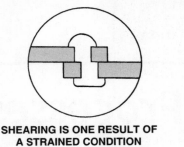

SHEARING IS ONE RESULT OF A STRAINED CONDITION

CRACKING IS A RESULT OF IMPROPER FORMING

Figure 7-1-1. Rivet shearing under load caused by strain

THIN MATERIAL CAN BE BENT MORE SHARPLY THAN THICK

SOFT MATERIAL CAN BE BENT MORE SHARPLEY THAN HARD

Figure 7-2-1. Radius of bend in thick or soft metal

or not at all, do not straighten a bend or a curve and try to reform it. Discard the piece of metal and start with a new one.

When making layouts, be careful not to scratch aluminum or aluminum alloys. A lead pencil is not satisfactory for marking. All marks on sheet metal should be made with a soft wax-charcoal pencil instead of a graphite one. Some examples are a Stabilo "8008", a Dixon "Phano", and a Blaisdell. Fine line felt tip pens can also be used. Scribers make scratches which induce fatigue failure but they may be used if the marking lines fall outside the finished part, that is, if the scribed line will be in the waste material.

Keep bench tops covered with material hard enough to prevent chips and other foreign materials from becoming imbedded in them (no carpet). Be sure, also, to keep bench tops clean and free from chips, filings, and the like. For the protection of the metals being worked, keep vise jaws covered with soft metal jaw caps.

Stainless steel can be formed by any of the usual methods but requires considerably more skill than aluminum or aluminum alloys. Since stainless steel work hardens very readily, it requires frequent annealing during the forming operations. Always try to press stainless steel parts out in one operation.

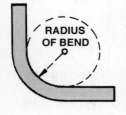

RADIUS OF BEND

Figure 7-2-2. Measuring the radius of bend

Section 2
Technical Forming Terms

When forming straight bends, you must consider the thickness of the material, its alloy composition, and its temper condition. Generally speaking, the thinner the material, the sharper it can be bent (the smaller the radius of bend) and the softer the material, the sharper the bend. Refer to Figure 7-2-1. The sharpest bend that can be placed in a piece of metal without critically weakening the part is called the minimum radius of bend. Other factors that must be considered when making straight line bends are bend allowance, set-back, and the brake or sight line.

Formulas and tables to be applied under the varying conditions have been established. Application of the formulas usually consists merely of substituting measurements, such as sheet stock thickness and degree of bends. All these tables and formulas are based on the decimal system; so if sheet stock thickness are given in gauge numbers, you must convert them to their decimal equivalent before you can proceed with your calculations.

Minimum Radius of Bend

The radius of bend of a sheet of material is the radius of the bend as measured on the inside of the curved material, as shown in Figure 7-2-2. The minimum radius of bend of a sheet of material is the sharpest curve to which the sheet can be bent without critically weakening that part at the bend. In general, the minimum radius from Table 7-2-1 may be used as starting estimates. If the radius of bend is too small, stresses and strains will weaken the metal and may result in cracking. A minimum radius of bend is specified for each type of aircraft sheet metal. The kind of material, thickness, and temper condition of the sheet are factors affecting it. You may bend annealed sheet to a radius approximately equal to its thickness. Stainless steel and 2024 aluminum alloy require a fairly large bend radius.

Bend Allowance

Suppose you were confronted with the problem of making a formed angle or a stringer to fit into a corner. The corner measures one inch on each side, but you realize that you cannot make a square bend in the metal and that it will not fit squarely into the corner but that it will have a curve. You know, also, that the curved distance will be shorter than the dis-

STEEL SHEET		ALUMINUM ALLOY SHEET				
ANNEALED		ANNEALED ALUMINUM ALLOY			HT ALUMINUM ALLOY	
THICKNESS	MINIMUM RADIUS	THICKNESS	MINIMUM RADIUS		MINIMUM RADIUS	
			STANDARD	SPECIAL	STANDARD	SPECIAL
0.025	$^1/_{32}$	0.016	$^1/_{64}$	-	$^3/_{32}$	$^3/_{64}$
0.031	$^1/_{32}$	0.020	$^1/_{64}$	-	$^3/_{32}$	$^3/_{64}$
0.038	$^1/_{32}$	0.025	$^1/_{32}$	$^1/_{64}$	$^1/_{8}$	$^1/_{16}$
0.050	$^1/_{16}$	0.032	$^1/_{32}$	$^1/_{64}$	$^1/_{8}$	$^1/_{16}$
0.063	$^1/_{16}$	0.040	$^1/_{16}$	$^1/_{32}$	$^3/_{16}$	$^3/_{32}$
0.078	$^1/_{8}$	0.051	$^1/_{16}$	$^1/_{32}$	$^3/_{16}$	$^3/_{32}$
0.094	$^1/_{8}$	0.064	$^1/_{8}$	$^1/_{16}$	$^1/_{4}$	$^1/_{8}$
0.125	$^1/_{8}$	0.072	$^1/_{8}$	$^1/_{16}$	$^1/_{4}$	$^1/_{8}$
0.188	$^3/_{16}$	0.081	$^1/_{8}$	$^3/_{32}$	$^1/_{4}$	-
0.250	$^1/_{4}$	0.091	$^5/_{32}$	$^3/_{32}$	$^3/_{8}$	-
-	-	0.102	$^3/_{16}$	$^3/_{32}$	$^3/_{8}$	-
-	-	0.125	$^1/_{4}$	$^1/_{8}$	$^1/_{2}$	-
-	-	0.188	$^3/_{8}$	$^3/_{16}$	$^3/_{4}$	-
-	-	0.250	$^1/_{2}$	$^1/_{4}$	1	-

NOTE:
The special minimum radii for aluminum alloy sheets may be used where the bend is 90° or less in special cases. For example, where clearance for rivet or bolt heads or attached parts is necessary.

Table 7-2-1. Minimum bend radii for sheet stock

tance into the corner and out. So when making a bend or fold in a sheet of metal, you must calculate bend allowance (BA) — the length of material required for the bend. This is shown by Figure 7-2-3.

Bend allowance depends on four factors—the degree of bend, the radius of the bend, the thickness of the metal, and the type of metal used. As mentioned in the paragraph on radius of bend, the radius of bend is generally proportional to the thickness of the material. Furthermore, the sharper the radius of bend can be made, the shorter will be the material needed for the bend.

Bending the strip would compress the material on the inside of the curve and stretch the material on the outside of it. However, some distance between these two extremes lies a space which is not affected by either force. This

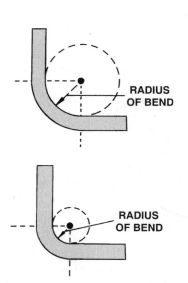

Figure 7-2-3. The sharper the bend, the shorter the material needed for the bend

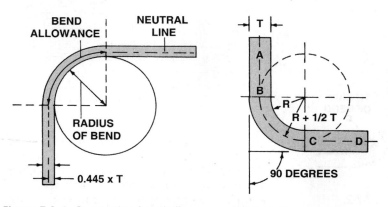

Figure 7-2-4. Computing bend allowance - 90° bend

is known as the neutral line or neutral axis. It occurs at a distance approximately 0.445 of the metal thickness (0.445 x T) from the inside of the radius of bend.

When bending metal to exact dimensions, the length of the neutral line must be determined in order that sufficient material can be allowed for the bend. To save you time in calculation of bend allowance, tables for various angles, radii of bends, material thickness, and other factors have been established for your use. However, in the absence of prepared bend allowance tables, it is of the utmost importance that the two following empirical bend allowance formulas be memorized and understood. Refer to Figure 7-2-4.

An empirical formula is one that has been derived solely by experiment and observation without reference to scientific principles. This information has been developed into the bend allowance chart shown in Table 7-2-2.

The formula:

$$= \frac{2\pi (R + \frac{1}{2}T)}{4}$$

is an empirical formula for a 90-degree bend only. It is formulated as follows:

To the radius of bend, R, add one-half the thickness of the metal, $\frac{1}{2}$ T. This gives:

$$R + \frac{1}{2} T$$

the radius of the circle at approximately the neutral axis.

Compute the circumference of this circle by multiplying the radius of curvature of the neutral line (R + $\frac{1}{2}$ T in illustration) by 2π. This gives the circumference as:

$$2\pi(R + \frac{1}{2} T)$$

Since a 90-degree bend is a quarter of the circle (Figure 7-2-4), divide the circumference by 4.

This gives:

$$= \frac{2\pi (R + \frac{1}{2}T)}{4}$$

Therefore, the bend allowance (BA) for a 90° bend:

$$= \frac{2\pi (R + \frac{1}{2}T)}{4}$$

EXAMPLE 1:

To use the formula in finding the bend allowance for a 90-degree bend having a radius of $\frac{1}{4}$ inch for material 0.051 inch thick, substitute in the formula as follows:

SOLUTION 1:

$$BA = \frac{2 \times 3.1416 \times \frac{1}{2} (0.051)}{4}$$

$$BA = \frac{6.2832 (0.250 + 0.0255)}{4}$$

$$BA = \frac{6.2832 (0.755)}{4}$$

$$BA = 0.4323 \text{ or } \frac{7}{16} \text{ inch}$$

The necessary bend allowance or the length of material required for the bend.

Another accepted empirical formula for practical use in sheet metal work which may be used in finding the bend allowance for any degree of bend is as follows:

$$BA = (0.01743 \times R) + (0.0078 \times T) \times N$$

Where:

R = Inside radius of bend

T = Thickness of metal sheet

N = Number of degrees that metal is to be bent.

The empirical formulas, while practically correct, are nevertheless slightly in error because actually the neutral line is not exactly in the center of the sheet being bent However, the amount of error incurred in any given problem is so slight that for most work (since the material used is thin) the formulas are satisfactory.

In most established sheet metal shops, bend allowance tables are available for use in order to save time and expedite the work.

To determine bend allowance for any degree of bend by use of the tables, find the bend allowance per degree for the thickness of the material and the radius of bend in question, then multiply by the number of degrees in the bend. For 90° bends, multiply by 90; for 85° bends, multiply by 85; for 120° bends, multiply by 120, and so on.

EXAMPLE 2:

To find the bend allowance when the sheet thickness is 0.051 inch, the radius of bend is $\frac{1}{4}$ inch (0.250), and the bend is to be 90°, proceed as follows:

SOLUTION 2:

From the Bend allowance table, the bend allowance per degree of bend for 0.051 inch sheet is 0.004756, when the radius of bend is $\frac{1}{4}$ inch. Multiplying 0.004756 by 90 gives 0.4280, the total bend allowance in inches.

GAUGE (INCHES) Thickness	BEND ALLOWANCE CHART						
	RADIUS						
	0.031 1/32	0.063 1/16	0.094 3/32	0.125 1/8	0.156 5/32	0.188 3/16	0.219 7/32
0.020	0.062 0.000693	0.113 0.001251	0.161 0.001792	0.210 0.002333	0.259 0.002874	0.309 0.003433	0.358 0.003974
0.025	0.066 0.000736	0.116 0.001294	0.165 0.001835	0.214 0.002376	0.263 0.002917	0.313 0.003476	0.0362 0.004017
0.028	0.068 0.000759	0.119 0.001318	0.167 0.001859	0.216 0.002400	0.265 0.02941	0.315 0.003499	0.364 0.004040
0.032	0.071 0.000787	0.121 0.001345	0.170 0.001886	0.218 0.002427	0.267 0.002968	0.317 0.003526	0.366 0.004067
0.038	0.075 0.000837	0.126 0.001396	0.174 0.001937	0.223 0.002478	0.272 0.003019	0.322 0.003577	0.371 0.004118
0.040	0.07 0.000853	0.127 0.001411	0.176 0.001952	0.224★ 0.002493	0.273 0.003034	0.323 0.003593	0.372 0.004134
0.051	—	0.134 0.001413	0.183 0.002034	0.232 0.002575	0.280 0.003116	0.331 0.003675	0.379 0.004215
0.064	—	0.144 0.001595	0.192 0.002136	0.241 0.002676	0.290 0.003218	0.340 0.003776	0.389 0.004317
0.072	—	—	0.198 0.002202	0.247 0.002743	0.296 0.003284	0.436 0.003842	0.394 0.004283
0.078	—	—	0.202 0.002249	0.251 0.002790	0.300 0.003331	0.350 0.003889	0.399 0.004430
0.081	—	—	0.204 0.002272	0.253 0.002813	0.302 0.003354	0.352 0.003912	0.401 0.004453
0.091	—	—	0.212 0.002350	0.260 0.002891	0.309 0.003432	0.359 0.003990	0.408 0.004531
0.094	—	—	0.214 0.002374	0.262 0.002914	0.311 0.003455	0.361 0.004014	0.410 0.004555
0.102	—	—	—	0.268 0.002977	0.317 0.003518	0.367 0.004076	0.416 0.004617
0.109	—	—	—	0.273 0.003031	0.321 0.003572	0.372 0.004131	0.420 0.004672
0.125	—	—	—	0.284 0.003156	0.333 0.003697	0.383 0.004256	0.432 0.004797
0.156	—	—	—	—	0.355 0.003939	0.405 0.004497	0.453 00.5038
0.188	—	—	—	—	—	0.417 0.004747	0.476 0.005288
0.250	—	—	—	—	—	—	—

NOTE: The top numbers in each box are for a 90° bend. The bottom numbers are the bend allowance for 1° of bend.

Table 7-2-2A. Bend allowance table

Handwritten notes:

$T = .040$

$R = 0.125$

$SB = .165$

$BA = .224$

$SB + BA - R = SL$

$SB = .165$

$BA = .224 +$

$.389 - .125$

$.264 = SL$

Gauge (Inches)	BEND ALLOWANCE CHART						
	Radius						
	0.250 1/4	0.281 9/32	0.313 5/16	0.344 11/32	0.375 3/8	0.438 7/16	0.500 1/2
0.020	0.406 0.004515	0.455 0.005056	0.505 0.005614	0.554 0.006155	0.603 0.006695	0.702 0.007795	0.799 0.008877
0.025	0.410 0.004558	0.459 0.005098	0.509 0.005657	0.558 0.006198	0.607 0.006739	0.705 0.007838	0.803 0.008920
0.028	0.412 0.004581	0.461 0.005122	0.511 0.005680	0.560 0.006221	0.609 0.006762	0.708 0.007862	0.805 0.007862
0.032	0.415 0.004608	0.463 0.005149	0.514 0.005708	0.562 0.006249	0.611 0.006789	0.710 0.007889	0.807 0.008971
0.038	0.419 0.004659	0.468 0.005200	0.518 0.005758	0.567 0.006299	0.616 0.006840	0.715 0.007940	0.812 0.009021
0.040	0.421 0.004675	0.469 0.005215	0.520 0.005774	0.568 0.006315	0.617 0.006856	0.716 0.007955	0.813 0.009037
0.051	0.428 0.004756	0.477 0.005297	0.527 0.005855	0.576 0.006397	0.624 0.006934	0.723 0.008037	0.821 0.009119
0.064	0.437 0.004858	0.486 0.005399	0.536 0.005957	0.585 0.006498	0.634 0.007039	0.732 0.008138	0.830 0.009220
0.072	0.443 0.004924	0.492 0.005465	0.542 0.006023	0.591 0.006564	0.639 0.007105	0.738 0.008205	0.836 0.009287
0.078	0.447 0.004963	0.496 0.005512	0.546 0.006070	0.595 0.006611	0.644 0.007152	0.745 0.008252	0.840 0.009333
0.081	0.449 0.004969	0.498 0.005535	0.548 0.006094	0.598 0.006635	0.646 0.007176	0.745 0.008275	0.842 0.009357
0.091	0.456 0.005072	0.505 0.005613	0.555 0.006172	0.604 0.006713	0.653 0.007254	0.752 0.008353	0.849 0.009435
0.094	0.459 0.005096	0.507 0.005637	0.558 0.006195	0.606 0.006736	0.655 0.007277	0.754 0.008376	0.851 0.009458
0.102	0.464 0.005158	0.513 0.005699	0.563 0.006257	0.612 0.006798	0.661 0.007339	0.760 0.008439	0.857 0.009521
0.109	0.469 0.005213	0.518 0.005754	0.568 0.006312	0.617 0.006853	0.665 0.008394	0.764 0.008493	0.862 0.009575
0.125	0.480 0.005338	0.529 0.005678	0.579 0.006437	0.628 0.006978	0.677 0.007519	0.776 0.008618	0.873 0.009700
0.156	0.502 0.005579	0.551 0.006120	0.601 0.006679	0.650 0.007220	0.698 0.007761	0.797 0.008860	0.895 0.0099421
0.188	0.525 0.005829	0.573 0.006370	0.624 0.006928	0.672 0.007469	0.721 0.008010	0.820 0.009109	0.917 0.010191
0.250	0.568 0.006313	0.617 0.006835	0.667 0.007412	0.716 0.007953	0.764 0.008494	0.863 0.009593	0.961 0.010675

NOTE: The top numbers in each box are for a 90° bend. The bottom numbers are the bend allowance for 1° of bend.

Table 7-2-2B. Bend allowance table

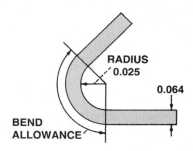

BEND ALLOWANCE FOR OTHER THAN
90 DEGREES IS OBTAINED BY MULTIPLYING
THE BEND ALLOWANCE FOR 1 DEGREE BY
THE NUMBER OF DEGREES REQUIRED

Figure 7-2-5. Bend allowance for more than 90°
bend.

EXAMPLE 3:

To find the bend allowance when the sheet thickness is 0.051, radius of bend is $1/4$ inch (0.250), and the bend is to be 120°, proceed as follows:

SOLUTION 3:

In this case, multiply 0.004756 by 120. The total bend allowance in inches will be 120 x 0.004756 which equals 0.57072.

Set-Back

When bending a piece of sheet stock, it is often desirable to know the starting and ending points of the bend so that the length of the flat of the stock can be determined. As you can see from the illustration on set-back, two factors are important in determining this—the radius of bend and the thickness of the material. Provision for these two factors is made in the process of set-back.

In Figure 7-2-4, note that set-back is the distance from the bend tangent line to the mold point. The mold point is the point of intersection of the lines extending from the outside surfaces, while the bend tangent lines are the starting and end points of the bend. Also note that set-back is illustrated only for the vertical flat and that a corresponding set-back exists for the horizontal flat.

To calculate the set-back for a 90° bend, merely add the inside radius of the bend to the thickness of the sheet stock. In formula form, this would read, SB = R + T. However, to calculate set-back for angles larger or smaller than 90°, you have to consult Set-back Tables (K-Chart) for a value, called K, then substitute this value in the formula:

SB = K (R + T)

The value for K varies with the number of degrees in the bend (Refer to Figure 7-2-5).

EXAMPLE 4:

To calculate the set-back for a 90° bend, if the material is 0.051 inch thick and the radius of bend is specified to be $1/8$ inch, proceed as follows:

SOLUTION 4:

Substitute in the formula:

SB = R + T

You would have:

SB = 0.125 + 0.051 = 0.176 inch

EXAMPLE 5:

To make a 120° bend with a radius of bend of 0.125 inch in a sheet 0.032 inch thick, you would calculate setback as follows:

SOLUTION 5:

Degree of Bend (A in the Set-Back Table) = 120°

Thickness of Sheet (T) = 0.032 inch

Radius (R) = 0.125 inch

K for 120° bend (from Set-Back Table) = 1.732

Set-Back = 1.732 (0.032 + 125)

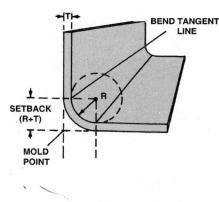

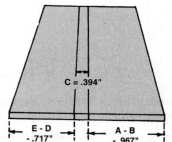

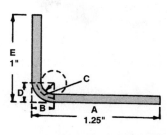

A - HORIZONTAL FLANGE LENGTH
B - SET BACK FOR H FLANGE
C - BEND ALLOWANCE
D - SET BACK FOR V FLANGE
E - VERTICAL FLANGE LENGTH

Figure 7-2-6. Layout of an angle

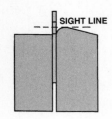

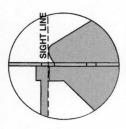

Figure 7-2-7. Locating the brake or sight line on a form block or a brake

= 1.732 x 0.157

= 0.272 inch (About 1/4 inch)

EXAMPLE 6:

Suppose you had to lay out and form the angle shown in Figure 7-2-6. The edge of the horizontal flange is to be $1^1/_4$ inch out and the top of the vertical flange is to be 1 inch above the outside surface. The material is to be 0.064 inch thick, the radius of bend is to be 0.219 inch, and the bend is to be 90°. Your procedure would be as follows:

SOLUTION 6:

Set-back 'B' for the first flat is: R + T, which is 0.219 + 0.064 = 0.283. The horizontal flat, A-B, is then equal to the distance A less this set-back. Mark it off at a distance of 1.25 - 0.283 which equals 0.967 inch as shown.

Next, calculate the bend allowance, C, for the bend by using the bend allowance formula:

$$BA = \frac{2\pi (R + {}^1/_2T)}{4}$$

$$BA = \frac{6.2832 (0.219 + 0.032)}{4} + 0.394 \text{ inches}$$

Mark this off as shown in Figure 7-2-6.

Set-back, D, for the vertical flat is also 0.283 inch. Now, lay off the vertical flat, E-D. This is equal to the distance E less the set-back, D, which is 1.00 - 0.283 which equals 0.717 inch. Mark it off as shown in Figure 7-2-6.

Add up the distances allowed for the horizontal flat (0.967 inch), the vertical flat (0.717 inch), and the bend allowance. The total will be 2.078 inches, or approximately 2.08 inches, the total length of the material necessary.

Brake or Sight Line

The brake or sight line, Figure 7-2-7, is the mark on a flat sheet which is set even with the nose of the cornice brake and serves as a guide in bending. You can locate the brake line by measuring out one radius from the bend tangent line which is to be inserted under the nose of the brake or against the radius form block.

If a bend is made without the sight line located properly, one of two things will happen:

  a. If too far from the clamp, the part will be long and will not fit.

  b. If too close to the clamp the part will be too short and still won't fit.

Section 3

Layout Procedures

Generally, in order to prevent waste of material and to get a greater degree of accuracy in the finished part, it is wise to make a layout, or pattern, of the part before forming it. Where straight angle bends are concerned, correct allowances must be made for set-back and bend allowance. If the shrinking or stretching processes are to be applied, an accurate estimate as to where the metal sheet is to be stretched or shrunk must be made so that the part can be turned out with a minimum amount of forming. Use the set back table shown in Table 7-3-1 as a starting point.

The layout procedures of the aircraft sheet metal worker can be classified into three general groups, flat layout, duplication of pattern, and projection through a set of points. All three processes require a good working knowledge of arithmetic and geometry.

Flat Layout

When it is necessary to lay out material for an angle or a channel, first determine set-back and bend allowance so you can establish the

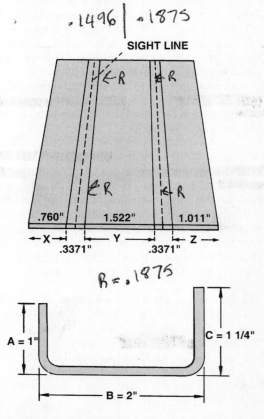

Figure 7-3-1. Layout and bend

Degree	Decimal	Degree	Decimal	Degree	Decimal	Degree	Decimal
1°	0.00873	46°	0.42447	91°	1.0176	136°	2.4751
2°	0.01745	47°	0.43481	92°	1.0355	137°	2.5386
3°	0.02618	48°	0.44523	93°	1.0538	138°	2.6051
4°	0.03492	49°	0.45573	94°	1.0724	139°	2.6746
5°	0.04366	50°	0.46631	95°	1.0913	140°	2.7475
6°	0.05241	51°	0.47697	96°	1.1106	141°	2.8239
7°	0.06116	52°	0.48773	97°	1.1303	142°	2.9042
8°	0.06993	53°	0.49858	98°	1.1504	143°	2.9887
9°	0.07870	54°	0.50952	99°	1.1708	144°	3.0777
10°	0.08749	55°	0.52057	100°	1.1917	145°	3.1716
11°	0.09629	56°	0.53171	101°	1.2131	146°	3.2708
12°	0.10510	57°	0.54295	102°	1.2349	147°	3.3759
13°	0.11393	58°	0.55431	103°	1.2572	148°	3.4874
14°	0.12278	59°	0.56577	104°	1.2799	149°	3.6059
15°	0.13165	60°	0.57735	105°	1.3032	150°	3.7320
16°	0.14054	61°	0.58904	106°	1.3270	151°	3.8667
17°	0.14945	62°	0.60086	107°	1.3514	152°	4.0108
18°	0.15838	63°	0.61280	108°	1.3764	153°	4.1653
19°	0.16734	64°	0.62487	109°	1.4019	154°	4.3315
20°	0.17633	65°	0.63707	110°	1.4281	155°	4.5107
21°	0.18534	66°	0.64941	111°	1.4550	156°	4.7046
22°	0.19438	67°	0.66188	112°	1.4826	157°	4.9151
23°	0.20345	68°	0.67451	113°	1.5108	158°	5.1455
24°	0.21256	69°	0.67728	114°	1.5399	159°	5.3995
25°	0.22169	70°	0.70021	115°	1.5697	160°	5.6713
26°	0.23087	71°	0.71329	116°	1.6003	161°	5.9758
27°	0.24008	72°	0.72654	117°	1.6318	162°	6.3137
28°	0.24933	73°	0.73996	118°	1.6643	163°	6.6911
29°	0.25862	74°	0.75355	119°	1.6977	164°	7.1154
30°	0.26795	75°	0.76733	120°	1.7320	165°	7.5957
31°	0.27732	76°	0.78128	121°	1.7675	166°	8.1443
32°	0.28674	77°	0.79546	122°	1.8040	167°	8.7769
33°	0.29621	78°	0.80978	123°	1.8418	168°	9.5144
34°	0.30573	79°	0.82434	124°	1.8807	169°	10.385
35°	0.31530	80°	0.83910	125°	1.9210	170°	11.430
36°	0.32492	81°	0.85408	126°	1.9626	171°	12.706
37°	0.33459	82°	0.86929	127°	2.0057	172°	14.301
38°	0.34433	83°	0.88472	128°	2.0503	173°	16.350
39°	0.35412	84°	0.90040	129°	2.0965	174°	19.081
40°	0.36397	85°	0.91633	130°	2.1445	175°	22.904
41°	0.37388	86°	0.93251	131°	2.1943	176°	26.636
42°	0.38386	87°	0.94896	132°	2.2460	177°	38.188
43°	0.39391	88°	0.96569	133°	2.2998	178°	57.290
44°	0.40403	89°	0.98270	134°	2.3558	179°	114.590
45°	0.41421	90°	1.00000	135°	2.4142	180°	Infinite (∞)

Table 7-3-1. Setback chart (K chart)

distances of the flats. Then lay off the measurements on a piece of flat stock so you can determine just where to begin and end each bend.

EXAMPLE 7:

Assume that you were to lay out a flat pattern, as illustrated in Figure 7-3-1, of a channel in which the left-hand flange, A, is to be one inch high, the right-hand flange, B, is to be $1^1/_4$ inches high, and the distance between the outside surfaces of the two flanges is to be 2 inches. The material is 0.051 inch thick and the radius of bend is to be $^3/_{16}$ inch. The angles are to be right angles, so use set-back and bend allowance for 90 degree angles and proceed as follows:

SOLUTION 7:

The set-back for the first bend is:

R + T

which is:

0.188 + 0.051 = 0.239

The first flat, X, is then equal to the distance A, less the set-back. Mark it off at a distance of:

1 - 0.239 = 0.761

This is shown in Figure 7-3-1.

Next, calculate the bend allowance for the first bend by using the bend allowance formula:

$$BA = \frac{2\pi (R + {}^1/_2 T)}{4}$$

$$BA = \frac{6.2832 (0.188 + 0.0255)}{4}$$

$$BA = 0.3371$$

Mark it off, then, lay off the second flat, Y. This is equal to the distance B less the set-back at each end, or:

B - (R + T + R + T)

which is:

2 - (0.188 + 0.051 + 0.188 + 0.051) = 1.522

Calculate the bend allowance for the second bend, using the bend allowance formula. It is the same as that for the first bend. So put down 0.3371.

Mark off the third flat, Z. It is equal to:

C - (R + T)

which is:

1.25 - (0.188 + 0.051) = 1.011

Add up all these figures. The sum will be 3.9882 or approximately 4.00 inches. Just totaling the three sides, 1 inch, 2 inches, and $1^1/_4$ inch, you would have 4.250 inches of material length; so now you can see how set-back and bend allowance affect material lengths in forming straight line bends. If the angles were not right angles, you would take the set-back values from Set-Back Tables or K-Charts and bend allowance from Bend Allowance Tables.

After all measurements are calculated, cut the material and mark off the brake and sight lines as shown on the preceding page. Now you are ready to apply the brake or the folder.

Sheet metal brakes are manufactured for different uses and various trades. However, the most common sheet metal brake encountered is one made for bending galvanized steel in light gauges as found in the commercial sheet metal trade. Galvanized steel is not critical as to the radius of bend. As a result, these brakes have a small, sharp, radius on the nose piece.

While additional nose pieces are desirable, they are expensive. In the case of older equipment they may not be available. This presents a problem in as much as aircraft metal work is critical as to its bend radius.

There is an easy way around the problem of inadequate radius on the nose piece. By placing a wide strip (12 inches or more) of annealed aluminum in the brake and adjusting for the thickness, bend it so as to form the sheet to the nose piece. In other words, bend it to it's maximum degree of bend.

As shown by Figure 7-3-2, the bent sheet will form a different radius on the outside of the

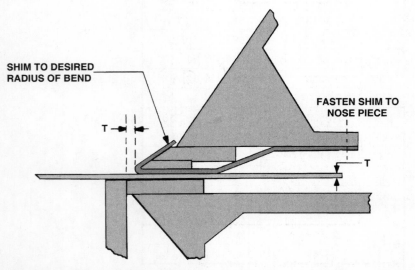

SHIM TO DESIRED RADIUS OF BEND

FASTEN SHIM TO NOSE PIECE

Figure 7-3-2. Adjusting brake bending radius

bend. This radius can be used for the work by using the formed piece as a shim for the nose piece. Depending on the thickness of the shim, different radii can be formed. While single shims are more easily handled, for larger radii one shim can be used to form another, then both can be used in combination (double thickness).

There are only a few rules for using nose piece shims:

1. The break must be adjusted properly for the thickness of the shim material as well as the material being formed over the shim. Each change of radius will require a different shim. Each change of thickness will require adjustment of the nose piece or the apron, depending on how the brake is manufactured.

2. As the radii get larger and the shims get thicker, be careful not to exceed the capacity of the break.

3. Some method of holding shims firmly against the nose piece is critical.

4. All bends in aircraft sheet metal using a commercial sheet metal break should be formed over a shim. Standard nose pieces are not suitable.

Section 4

Duplication of Pattern

When it is necessary to duplicate an aircraft part and blueprints are not available, you may take measurements directly from the original or from a similar part. In studying the following steps for laying out a part to be duplicated, refer to the accompanying illustrations.

Draw reference (datum) line, AB, on the sample part and a corresponding line on the template material. Next, with point A on the sample part as a center, draw an arc having a radius of approximately $1/2$ inch and extending to the flanges. Number the arc as it passes through the reference line.

Draw similar arcs each with a radius $1/2$ inch greater than the previous one until you have marked the entire part. In case there is an extremely sharp curve in the object, decrease the distance between the arcs to increase the number of arcs. This procedure will increase the accuracy of the layout. An arc must pass through every corner of the part; one arc may pass through more than one corner.

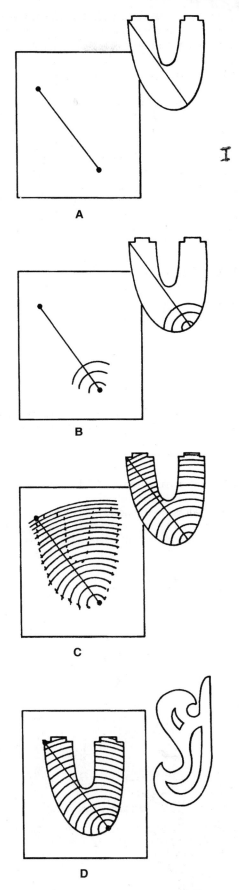

Figure 7-4-1. Connecting points by use of a french curve

Fraction	Decimal	Fraction	Decimal	Fraction	Decimal	Fraction	Decimal
1/64	0.015625	17/64	0.265625	33/64	0.51625	49/64	0.765625
1/32	0.03125	9/32	0.28125	17/32	0.53125	25/32	0.78125
3/64	0.046875	19/64	0.296875	35/64	0.546875	51/64	0.796875
1/16	0.0625	5/16	0.3125	9/16	0.5625	13/16	0.8125
5/64	0.078125	21/64	0.328125	37/64	0.578125	53/64	0.828125
3/32	0.09375	11/32	0.34375	19/32	0.59375	27/32	0.84375
7/64	0.109375	23/65	0.359375	39/64	0.609375	55/64	0.859375
1/8	0.125	3/8	0.375	5/8	0.625	7/8	0.875
9/64	0.140625	25/64	0.390625	41/64	0.640625	57/64	0.890625
5/32	0.15625	13/32	0.40625	21/32	0.65625	29/32	0.90625
11/64	0.171875	27/64	0.421875	43/64	0.671875	59/64	0.921875
3/16	0.1875	7/16	0.4375	11/16	0.6875	15/16	0.9375
13/64	0.203125	29/64	0.453125	45/64	0.703125	61/64	0.953125
7/32	0.21875	15/32	0.46875	23/32	0.71875	31/32	0.96875
15/64	0.234275	31/64	0.484375	47/64	0.734375	63/64	0.984375
1/4	0.250	1/2	0.500	3/4	0.750	1	1.000

Table 7-4-1. Decimal equivalent chart

Locate the coordinate point on the layout by measuring on the part with dividers. Be careful to always measure the distance from the reference point to the beginning of the bend line on the flange of the part.

After you have similarly located all points, draw a line through them, using a French curve to insure a smooth pattern.

Allow for additional material for forming the flange and locate the inside bend tangent line by measuring inside of the sight line, a distance equal to the radius of bend of the part.

Using the intersection of these lines as a center, locate the required relief holes. Then cut out and form as necessary.

Figure 7-4-1 illustrates the complete process.

Relief of Bending Strains

Wherever two bends intersect, material must be removed to make room for the material contained in the flanges. Holes are therefore drilled at the intersection. These holes, called relief holes, prevent strains from being set up at the intersection of the inside bend tangent lines. Such strains may cause the metal to crack. Then, too, relief holes provide a neatly trimmed corner where the excess material is trimmed away.

The size of relief holes varies with thickness of the material, but they should not be less than $1/8$ inch in diameter for aluminum alloy sheet stock up to and including 0.064 inch thick, or $3/16$ inch for stock ranging in thickness from 0.072 inch to 0.128. The most common method of determining the diameter of a relief hole is to use the radius of bend for this dimension, provided it is not less than the minimum allowance ($1/8$ inch).

Use the decimal equivalent chart, Table 7-4-1, to convert thickness and hole sizes to matching measurements.

Relief holes must at least touch the intersection of the inside bend tangent lines. To allow for possible error in bending, make relief holes extend $1/32$ to $1/16$ of an inch behind the inside bend tangent lines. It is good practice to use the intersection of these lines as center of the holes. Also note that the line on the

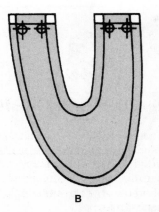

A   B

Figure 7-4-2. Locating relief holes

inside of the curve is cut at an angle toward the relief holes to allow for the stretching of the inside flange. Figure 7-4-2 illustrates relief hole placement.

Layout of a Faired Curve Through a Set of Points

Airworthiness Directive (AD Note) compliance may require modifications which make it necessary to design and form a fairing to fit over a projection on the airplane or engine. The following is a simple procedure for obtaining the pattern for such a fairing (refer to Figure 7-4-3).

First, establish the points A, O, and B as locations for clearance. Then draw a base line. X - X[1] through point A, then draw Y - Y[1] through point A, perpendicular to line X - X[1]. Through point B, draw a line Z - Z[1], perpendicular to line Y - Y[1], establishing point C where the two lines intersect. Next, draw line BE and AD through point O.

Now, divide the distances BO and AO into segments of different lengths, making the increments smaller as you approach the critical point, O.

Draw line AF through a segment point on line BE and draw line CG through this inter section point.

Then draw line BH through the point of intersection of lines CG and AD. The point of intersection between lines BH and AF locates a point on the faired line.

Continue this procedure for all segment points on lines BE and AD. Then, using a French curve, connect all these points, making a true faired curve through points AOB.

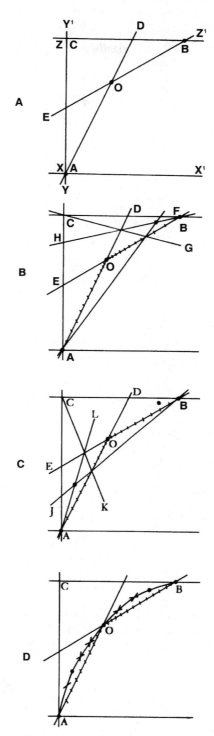

Figure 7-4-3. Layout for a faired curve through a set of points

Section 5

Hand-Forming Procedures

All forming revolves around the processes of shrinking and stretching, and hand-forming processes are no exception. If a formed or extruded angle is to be curved, you either stretch one leg or shrink the other, whichever will make the part fit the job at hand. In bumping, you stretch the material in the bulge to make it balloon, and in joggling, you stretch the material between the joggles. Material in the edge of lightening holes is often stretched to form a beveled reinforcing ridge around them.

Straight Line Bends

The cornice brake and bar folder are ordinarily used to make straight bends. Whenever such machines are not available, you may bend comparatively short sections by hand with the aid of wood or metal bending blocks by proceeding as follows:

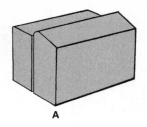

A

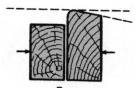

B

THE FORM BLOCK IS ROUNDED TO THE CORRECT RADIUS OF BEND AND IS CUT BACK TO ALLOW FOR SPRING BACK OF THE MATERIAL

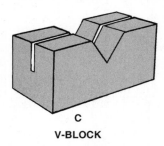

C

V-BLOCK

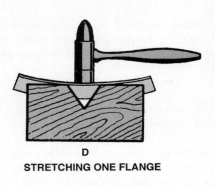

D

STRETCHING ONE FLANGE

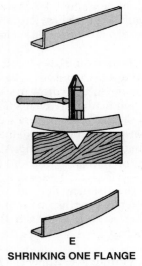

E

SHRINKING ONE FLANGE

Figure 7-5-1. Uses of forming blocks

After you have laid out and cut the blank to size, clamp it rigidly along the bending line between two wood blocks held in a vise. Note that the wooden forming block has one edge rounded to give the desired radius of bend. See Figure 7-5-1.

By tapping lightly with a rubber, plastic, or raw-hide mallet, bend the metal protruding beyond the bending blocks to the desired angle. Start tapping at one end, and work back and forth along the edge, making the bend gradually and evenly.

Continue this process until the protruding metal is forced down to the desired angle against the forming block. Allow for spring back by driving the material slightly farther than the actual bend. Note in the illustration that the forming block is curved slightly beyond the 90° point to allow for spring back. If a large amount of metal extends beyond the bending blocks, maintain hand pressure against the protruding sheet to prevent bouncing.

Remove any irregularities by holding a straight block of hardwood edgewise against the bend and striking it with heavy blows of a mallet or hammer. If the amount of metal protruding beyond the bending blocks is small, make the entire bend by using the hardwood block and hammer.

Curving Formed or Extruded Angles

Both formed and extruded types of angles can be conveniently curved (not bent sharply) by stretching or shrinking either of the flanges. Curving by stretching the one flange is usually preferred since that process requires only a V-block and a mallet and is very easily accomplished.

By Stretching One Flange

In the stretching process, place the flange to be stretched in the groove of the V-block. Using a stretching mallet, strike the flange directly over the V-portion with light, even blows and gradually force it downward into the V. Too heavy a blow will buckle the angle strip. Keep moving the angle strip across the V-block. Always strike the spot directly above the V. Form the curve gradually and evenly by moving the strip slowly back and forth, distributing the hammer blows at equal spaces on the flange.

Lay out a full-sized, accurate pattern on a sheet of paper or plywood and periodically check the accuracy of the curve. By comparing the angle with the pattern, you can tell exactly how the curve is progressing and just where it needs to be increased or decreased. It is better to get the curve to conform roughly to the desired shape before attempting to finish any one portion, because the finishing or smoothing of the angle may cause some other portion of the angle to change shape. If any part of the angle strip is curved too much, reduce the curve by reversing the angle strip on the V-block, with the bottom flange up, and striking it light blows with the mallet.

Try to form the curve with a minimum amount of hammering, for excessive hammering will work harden the metal. Work hardening can be recognized by a lack of bending response or by springiness in the metal. It can be recognized very readily by an experienced worker. In some cases you may have to anneal the part during the curving operation. If you do, be sure to heat-treat the part again before installing it on the airplane.

By Shrinking One Flange

Curving an extruded or a formed angle strip by shrinking may be accomplished by either of two methods, the V-block method and the shrinking block method. Of the two, the V-block is, in general, more satisfactory since it is faster, easier, and affects the metal less. However, very good results can be obtained by the shrinking block method.

In the V-block method, place one flange of the angle strip flat on the V-block with the other flange extending upward as shown. Hold it firmly, so that it does not bounce when hammered, and strike the edge of the upper flange with light blows of a round, soft-faced mallet. Begin at one end of the angle strip and, working back and forth, strike light blows directly over the 'V' portion of the block. Strike the edge of the flange at a slight angle as this tends to keep the vertical flange from bending outward.

Occasionally, check the curve for accuracy with the pattern. If a sharp curve is made, the angle (cross-section of the formed angle) will close slightly. To avoid such closing of the angle, clamp the angle strip to a hardwood board with the hammered flange facing upward. Use small C-clamps on which the jaws have been covered with masking tape. If the angle has already closed, you can bring the flange back to the correct angle with a few blows of a mallet or with the aid of a small hardwood block. If any portion of the angle strip is curved too much, reduce it by reversing the angle on the

Figure 7-5-2. Crimping a flange

V-block and hammering with a suitable mallet, as explained in the previous paragraph on stretching. When you have obtained the proper curve, smooth the entire angle by planishing with a soft-faced mallet.

If the curve in a formed angle is to be quite sharp or if the flanges of the angle are rather broad, the shrinking block method must be used. In this process, crimp the flange which is to form the inside of the curve. When making a crimp, hold the crimping pliers so that the jaws are about $1/8$ inch apart, and by rotating the wrist back and forth, bring the upper jaw of the pliers into contact with the flange, first on one side and then on the other side of the lower jaw. Complete the crimp by working a raised portion into the flange, gradually increasing the twisting motion of the pliers. Do not make the crimp too large as it will be difficult to work out. The size of the crimp depends upon the thickness and softness of the material, but usually about $1/4$ inch is sufficient. Place several crimps spaced evenly along the desired curve with enough space left between each crimp so the jaws of the shrinking block can be easily attached. Crimping is illustrated in Figure 7-5-2.

After completing the crimping, place the crimped flange in the shrinking block so that one crimp at a time is located between the jaws as shown in Figure 7-5-3. Flatten each crimp with light blows of a soft-faced mallet, starting at the apex (the closed end) of

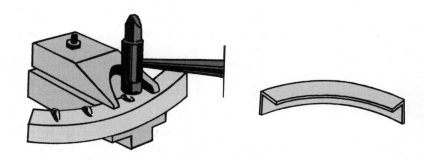

Figure 7-5-3. Shrinking out crimps on a shrinking block

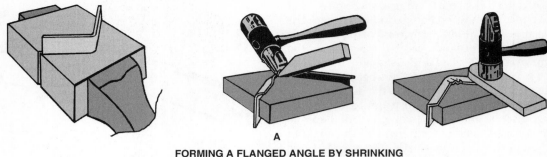

FORMING A FLANGED ANGLE BY SHRINKING

A

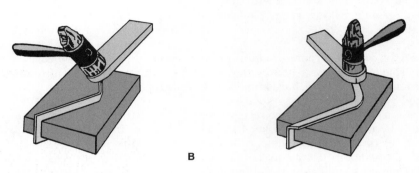

B

FORMING A FLANGED ANGLE BY STRETCHING

Figure 7-5-4. Wooden forming blocks

the crimp and gradually working toward the edge of the flange. Check the curve of the angle with the pattern periodically during the forming process and again after all the crimps have been worked out. If it is necessary to increase the curve, add more crimps and repeat the process. Space the additional crimps between the original ones so that the metal will not become unduly work hardened at any one point. If the curve needs to be increased or decreased slightly at any point, use the V-block. After obtaining the desired curve, you may planish the angle over a stake or a wooden form.

Forming Flanged Angles

The forming process for these two flanged angles is slightly more complicated than that just discussed in that the bend is shorter (not gradually curved) and necessitates shrinking or stretching in a small or concentrated area. If the flange is to point toward the inside of the bend, the material must be shrunk; if it is to point toward the outside, it must be stretched.

By Shrinking

In forming a flanged angle by shrinking, use wooden forming blocks similar to those shown and proceed as follows:

Cut the metal to size, allowing some for trimming after forming. Determine bend allowance for a 90° bend and round the edge of the forming block accordingly (Figure 7-5-4.)

Clamp the material in the form blocks as shown, and bend the exposed flange against the block. After bending, tap the blocks slightly. This induces a setting process in the bend.

Using a soft-faced shrinking mallet, start hammering near the center and work the flange down gradually toward both ends. The flange will tend to buckle at the bend because the material is made to occupy less space. Work the material into several small buckles instead of one large one; and work each buckle out gradually by hammering lightly and gradually compressing the material in each buckle. The use of a small, hardwood wedge block, as shown, will aid in working out the buckles.

Planish the flange after it is flattened against the form block, and remove small irregularities. If the form blocks are made of hardwood, use a metal planishing hammer; if the forms are made of metal, use a soft-faced mallet. Trim the excess material away and file and polish.

By Stretching

To form a flanged angle by stretching, use the same forming blocks, the wooden wedge block,

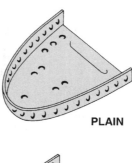

PLAIN

WITH RELIEF HOLES

WITH CRIMPS AND BEADS

WITH CRIMPS, RELIEF HOLES AND BEADS

Figure 7-5-5. Nose ribs representing various types of forming

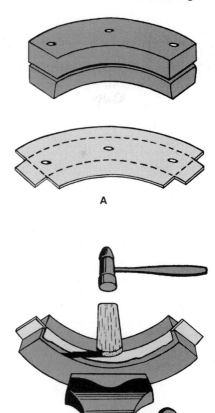

A

B

Figure 7-5-6. Forming the concave flange

and the mallet as in the shrinking process, and proceed as follows:

- Cut the material to size (allowing for trim), determine bend allowance for a 90° bend, and round off the edge of the block to conform to the desired radius of bend.

- Clamp the material in the form blocks as illustrated.

- Using the soft faced stretching mallet, start hammering near the ends and work the flange down gradually toward the center from both ends. Work the flange down smoothly and gradually to prevent cracking and splitting. Planish the flange and angle, as in the previous procedure and trim and smooth the edges, if necessary.

Forming Curved Flanged Parts

Curved flanged parts are usually hand formed. Of the types shown in Figure 7-5-5, the second (with relief holes) is probably the simplest to form and is, therefore, the most popular. It has a concave flange (the inside flange) and a convex flange (the outside one). The concave flange is formed by stretching; the convex flange by with the aid of hardwood or metal forming blocks, which usually are made in pairs.

The block over which the metal is formed is called the forming block, and the block that holds the metal to the forming block is called the clamping block. They are made specifically for the particular part to be formed, fit each other exactly, and conform to the actual dimensions and contour of the finished article. The mating parts are usually equipped with aligning pins to aid in lining up the blocks and hold the metal in place. The blocks may be held together by C-clamps or a vise.

The blocks may also be held together with bolts by drilling through both forms and the metal, provided the holes do not affect the strength of the finished part. The edges of the forming

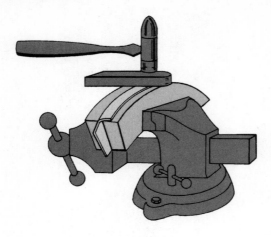

Figure 7-5-7. Forming the convex flange

block are rounded to give the correct radius of bend to the part, and are undercut to allow for springback of the metal. The undercut is especially necessary if the material is hard or if the bend must be highly accurate.

Note the various types of forming represented. In the plain nose rib, only one large convex flange is used, but because of the great distance around the part and the easy occurrence of buckles in forming, it is rather difficult to form. However, the flange and the beaded rib provide sufficient strength to make this a very good type to use.

In the type with relief holes, the concave flange is the only part of the forming process that will give you trouble; the outside flange is broken up into smaller sections by relief holes (notches inserted to prevent strains in a bend) (Figure 7-5-6).

In the type with the crimps, note that crimps are inserted at equally spaced intervals. The crimps, of course, are placed to absorb material—to cause curving— but at the same time they provide strength to the part. The two minor beads and the large beaded flange (placed on the inside of the curve) provide the necessary strength. These beads are easily made on a rotary beading machine. In the fourth nose rib illustrated, note that a combination of the four common forming methods are applied. They are crimping, beading, putting in relief holes, and using a formed angle (riveted on at each end). The beads and the formed angles provide strength for the part.

Some of the major steps in forming a curved flange part are as follows:

- Cut the material to size (allowing for trim), locate and drill holes for alignment pins, and remove all burrs (jagged edges).

- Place the material between the wooden blocks and clamp them tightly in a vise so that the material will not move or shift. To prevent strain on the form blocks and to keep the metal from slipping, clamp the work in the vise as closely as possible to the particular area being hammered.

- Bend the flange on the concave curve first, because in stretching the metal the flange may split open or crack and a new piece may have to be made. Using a soft mallet or wood wedge block, start hammering at a point a short distance away from the beginning of the concave bend and continue toward the center of the bend.

This procedure permits some of the excess metal along the tapered portion of the flange to be worked into the curve where it will be needed. Continue hammering until the metal is gradually worked down over the entire flange, flush with the form block.

Starting at the center of the curve and working towards both ends, hammer the convex flange down over the form. Strike the metal with glancing blows, at an angle of approximately 30° off perpendicular and with a motion that will tend to pull the part away from the block. Refer to Figure 7-5-7.

Stretch the metal around the radius bend and remove the buckles gradually. The wedge block aids in removing the buckles.

While working the metal down over the form, keep the edge of the flange as nearly perpendicular to the block as possible. The wedge block helps keep the edge of the metal perpendicular to the block and lessens the possibility of buckles and of splitting or cracking the metal

Finally, trim the flanges of excess metal planish, remove burrs, round the corners (if any), and check the part for accuracy.

Bumping

Bumping on a form block or female die and bumping on a sandbag are the two common types practiced. In either method only one form is required - a wooden block, lead die, or sandbag. A good example of a part made by the block or die type of bumping is the blister or streamlined cover plate. Wing fillets constitute a good example of parts that are usual formed by bumping on a sandbag.

Form Block or Die Bumping

The lead die or the wood block designed for bumping must have the same dimensions and

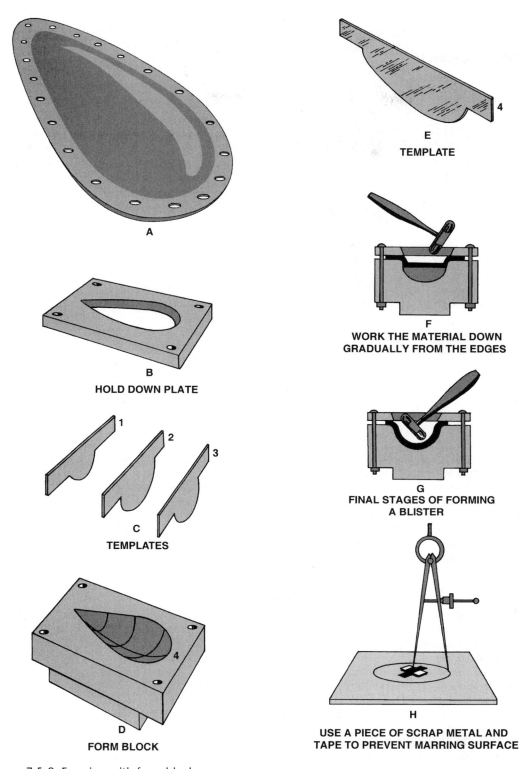

E
TEMPLATE

F
**WORK THE MATERIAL DOWN
GRADUALLY FROM THE EDGES**

G
**FINAL STAGES OF FORMING
A BLISTER**

H
**USE A PIECE OF SCRAP METAL AND
TAPE TO PREVENT MARRING SURFACE**

A

B
HOLD DOWN PLATE

C
TEMPLATES

D
FORM BLOCK

Figure 7-5-8. Forming with form blocks

contour as the outside of the blister. To provide sufficient bucking weight, and to give sufficient bearing surface for fastening the metal, the block or die should be at least one inch larger in all dimensions than the form requires.

When forming the wood block, hollow it out with saws, chisels, gouges, files, and rasps.

Smooth and finish it with sandpaper. Make the inside of the form as smooth as possible, because any slight irregularity will show up on the finished part. Prepare several templates (patterns of the cross section) such as those shown with the form block for the blister so that the form can be checked for accuracy. Refer to Figure 7-5-8.

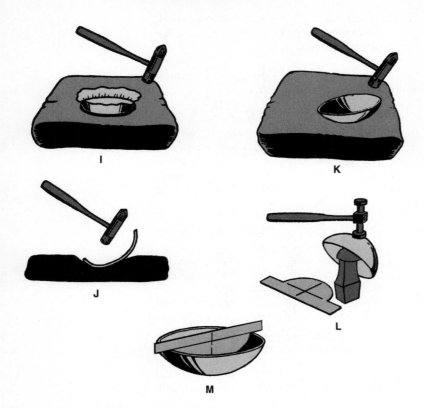

Figure 7-5-9. Forming metal by bumping

Shape the contour of the form at points 1, 2 and 3 to the exact contour of templates 1, 2 and 3. Shape the areas between the template check points to conform to the remaining contour and to template 4. Shaping of the form block requires particular care because the more nearly accurate it is in all details, the less time it will take to produce a smooth, finished part.

Correct clamping of the material to the form block is an important part of the block forming operation. Several methods are possible. For parts such as the blister, one of the best means of clamping the material is to use a full metal cutout or steel hold-down plate as shown. In this process, place the hold-down plate directly over the material to be formed and clamp it in position with bolts or C-clamps. Tighten the C-clamps or bolts just tight enough to hold the material flat against the face of the form block, but not so tight that the metal cannot be drawn into the form. If the material is not held flat against the face of the form, it will bend up or buckle away from the block, and if it is not permitted to slip into the concave depression a little, the blister portion will become very thin in places. Hold-down plates should be of heavy steel, $1/8$ inch for small forms and $1/4$ inch or heavier for large forms.

If the material for making a full metal hold down plate is not available, use a hardwood cutout. Make the cutout and use it in the same

manner as the steel plate, but take greater precautions to make sure that the material is held as desired.

You may use pieced form-clamps if a full metal hold-down plate or hardwood cutout is not available or if a full cutout cannot be used. Be careful to clamp them properly and locate them so that they line up with the edge of the form If they are not lined up accurately, the material will bulge.

After preparing and checking the form, perform the bumping process according to the following general steps.

Cut a metal blank to size, allowing an extra $1/2$ to 1 inch to permit drawing.

Apply a thin coat of light oil to the block and to the aluminum to prevent galling (scraping on rough spots).

Clamp the material between the block and steel plate, as previously described, so that it will be firmly supported yet able to slip a little toward the inside of the form.

Clamp the bumping block in a bench vise. With a soft faced mallet or with a hardwood drive block and suitable mallet, start the bumping near the edges of the form.

With light blows of the mallet, work the material down gradually from the edges. Remember that the object of the bumping process is to work the material into shape by stretching it, rather than by forcing it into the form with heavy blows. Always start bumping near the edge of the form—never start near the center of the blister.

Smooth the work as much as possible before removing it from the form. You can do this by rubbing the work with the rounded end of a maple block or with the round end of a stretching mallet.

Remove the blister from the bumping block and trim it, leaving a $1/2$ inch flange.

Finally, drill the rivet holes, chamfer the edges 45°, and clean and polish the part.

Sandbag Bumping

Bumping on a sandbag is one of the most difficult types of sheet metal hand forming. There is no exact form block to serve as a guide. During this type of forming operation, you force a depression in a sandbag to take the shape of the hammered portion of the metal. The depression, or pit, has a tendency to move or shift from the hammering; therefore, you have to readjust it from time to time during the bumping process. The degree of shifting depends largely on the contour or shape of the piece being formed and whether glancing blows must be struck, in order to stretch, draw, or shrink the metal (Figure 7-5-9).

When forming by this method, prepare a contour template, or some sort of a pattern to serve as a working guide and to insure accuracy of the finished part. Make the pattern from ordinary paper, cut and folded around the part to be duplicated. Cut the paper cover at the points where it would have to be stretched to fit, and attach additional pieces of paper with masking tape to cover the exposed portions.

After completely covering the part, trim the pattern to exact size. Then open it and lay it out on the metal from which the part is to be formed. The pattern will not lie flat, however, it will give you a fairly accurate idea of the approximate shape of the metal to be cut, and the pieced-in sections will indicate where the metal is to be stretched. Place the paper pattern on the material and mark the outline of the part and the portions to be stretched. Add at least one inch of excess metal when cutting the material to size. You can trim off this excess metal after bumping the part into shape.

If the part to be formed is radially symmetrical, it will be fairly easy to form, since a simple contour template can be used a working guide and a pattern to indicate the portions of unequal stretching need not be made. However, the procedure for bumping sheet metal parts on a sandbag follows certain basic rules which can be applied to any part, regardless of its contour or shape.

Lay out and cut the contour template. This can be made of sheet metal, medium heavy cardboard, or thin plywood.

Determine the amount of metal needed, lay it out, and cut it to size, allowing at least $1/2$ inch excess.

Place a sandbag on a solid foundation capable of supporting heavy blows and, with the aid of a smooth-faced mallet, make a pit in the bag. Analyze the part to determine the correct radius of the pit for the forming operation. The pit will not retain its shape but will change with the hammering it receives. Consequently, as the bumping proceeds, you will have to readjust the pit.

Select a soft, round-faced or bell-shaped mallet having a contour slightly smaller than the contour desired on the sheet metal part.

Holding one edge of the metal in one hand, place the portion to be bumped near the edge of the pit on the sandbag.

Strike the metal with light glancing blows, about $1/2$ to 1 inch from the edge.

Continue bumping toward the center, revolving the metal and working gradually inward until the desired shape is obtained. Shape the entire part as a unit; if you shape one portion completely and continue hammering on some other portion, the completed portion will be thrown out of shape.

At frequent intervals during the bumping process, check the part for accuracy of shape by applying the template. If wrinkles are formed, work them out before they become too large.

Finally, with the aid of a suitable stake and planishing hammer, or with a hand dolly and planishing hammer, remove small dents and hammer marks.

With a pair of dividers, mark around the inside of the object, and trim the edge and file smooth. Clean and polish the part.

A
JOGGLE DIES

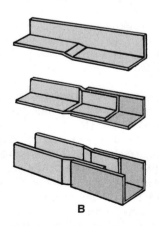

B

THREE METHODS OF JOGGLING

Figure 7-5-10. Joggling

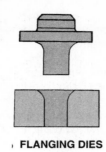

FLANGING DIES

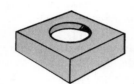

CHAMFERED FLANGING BLOCK

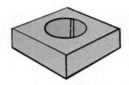

PLAIN FLANGING BLOCK

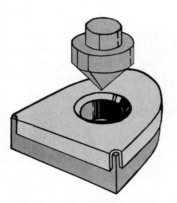

**CONE SHAPED MALE DIE AND
CHAMFER BLOCK**

Figure 7-5-11. Flanging

Joggling

A joggle is an offset formed on an angle strip to provide clearance for a sheet or an extrusion. Joggles are often found at the intersection of stringers and formers. One of these members, usually the former, has the flange joggled to fit flush over the flange of the stringer. The amount of offset is usually small; therefore, the depth of the joggle is generally specified in thousandths of an inch. The thickness of the material to be cleared governs the depth of the joggle. In determining the length of the joggle necessary, it is common practice to allow an extra $1/16$ inch to give enough added clearance

to assure a fit between the joggled (overlapped) part. Refer to Figure 7-5-10 for examples.

There are a number of different methods by which you may form joggles. If the joggle is to be made on a straight flange or flat piece of metal, form it on a cornice brake by inserting and bending up along the line of the joggle; then hold a piece of metal of the correct thickness to give the desired offset under the bent up portion and pound the flange down while the metal is still in the same position in the brake.

Where a joggle is necessary in a curved flange, forming blocks or dies made of hardwood, steel, or aluminum alloy may be used. If the die is to be used only a few times, hardwood is satisfactory as it is easily worked. If a number of similar joggles are to be produced, then use steel or aluminum alloy dies. Dies of aluminum alloy are preferred, since they are easier to fabricate than steel ones and will wear about as long. Then, too, they are sufficiently soft and resilient to permit forming aluminum alloy parts on them without marring, and to allow nicks and scratches to be easily removed from their surfaces.

When using joggling dies for the first time, test them for accuracy on a piece of waste stock. In this way you will avoid the possibility of ruining already fabricated parts. Always keep the surfaces of the blocks free from dirt, filings, and so on, so that the surfaces of the work will not be marred.

Note that in the simple joggle blocks shown, both blocks are matched to the exact dimensions of the joggle desired. When forming a joggle, place the flange to be joggled between the blocks and squeeze the blocks together in a vise The unjoggled flange will spring away from the blocks slightly, so hammer it back into position before removing the angle from the die.

Forming Lightening Holes

Occasionally, holes are cut in rib sections, fuselage frames, and other structural parts to decrease weight. Such holes are known as lightening holes. To keep from weakening the member (by removal of the material), flanges are often pressed around the holes to strengthen the area from which the material was removed. These holes should never be cut in any structural part unless authorized. The size of the lightening hole and the width of the flange formed around the hole are determined by design specifications. Margins of safety are considered in the specifications so that the weight of the part can be decreased and still retain the necessary strength. You may cut out lightening holes by any one of the following methods:

1. Punching out if the correct size punch die is available.

2. Cutting out with a fly-cutter mounted on a drill.

3. Scribing circumference of the hole with dividers and drilling around the entire circumference with a small drill, allowing enough clearance to file smooth.

4. Scribing the circumference of the hole with dividers; drilling the hole inside the circumference large enough to insert aviation snips; cutting out excess metal; and filing smooth.

You may form the flange by use of a flanging die or some hardwood or metal form blocks. Flanging dies consist of two matching parts, a female die and a male die. For flanging soft metal, dies can be of hardwood, such as maple; for hard metal or for more permanent use, they should be made of steel. The pilot guide should be the same size as the hole to be flanged and the shoulder should be the same width and angle as the desired flange.

When flanging lightening holes, place the material between the mating parts of the die and form it by hammering or squeezing the dies together in a vise or in an arbor press. The dies will work more smoothly if they are coated with light machine oil.

Note that in the two form blocks shown in Figure 7-5-11, the hole in the upper block is the same size as the hole to be flanged and is chamfered to the width of the flange and the angle desired, while in the lower block, the hole is the same diameter as that of the flange. You may use either type. When using the upper block, center the material to be flanged and hammer it with a stretching mallet round and round until the flange conforms to the chamfer. When using the lower block, center the lightening hole over the hole in the block, then stretch the edges, hammering the material into the hole, round and round, until the desired flange is obtained. Occasionally the chamfer is formed with a cone-shaped male die used in conjunction with the form block with which the part was formed.

Section 6
Working Stainless Steel

When working with stainless steel make sure that the metal does not get unduly scratched or marred. Also take special precautions when shearing, punching, and drilling this metal. It takes about twice as much pressure

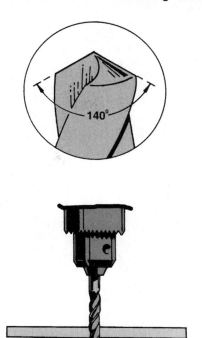

Figure 7-6-1. Drill cutting-angle for stainless steel

to shear or punch stainless steel as it does to cut mild steel. Keep the shear, or punch and die, adjusted very closely. Too much clearance will permit the metal to be drawn over the edge of the die and cause it to become work hardened, resulting in excessive strain on the machine.

In drilling stainless steel, use a high speed drill ground to an included angle of 140 degrees (Figure 7-6-1.) Some special drills have an offset point while others have a chip curler in the flutes. When using an ordinary twist drill, grind its point to a stubbier angle than the standard drill point. Keep the drill speed about one-half that required for drilling mild steel, but never exceed 750 r.p.m. Keep a steady pressure on the drill so the feed is steady at all times. Drill the material on a backing plate, such as cast iron, which is hard enough to permit the drill to cut all the way through the stock without pushing the metal away from the drill point. Spot the drill before turning on the power and also make sure that when the power is turned on, pressure is being exerted.

To avoid overheating, dip the drill in water after drilling each hole. When it is necessary to drill several deep holes in stainless steel, use a liquid coolant. Apply the coolant to the material immediately upon starting the drill. Due to high temperatures developed by high-speed drill rotation, high-speed portable hand-drills have a tendency to burn the drill points and excessively work-harden the material at

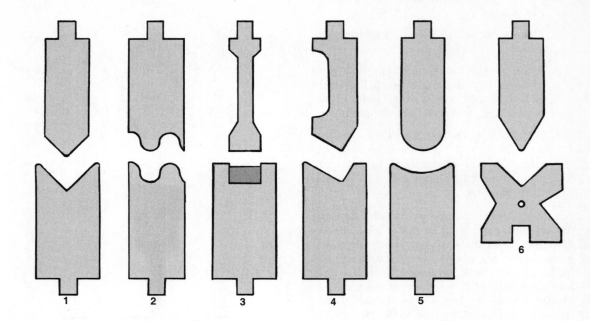

Figure 7-7-1. Various press brake dies and punches

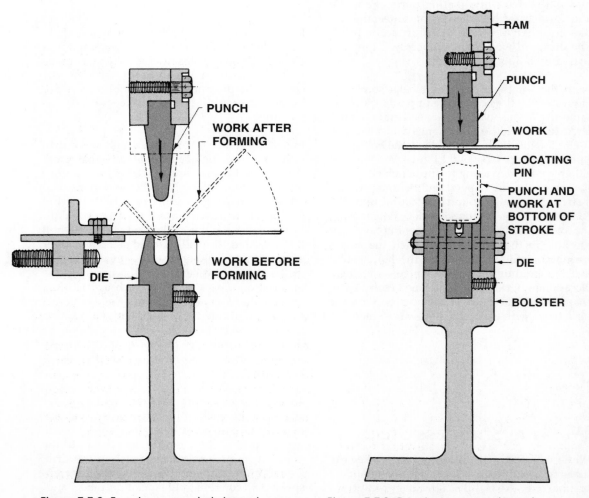

Figure 7-7-2. Forming a rounded channel or an angle with a large radius

Figure 7-7-3. Forming an open channel

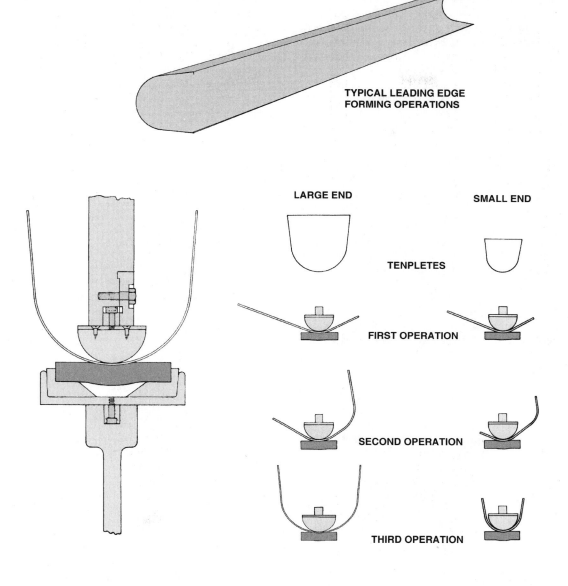

Figure 7-7-4. Using special punches and a rubber sheet, compound tapered curves are possible

the point of contact. Therefore, the high-speed portable hand-drill should not be used. Use an electric variable speed drill motor, or a drill press with adjustable speeds.

Section 7

Press Brake Work

Standard sheet metal brakes are rather severely limited as to capacity. This becomes very obvious as the size of the airplane on which you are working becomes larger. The material is simply too thick for a leaf brake. This is where the press brake comes in.

Press brakes are capable of bend a very large range of material thickness. They are expensive, therefore they are found only in large, or progressive, shops. They can, however, form a larger variety of shapes not possible on a leaf brake.

Most press brakes are hydraulically operated and have infinite control of the punch pressure and travel. This makes them even more controllable. Extremely accurate work over a wide range of shapes is possible. Figure 7-7-1 illustrates an assortment of punches and dies that can be used for most straight line bending operations.

Controlling the Radius of Bend

Most shops will not be fortunate enough to have a large variety of punches and dies. To control the radius of bend, shoes similar to those used on leaf brakes can be used. They must be held tightly against the punch, but no further adjustment is necessary. The pressure applied on the downward stroke of the die will take care of adjustments by itself.

> **CAUTION:** *When working on or around a press brake, be careful. Should you get a hand or arm under the punch, the hydraulically driven punch will not even slow down. Severe injury can and has resulted.*

Production Forming

Figures 7-7-2 and 7-7-3 show special tooling that has been fabricated for production line forming. The press brake lends itself to rapid, more complete, single operation forming than do leaf brakes. A very large number of identical parts can be formed in very little time. Similar parts requirements for repair operations can be formed using tooling that has been somewhat simplified. Many of the automatic stops can be replaced with careful setup and handling.

Forming wing and empennage leading edges is another item commonly produced on a press brake. A careful look at Figure 7-7-4 will show what is possible. In this illustration, not only is a rounded leading edge being formed, the part is also tapered. This type of part is very difficult to form by any other method. A press brake, however, can handle it with ease. The punch is made of hardwood and the die

is a rubber blanket, or strip, glued onto the special die holder. The special tooling is not difficult to fabricate. By careful manipulation of the part, with special attention to the center of the bend and the amount of pressure on the ram, curved leading edges of very heavy material can be formed. In cases using thick material, the part may be formed from annealed sheet and heat treated after forming.

Section 8

Roll Forming

Many parts can be formed by using a rolling machine. The most common form of rolling machine is called a slip roll. This is because the top roll can be released on one end. This lets the top roll be lifted out of the way so the work be removed. With a tightly rolled part, it can be removed no other way.

Slip rolls have been around for a long time. They can be used to form buckets, tubs, pans, and some funnels. Many aircraft parts can be formed on slip rolls. Especially patches that must conform to a curve. Most commercial uses require some additional finish work on a bench block and stakes.

Forming on a slip roll does require some practice to do well. If you look at the side views of

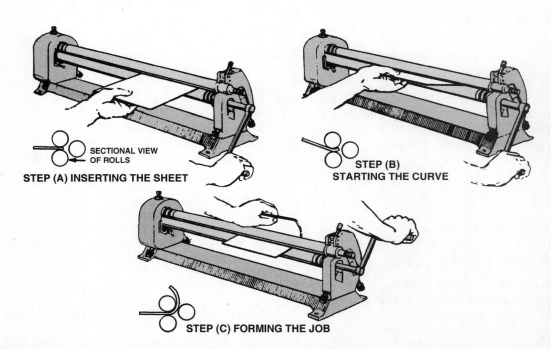

STEP (A) INSERTING THE SHEET
SECTIONAL VIEW OF ROLLS

STEP (B) STARTING THE CURVE

STEP (C) FORMING THE JOB

Figure 7-8-1. The various steps in rolling a part on a slip roll

the work in progress shown in Figure 7-8-1, you will see a problem in the process of being created. When the end of a sheet tries to go completely through the rolls, the end will come out with a flat spot. This is because there is no support after the edge leaves the first bottom roll. The finished part will have two flat spots; one for each edge.

If the part is not a tightly rolled one, it is possible to start with a longer sheet than necessary, then be trimmed when finished rolling it. In many cases this is not possible. The answer is to form the part sandwiched between two pieces of additional material that are longer, or wider, depending on the shape. This will allow the real part to have support all the way to the edge and leave no flat spots. As with all forming operations, think it out first.

Section 9
Flanging Machines

A group of specialized machines that form flanges are available. They are very specialized and require some training to operate. For the shop that can afford them, they are especially useful. The hammer marks and such that come from hand forming do not exist with a part formed in a flanger. Using annealed material, rather heavy parts can be formed.

Even though they form material very well, flangers are not in common use. These machines are mentioned here only to let you know they are available.

8

Structural Repair

Section 1

Methods

Methods of repairing structural portions of an airplane are varied. No set of specific repair patterns have been devised which will apply in all cases. In general, since design loads acting in various structural parts of an airplane are seldom available to the field repairman, the problem of repairing a damaged section is usually solved by an attempt to duplicate the original part in strength, kind of material, and thickness. In this connection, general rules concerning the selection of material and the forming of parts can be set down and can be applied universally.

In this chapter, there are several examples of common repairs that are encountered in the maintenance of airplane that apply these general principles. The procedures in these examples are representative only. When the aircraft structural repair manual does not exist, refer to FAA Advisory Circular AC43.13 or other approved information. If service manual instructions or structural repair manuals are available, always give them precedence. How to obtain these manuals is discussed later in the chapter.

Learning Objective

DESCRIBE
- repair of structural members
- skin repair procedures

EXPLAIN
- how to identify stressed structural members

APPLY
- inspect and classify damage
- determine which standards apply to a repair

Section 2

Stresses in Structural Members

Forces acting on an airplane, be it on the ground or in flight, cause pulling, pushing, or twist-

Left. Structures often require repair due to damage or fatigue during their service life.

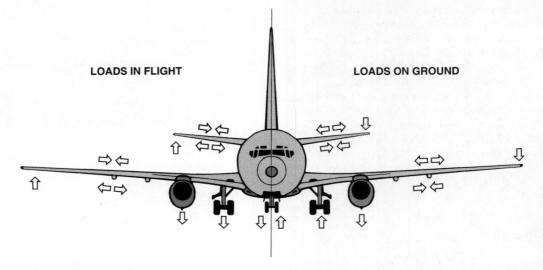

Figure 8-2-1. Whether in flight or at rest, stresses are always present.

ing within the various members of the airplane structure. While the airplane is on the ground, the weight of the wings, fuselage, engines, and empennage causes forces to act downward on the wing and stabilizer tips, along the spars and stringers, and on the bulkheads and formers. This is illustrated in Figure 8-2-1. These forces are passed on from member to member, causing bending, twisting, pulling, compression, and shearing.

As the airplane takes off, most of the forces in the fuselage continue to act in the same direction, but due to the motion of the airplane, they increase in intensity. The forces on the wing tips and the wing surfaces, however, reverse direction and instead of being downward forces of weight, they become upward forces of lift. The forces of lift are exerted first against the skin and stringers, then are passed on to the ribs, and finally are transmitted through the spars to be distributed through the fuselage to any dead weight items carried in the fuselage. The wings bend upward at the end and may flutter slightly during flight. This wing bending cannot be ignored by the manufacturer in the original design and construction and cannot be ignored by the sheet metal technician during maintenance. It is quite surprising how an aircraft structure composed of structural members and skin rigidly riveted or bolted together, such as a wing, can bend or act much like a large spring leaf.

Stresses in an airplane can be classified into five types—tension, compression, shear, bending, and torsion (or twisting). The first three are commonly called the basic stresses, the last two, the combination stresses. Stresses rarely act singly—usually in combinations. The most important types of stresses from

your standpoint—the standpoint of the sheet metal technician—are bending, torsion, and shear.

Tension

Tension (or tensile stress) is the force per unit area tending to stretch a structural member. In Figure 8-2-2, note the condition of the metal strap before and after stretching. Drilling a hole in the strap has removed much of the material and has reduced the cross-sectional area of the strap. Since the load is constant from one end of the strap to the other, and the hole cannot carry any of the load, the stress in the reduced section is greatly increased (per unit area). The area on each side of the hole is carrying not only its normal share of the load, but also that part of the load which should have been carried by the removed material. Obviously, if the load were increased until the strap failed, the break would occur in the material near the hole.

The strength of a member in tension is determined on the basis of its gross area (or total area), but calculations involving tension must take into consideration the net area of the member. Net area is defined as the gross area minus that removed by drilling holes or by making other changes in the section. Placing rivets or bolts in holes makes no appreciable difference in added strength, as the rivets or bolts will not transfer tensional loads across holes in which they are inserted.

Compression

Compression (or compressive stress) is the force per unit area which tends to shorten (or compress) a structural member at any cross-section. Under a compressive load, an undrilled member will be stronger than an identical member with holes drilled through it. However, if a plug of equivalent or stronger material is fitted tightly in a drilled member, it will transfer compressive loads across the hole and the member will carry approximately as large a load as if the hole were not there. Thus, for compressive loads the gross or total area may be used in determining the stress in a member if all holes are tightly plugged with equivalent or stronger material.

Shear

Shear is the force (per unit area) which acts in such a way as to slide adjacent particles of material past each other. The term shear is used because it is a sideways stress of the type that is put on a piece of paper or a sheet of metal when it is cut with a pair of shears. Shear stress concerns you chiefly from the standpoint of rivet and bolt applications, particularly when attaching sheet stock, for if a rivet used in a shear application gives way, the rivet parts are pushed sideways.

Bending

Bending (or beam stress) is actually a combination of two forces acting upon a structural member at one or more points. In Figure 8-2-3 note that the bending stress causes a tensile stress to act on the upper half of the beam and a compressive stress on the lower half. These stresses act opposite on the two sides of the center line of the member, which is called the neutral axis. Since these forces acting in opposite directions are next to each other at the neutral axis, the greatest shear stress occur along this line, and none exists at the extreme upper or lower surfaces of the beam.

Torsion

Torsion (or twisting stress) is the force which tends to twist a structural member. The stresses arising from this action are shear stresses caused by the rotation of adjacent planes past each other about a common reference axis at right angles to these planes. This action may be illustrated by a rod fixed solidly at one end and twisted by a weight placed on a lever arm at the other, producing the equivalent of two equal and opposite forces acting on the rod at some distance from each other. A shearing action is set up all along the rod, with the center line of the rod representing the neutral axis.

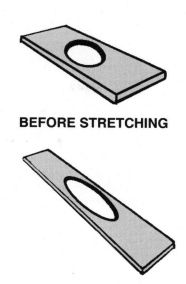

BEFORE STRETCHING

AFTER STRETCHING

Figure 8-2-2. Effects of tension on a metal strip

Section 3

Basic Principles of Repair

The first and one of the most important steps in repairing a structural damage is sizing up the job and making an accurate estimate of what is to be done. This sizing up includes an estimate of the best type and shape of patch to use; the type, size, and number of rivets needed; and the strength, thickness, and kind of material required to make the repaired member no heavier (or only slightly heavier) and just as strong as the original. You must also inspect the surrounding members for evidence of corrosion and load damage so that you can estimate accurately the extent of the clean out of the old damage required. After completing the clean out, make the layout of the patch first

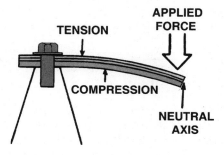

Figure 8-2-3. Bending is a combination of two forces

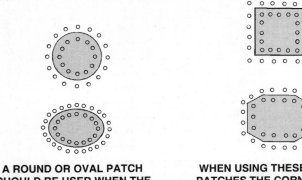

A ROUND OR OVAL PATCH SHOULD BE USED WHEN THE DIRECTION OF STRESS IS UNKNOWN

WHEN USING THESE TYPES OF PATCHES THE CORNERS MUST BE ROUNDED AS SPECIFIED

Figure 8-3-1. Typical small hole patches

on paper, then transfer it to the sheet stock selected. You then cut and chamfer the patch, form it so it matches the contour of that particular area, and apply it.

Maintaining Original Strength

When making any repair, you must observe certain fundamental rules if the original strength of the structure is to be maintained. The patch plate should have a cross-sectional area equal to or greater than that of the original damaged section. If the member is subjected to compression or to bending loads, place the splice on the outside of the member to secure a higher resistance to such loads. If you cannot place the splice on the outside of the member, use material of a weight next heavier than the weight of the material used in the original.

In order to reduce the possibility of cracks starting from the corners of cutouts, try to make cutouts either circular or oval in shape as shown in Figure 8-3-1. Where it is necessary to use a rectangular cutout, make the radius of curvature at each corner no smaller than one-half inch. Either replace buckled or bent members or reinforce them by attaching a splice over the affected area.

Be sure the material used in all replacements or reinforcements is similar to the material used in the original structure. If it is necessary to substitute an alloy weaker than the original, use material of a heavier gauge to give equivalent cross-sectional strength. But never practice the reverse, that is, substituting a lighter gauge, stronger material for the original. This apparent inconsistency is due to the fact that one material can have greater tensile strength than another but less compressive strength, or vice versa. The different strengths of various alloys can be found in MIL Handbook 5.

Similarly, the buckling and torsional strength of many sheet metal and tubular parts are dependent primarily upon the thickness rather than the allowable compressive and shear strength of the material. Therefore, a substitute thinner than the original will reduce considerably the buckling and torsional strength of a part, even though the thinner substitute material has higher compressive and shear strengths.

When forming is necessary, be particularly careful. Heat-treated and cold-worked alloys will stand very little bending without cracking. Soft alloys, on the other hand, are easily formed but are not strong enough for primary structures. Strong alloys can be formed in their annealed condition and heat treated to develop their strength before assembling. In some cases, if the annealed metal is not available, you can heat the metal, quench it according to regular heat-treating practices, and form it before age hardening sets in. The forming should he completed in about one-half hour after quenching or the material will become too hard to work. If you use a brake to form a section, place a thin piece of soft metal over the brake jaws to prevent scraping and scratching the surface of the sheet.

You can determine the size of rivets for any repair by referring to the rivets used by the manufacturer in the next parallel rivet row inboard on the wing, or forward on the fuselage. Another method of determining the size of rivets to be used is to multiply the thickness of the thickest skin by three and use the nearest larger size rivet corresponding to that figure. Thus, for example, if the skin thickness is 0.040 inch, multiply 0.040 by 3 which equals 0.120 and use the next larger size rivet - $1/8$ inch (0.125 inch).

COMPOSITION OF RIVET (ALLOY)	ULTIMATE STRENGTH OF RIVET METAL (p.s.i.)	DIAMETER OF RIVET (INCHES)							
		1/16	3/32	1/8	5/32	3/16	1/4	5/16	3/8
2117 T	27,000	83	186	331	518	745	1,325	2,071	2,981
2017 T	30,000	92	206	368	573	828	1,472	2,300	3,313
2024 T	35,000	107	241	429	670	966	1,718	2,684	3,865
NOTE: Double-shear strength is found by multiplying the above values by 2.									

Table 8-3-1. Single-shear strength of aluminum-alloy rivets (pounds)

THICKNESS OF SHEET (INCHES)	DIAMETER OF RIVET (INCHES)							
	1/16	3/32	1/8	5/32	3/16	1/4	5/16	3/8
0.014	71	107	143	179	215	287	358	430
0.016	82	123	164	204	246	328	410	492
0.018	92	138	184	230	276	369	461	553
0.020	102	153	205	256	307	410	412	615
0.025	128	192	256	320	284	512	640	768
0.032	164	245	328	409	492	656	820	984
0.036	184	276	369	461	553	738	922	1,107
0.040	205	307	410	512	615	820	1,025	1,230
0.045	230	345	461	576	691	922	1,153	1,383
0.051	261	391	522	653	784	1,045	1,306	1,568
0.064	–	492	656	820	984	1,312	1,640	1,968
0.072	–	553	738	922	1,107	1,476	1,845	2,214
0.081	–	622	830	1,037	1,245	1,660	2,075	2,490
0.091	–	699	932	1,167	1,398	1,864	2,330	2,796
0.102	–	784	1,046	1,307	1,569	2,092	2,615	3,138
0.125	–	961	1,281	1,602	1,922	2,563	3,203	3,844
0.156	–	1,198	1,598	1,997	2,397	3,196	3,995	4,794
0.188	–	1,445	1,927	2,409	2,891	3,854	4,818	5,781
0.250	–	1,921	2,562	3,202	3,843	5,125	6,405	7,686
0.313	–	2,405	3,208	4,009	4,811	6,417	7,568	9,623
0.375	–	2,882	3,843	4,803	5,765	7,688	9,068	11,529
0.500	–	3,842	5,124	6,404	7,686	10,250	12,090	15,372

Table 8-3-2. Bearing strength (pounds)

All repairs made on structural parts of aircraft require a definite number of rivets in order to restore the original strength. This number varies according to the thickness of the material being repaired and the size of the damage. You can determine the number of rivets or bolts required by referring to a similar splice made by the manufacturer or by using this rivet formula:

The number of rivets to be used on each side of the break is equal to:

Length of break × thickness of original material × 75,000

Divide by shearing or bearing strength (smaller of the two).

To find the numerical values to substitute in this formula, proceed as follows:

Length of break—Measure this distance perpendicular to the direction of the general stress running through the damaged area.

Thickness of original material— Measure the thickness of the material in 1,000ths of an inch.

75,000—This is an assumed stress load value of 60,000 psi increased by a safety factor of 25 percent. It is a constant value.

Shear strength—Take this from prepared tables. See Shear Strength Table 8-3-1. It is the amount of force required to cut a rivet holding two or more sheets together. If the rivet is holding two sheets or two parts, it is under single shear, and if it is holding three sheets or three parts, it is under double shear.

Bearing strength—Take this value from prepared tables. See Bearing Strength Table 8-3-2. It is the amount of tension required to pull a rivet through the edge of two sheets, riveted together, or to elongate the rivet hole.

Figure 8-3-2 illustrates the failure methods from choosing the wrong size and/or strength rivet for the job.

EXAMPLE:

To use the formula in calculating the number of 2117–T rivets necessary to repair a break to

BEARING STRENGTH OF THE SHEET IS GREATER THAN SHEAR STRENGTH OF RIVET

SHEAR STRENGTH OF THE RIVET IS GREATER THAN THE BEARING STRENGTH OF THE SHEET

Figure 8-3-2. Bearing strength and shear strength

be $2\frac{1}{4}$ inches in length in material 0.040 inch thick, proceed as follows:

SOLUTION:

Multiply 2.25 × 0.040 = 0.090

Multiply 0.090 × 75,000 = 6750

Determine the size of the rivet required by multiplying the skin thickness by three:

0.040 × 3 = 0.120

So in this case, use a $\frac{1}{8}$ inch rivet. Determine the shear strength of a $\frac{1}{8}$ inch rivet by consulting the Shear Strength Table. In the table, the value of S for a $\frac{1}{8}$ inch rivet equals 331.

By consulting the Bearing Strength Table, determine the bearing strength of a 0.040-inch sheet using a $\frac{1}{8}$ inch rivet. From the table, the

value of B for a 0.040-inch sheet is 410. Since in this case the shear strength is less than the bearing strength, divide the 6750 by 331 (the shear strength). The result is 20.39+. Thus, the number of rivets to be used on each side of this damage will be 20.39+. Since any part of a fraction must be considered as a whole number, 21 rivets must be used on each side of the damage, or 42 for the whole patch.

Maintaining Original Contour

Form all repairs in such a manner that they will fit the original contour perfectly. A smooth contour is especially desirable when making patches on external skins.

Keeping Weight to a Minimum

Keep the weight of all repairs to a minimum. Make the size of the patch as small as practicable and use no more rivets than are necessary. In many cases, repairs disturb the original balance of the structure. By adding excessive weight in each repair, you may unbalance the airplane so much that it will require adjustment of the trim and balance tabs. In places such as the spinner on the propeller, a repair will require application of balancing patches so that a perfect balance of the propeller assembly can be maintained.

Protecting Against Corrosion

Unless otherwise specified, treat all contacting surfaces for resistance to corrosion, regardless of the composition of the material. Thoroughly clean all surfaces and condition them in an atmosphere of sufficiently low humidity to insure freedom from moisture during the application of any paint coating.

Classifying Damage

Damages can he classified into three general classes, as shown in Figure 8-3-3. In many eases, the availability or lack of materials and time are the prime factors which determine whether parts should be replaced or be repaired. Here is a classification of damages and a general description of each.

Negligible damage. Damages such as small dents, scratches, cracks, or small holes which can be smoothed, sanded, or hammered out, or can be repaired without the use of additional repair material.

Repairable damage. Damages that can be repaired by patching, splicing, and insertion without impairment of the original strength.

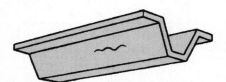

NEGLIGIBLE DAMAGE-SMALL NICKS, DENTS, OR CRACKS WHICH DO NOT WEAKEN THE STRUCTURE

REPAIRABLE DAMAGE-INVOLVES ONE SURFACE; CAN BE REPAIRED BY PATCHING

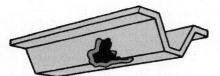

REPAIRABLE DAMAGE-SHOULD BE REPAIRED BY INSERTING A FILLER, THEN SPLICING

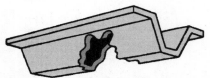

DAMAGE REQUIRING REPLACEMENT-PART IS BEYOND REPAIR AND MUST BE REPLACED AS A NEWLY FORMED PART

Figure 8-3-3. Types of damage

Damage necessitating replacement. Damages so severe that the part cannot be restored to its original strength or requires the use of more repair material than is practicable. These parts must be replaced.

Inspecting Damage

When making a visual inspection of damage, remember that there may be other kinds of damage than those caused by flying rocks. A rough landing may overload one of the landing gear, causing it to become sprung.

Such damage would be classified as load damage, and during inspection of the damage and sizing up of the repair job, you must consider how far the damage caused by the sprung shock strut extends to supporting structural members.

A shock occurring at one end of a member will be transmitted throughout its length; therefore, inspect closely all rivets, bolts, and attaching structures along the complete member for evidence of damage. Make a close examination for rivets that have partially failed and for holes which have been elongated.

Another kind of damage for which you must watch is that caused by weathering or corrosion. This is known as corrosion damage. You can detect corrosion damage of all aluminum material by the white crystalline deposit that may be found around loose rivets, scratches, or any portion of the structure that may be a natural spot for moisture to settle.

If you cannot make visual inspection of the inside skin surfaces without disassembly, then inspect the part by rapping the outside skin in various places with the knuckles.

The presence of severe corrosion will become evident when light rapping causes slight dents in the material or causes a white dust to rise. Ultrasonic thickness testers can give you an extremely accurate readout of the material and are excellent.

Removing Damage

Remove all material from the damaged area. Trim away enough material to include all cracks and buckles which extend out from the damage. Use aviation snips or a reamer when working on sheet stock, and a hack saw when trimming extrusions or formed sections. With a file, smooth all trimmed edges and remove snip and saw marks, burrs, and other scratches on the surfaces by use of a fine grade emery cloth.

Section 4
Specific Repair Types

Smooth Skin Repair

You can repair minor damage to the skin by applying a patch on either the inside or the outside of the sheet. If you place the patch on the inside, use a filler plug to fill the hole and to form a smooth outside surface. The method of applying the patch to the external surface is the same except that no plug is used and the edges of the patch are chamfered— that is, beveled so as not to leave sharp corners or edges.

The size and shape of the patch is determined in general by the number of rivets required in

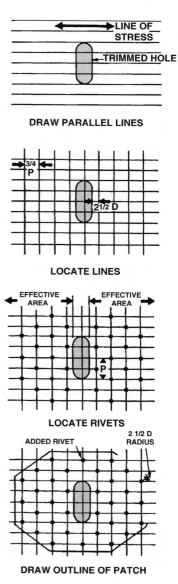

Figure 8-4-1. Damage-repair layout

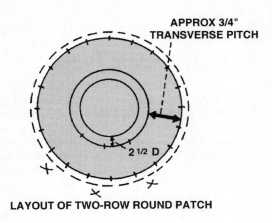

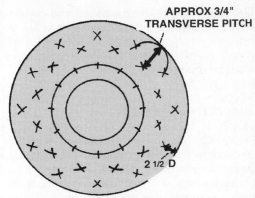

Figure 8-4-2. Round patch rivet pattern

the repair. If not otherwise specified, calculate the required number of rivets by using the rivet formula. Make the patch plate of the same material as the original skin and of the same thickness or of the next greater thickness.

Whenever possible, use an elongated octagonal patch for repair of the smooth skin. This type of patch provides a good concentration of rivets within the critical stress area, eliminates dangerous stress concentrations, and is very simple to lay out. This patch may vary in length according to the conditions of the repair. Follow the steps shown in Figure 8-4-1 for the layout of this patch.

First, draw the outline of the trimmed-out damage. Then, using a spacing of 3 to 4 diameters of the rivet to be used, draw lines running parallel to the line of stress. Locate the lines for perpendicular rows $2^1/_2$ rivet diameters from each side of the cutout, and space the remaining lines $^3/_4$ rivet pitch apart. Locate the rivet spots on alternate lines perpendicular to the stress lines in such a way as to produce a stagger between the rows and to establish a distance between rivets (in the same row) of about 6 to 8 rivet diameters. After you have located the proper number of rivets on each side of the cutout, add a few more if necessary so that the rivet distribution may be uniform. At each of the eight corners, swing an arc of $2^1/_2$ rivet diameters from each corner rivet. This locates the edge of the patch. Using straight lines, connect these arcs to complete the layout. Figure 8-4-1 shows how the layout will look during development.

Use the round patch for both external and flush repairs of small holes in smooth sheet sections. The uniform distribution of rivets around its circumference makes it an ideal patch to use in places where the direction of the stress is unknown or where it is known to change frequently.

If you use a two-row round patch, first draw the outline of the trimmed area on paper (Figure 8-4-2). Draw two circles, one with a radius equal to the radius of the trimmed area plus the edge distance, and the other with a radius $^3/_4$ inch larger. Determine the number of rivets to be used and space two-thirds of them equally along the outer row. Using any two adjacent rivet marks as centers, draw intersecting arcs, then draw a line from the point of intersection of the arcs to the center of the patch. Do the same with each of the other pairs of rivet marks. This will give half as many lines as there are rivets in the outer row. Locate rivets where these lines intersect the inner circle. Then transfer the layout to the patch material, adding regular outer edge material of $2^1/_2$ rivet diameters to the patch.

Use a three-row round patch (Figure 8-4-2) if the total number of rivets is large enough to cause a pitch distance smaller than the minimum for a two-row patch. Draw the outline of the area on paper, then draw a circle with a radius equal to that of the trimmed area plus the edge distance. Equally space one-third of the required number of rivets in this row.

Using each of these rivet locations as a center, draw arcs having a $^3/_4$ inch radius. Where they intersect, locate the second row of rivets. Locate the third row in a similar manner, then allow extra material of $2^1/_2$ rivet diameters around the outside rivet row.

Transfer the layout to the patch material. After laying out and making the patch, remove the burrs from all edges. Chamfer the edges of all external patches to a 45-degree angle and turn them slightly downward, so that they will fit close to the surface.

A spray can of 3M Artist Adhesive will allow you to glue the paper layout to the material.

When the marks are transferred, the paper layout can be peeled off, leaving no residue.

Panel Repair

In aircraft construction, a panel is any single sheet of metal covering. A panel section is the part of a panel between adjacent stringers and bulkheads. Where a section of skin is damaged to such an extent that it is impossible to install a standard skin repair, a special type of repair is necessary. The particular type of repair required depends on whether the damage is repairable outside of the member, inside the member (Figure 8-4-3), or to the edges of the panel.

A damage which after being trimmed has less than $8^1/_2$ manufacturer's rivet diameters of material inside the members requires a patch which extends over the members, plus an extra row of rivets along the outside of the members.

On damages which after being trimmed have 8X rivet diameters or more of material, extend the patch to include the manufacturer's row of rivets and add an extra row inside the members. Damages which extend to the edge of a panel require only one row of rivets along the panel edge (unless the manufacturer used more than one row). The repair procedure for the other edges of the damage follows the previously explained methods.

The procedures for making all three types of panel repairs are similar. Trim out the damaged portion to the allowances mentioned in the preceding paragraph. For relief of stresses at the corners of the trim out, round them to a minimum radius of $1/_2$ inch. Lay out the new rivet row with a transverse pitch of approximately 5 rivet diameters and stagger the rivets with those put in by the manufacturer, as shown in Figure 8-4-4.

Cut the patch plate from material of the same thickness as the original, or the next greater thickness, allowing an edge distance of $2^1/_2$

rivet diameters. At the corners, strike arcs having the radius equal to the edge distance. Chamfer the edges of the patch plate for a 45-degree angle and form the plate to fit the contour of the original structure.

Turn the edges downward slightly so the edges fit closely. A good method to use is as follows; using a hardwood block, make a thin saw cut long enough to fit the longest edge of the patch and about $3/_8$ inch or less deep. The edges can be turned down simply and quickly. Be careful to only turn the edges down, not bend them down. There is a difference.

Place the patch plate in its correct position, drill one rivet hole and temporarily fasten the plate in place with a Cleco. Using a hole finder, locate the position of a second hole, drill it, and insert a second fastener. Then, from the back side and through the original holes, locate and drill the remaining holes. Remove the burrs from the rivet holes and apply corrosion protective material to the contacting surfaces before riveting the patch into place.

Installation of Access Doors

Access doors are located on the exterior surfaces of the airplane fuselage, wing, or empennage to provide access to the interior of the unit. Access holes are for making repairs, inspections, and adjustments of internal mechanisms, for lubrication purposes, and to provide access to fuel and oil tank filler necks and caps. The number of access doors on an airplane is determined by the manufacturer in the original design. Installation of additional access doors is limited by these rigid restrictions:

Access doors are permissible only when existing openings do not permit access to the damaged area.

They may be installed only upon approval of the FAA Designated Engineering Representative (DER). He must be given full particulars, such as reasons which make the installation neces-

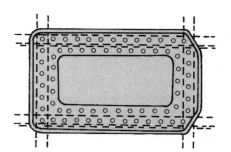

Figure 8-4-3. Damage repairable inside of members

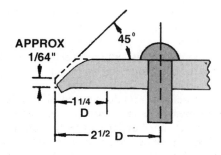

Figure 8-4-4. Chamfering and turning edge of patch

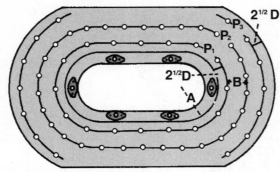

A RADIUS OF SKIN OPENING AND COVER PLATE
B TRANSVERSE PITCH 3/4" P₂ PITCH CENTER ROW
P₁ PITCH INNER ROW   P₃ PITCH OUTER ROW

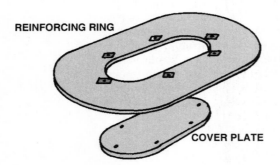

Figure 8-4-5. Access door layout

sary, the exact location of all present doors, and the proposed location for the new door or doors.

Access doors are never installed in the upper surfaces of wings or horizontal stabilizers, but in an emergency may be installed on either side of the vertical stabilizer.

The type of access door to be installed (if one is to be added) is usually described in service manuals for the aircraft. However, if instructions are inadequate, or if a repair manual is not available, follow the same general pattern as that used by the manufacturer during his installation of other access doors. The size of an access door is determined by two factors: the space in which it is being installed, and the work to be accomplished through the opening. The size must be kept to a minimum (Figure 8-4-5).

An access door consists of two parts—the supporting or reinforcing ring, and the cover plate. The supporting ring encircles the opening and is riveted onto the inside surface of the skin. The cover plate is flush with the outside surface of the skin and is fastened, either by screws or quick-fastening devices, to the reinforcing ring. The supporting ring may have two rows of rivets around it or may have two or more rows on either end with one or two rows on the

sides, as shown in Figure 8-4-5. The reinforcing ring should extend sufficiently beyond the inside of the skin opening to allow space for the plate nuts or fastening springs to which the cover plate is to be fastened. The material used for the reinforcing ring must be one thickness heavier than the original skin at that point. Use any recommended type of self-locking nut or quick-fastening device to fasten the cover plate. Do not skimp on plate nuts or other fastening devices.

When making the layout for an access door, first determine the size of the opening, then, by use of the rivet formula, determine the number of rivets required for attaching the reinforcing plate. Proceed as you would for a patch repair, using twice the distance A as the length of the break (Figure 8-4-5). Treat the layout as if it were two halves of a round patch—place all rivets in the ends of the plate. Place two additional rows of rivets along the sides of the opening. These rivets are not considered as carrying a load; therefore, space them in such a way that they do not exceed the maximum rivet pitch (12 diameters) and stagger them.

Leading Edge Repair

Leading edge patches should be flush with the surface, particularly on lighter, faster type airplanes. Make all leading edge repairs very carefully so that the original contour of the airfoil will be preserved and a smooth skin surface will be maintained. Figure 8-4-6 shows the arrangement of the repair.

If the damage requires trimming out the leading edge from cap strip to cap strip, use the method shown in the illustration of a typical leading edge damage and repair. When calculating the number of rivets, consider the length of the break as the distance around the leading edge from cap strip to cap strip. Place the required number of rivets in each splice plate, maintaining the rivet pitch and transverse pitch adopted by the manufacturer and used in the cap strips. Material for the splice plates must be one thickness heavier than the original skin; material for the patch plate may be the same thickness as that of the original skin.

If the damage does not require removal of the leading edge to the cap strips, use splice plates around the entire opening. The splice plates parallel to the cap strips should have the same number of rivets, rows, and spacing as that found in the cap strips. For installing rivets, use access doors provided to get to the interior of the leading edge. In case the existing openings are not large enough to receive the necessary riveting tools, make a specially located access door as described previously.

Corrugation Repair

On some airplanes, corrugated sheets are placed between the skin and attaching structures to reinforce the skin. When the skin is penetrated and requires repair, the underlying corrugated sheet is usually pierced also, and must be repaired along with the skin. In the standard nesting type, the inside radius of a crest fits into the outside radius of a valley, making it possible to overlap sections. In the standard type, these crests and valleys do not fit into each other, hence sections cannot be overlapped.

Corrugation repairs can be made in several ways, as shown in Figure 8-4-7. The most common and the easiest method is to form strips of sheet stock separately to fit each individual crest or valley.

When cleaning out the damaged area, round all corners to $1/2$ inch radius. With a flexible rule bent along the contour of the corrugations, measure the length of the break in the corrugated sheet. Substitute this measurement in the rivet formula and determine the number of rivets required in the repair. Since the rivets will be in double shear, use the double shear value of the rivet in your calculations.

The number of formed sections must be the same as the number of valleys and crests in the damaged area. These sections must extend far enough to include one row of rivets beyond each chordwise side of the cutout. The number of rows of rivets must be equal to the number of formed sections plus one. The number of rivets, found by the rivet formula, must be equally divided among the rows; add rivets for balance.

Determine the rivet pitch in the repair by dividing the manufacturer's rivet pitch equally so as to obtain an average spacing of 6 to 8 diameters and never less than 4 diameters. Locate the first rivets at spots not less than $2^1/2$ diameters from the edge of the cutout in the corrugated sheet and approximately in line, chordwise, with the manufacturer's rivets in the external skin.

Next determine the location of the remainder of the required rivets in the formed sections by using the repair rivet pitch and allowing a minimum edge distance of $2^1/2$ diameters. All rivets in the formed sections should align approximately in the chordwise direction with the rivets in the external skin.

Make the formed sections of 2024-T material and of the same thickness or one thickness heavier than the original corrugation. Where the original corrugations have been removed, add shims to make up the difference in thick-

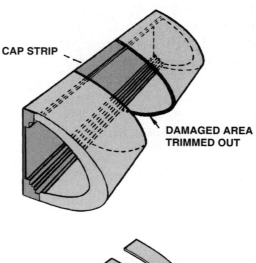

Figure 8-4-6. Leading edge repair

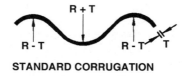

STANDARD CORRUGATION

REPAIR OF STANDARD CORRUGATION

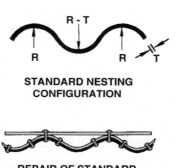

STANDARD NESTING
CONFIGURATION

REPAIR OF STANDARD
NESTING CONFIGURATION

Figure 8-4-7. Corrugation repair

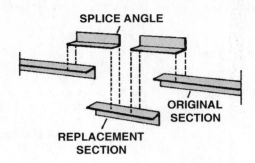

SPLICE ANGLE

ORIGINAL
SECTION

REPLACEMENT
SECTION

Figure 8-4-8. Stringer repair

ness in the old and new corrugated formed sections.

In repairing the smooth skin portion of the damage, extend the length of the smooth skin cutout spanwise beyond the corrugation cutout the same distance as the stiffeners. This point of extension should be approximately half-way between the cutout and the first row of rivets, but in no case should it be closer to a rivet than $2^1/_2$ diameters. Extend the smooth skin cutout chordwise beyond the corrugation cutout to within $2^1/_2$ diameters of the nearest row of manufacturer's rivets. Round all corners of the smooth skin cutout so they have a minimum radius of $^1/_2$ inch.

Taking the chordwise width of the smooth skin opening as the length of the break, use the rivet formula and calculate the number of rivets required for the skin patch. In laying out the smooth skin patch, extend it chordwise beyond the cutout to include at least two rows of manufacturer's rivets on each side. For the rivet spacing, use the same pitch as you did in the corrugation repair. The manufacturer's rivets in the patch within the effective area are considered a part of the required number.

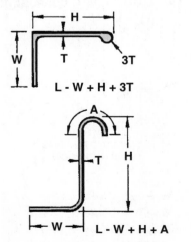

H

W   T   3T

L - W + H + 3T

A

T   H

W   L - W + H + A

Figure 8-4-9. Determining length of break on stringers

Cut the skin patch plate from 2024–T stock one thickness greater than the original skin and round the corners to a radius of 2-1/2 rivet diameters. Chamfer and turn the edges.

Cut shims of the same thickness and material as the original skin and fit them into the opening between the smooth skin and corrugation. The shims should be at least five rivet diameters wide.

Apply zinc chromate to all surfaces to be riveted together. When riveting the corrugation into place, put no rivets in the crests of the corrugation until the smooth skin patch is being applied.

If the corrugation is of the nesting type, cut a piece of similar material to size and place it under the original corrugation in the form of a patch-plate. Rivet calculations and layout procedure are the same as for the formed plate method of repair.

Stringer Repair

Stringer repairs are usually combination repairs involving the skin as well as internal members. In most cases, the repair requires the use of an insert and splice plates, as shown in Figure 8-4-8. If the damage occurs close to a bulkhead, cut the damaged stringer back so that only the insert extends through the opening in the bulkhead, for if the opening should be enlarged to accommodate both stringer and splice plate, the bulkhead would be weakened. Repair pieces for the various types of stringers may be either formed from sheet stock or cut from sections of similar stringer stock.

When calculating the number of rivets to be used in the repair, first determine the length of the break. In bulb angle stringers, the length is equivalent to the cross-sectional length plus three times the thickness of the material in the standing leg (to allow for the bulb) plus the actual cross-sectional length for the formed stringers and straight angles.

Substitute the value obtained as the length of the break in the rivet formula and calculate the number of rivets required.

The rivet pitch should be the same as that used by the manufacturer for attaching the skin to the stringer. In case this pitch exceeds the maximum range of ten rivet diameters, locate additional rivets between the original rivets. However, never make the spacing less than 4 diameters.

When laying out this spacing on paper, allow $2^1/_2$ rivet diameter for edge distance on each side of the break until all required rivets are located. There must be at least five rivets inserted on each end of the splice section.

Figure 8-4-9 shows how the original stringer is cut to allow the splice piece to be placed a minimum of $^1/_{32}$ inch clear of the bulkhead and yet accommodate the required number of rivets.

Prepare an insert piece to fit into the opening and replace the damaged section; be sure this piece has a clearance of $^1/_{32}$ inch on each end (between the ends of the original stringer). Cut the splice pieces to their proper length and drill the rivet holes.

Apply zinc chromate to all contacting surfaces and rivet the splice pieces to the insert section; then rivet the entire assembly into the original structure.

In some cases, the splices may be made from formed angles and placed on the face of the original stringers or back to back with them. Make the layout for this type of repair in the same manner as for repairs using sheet stock.

If you apply the splice piece as shown in Figure 8-4-10, then you must maintain the original cross-sectional area by using material thicker than that used in the original stringer; if you apply the splice piece as shown in Figure 8-4-10, the material may be the same thickness as the original stringer.

Former or Bulkhead Repair

Formers or bulkheads are usually designed to carry concentrated loads. Therefore, their repair is of prime importance. If not more than one-third of the cross-sectional bulkhead area must be removed in cleaning out the damage, use a patch plate and filler plate, shown in Figure 8-4-11.

Apply the rivet formula to determine the number of rivets required so you can establish the size of the patch plate. For length of the break, use the depth of the cutout area plus the length of the flange.

If more than one-half of the cross-sectional area of a bulkhead is damaged, remove the entire section and make a splice repair, including an insert. Measure the length of the break, as shown in Figure 8-4-12, and determine the number of rivets required by substituting this value in the rivet formula.

Since the rivets are in double shear, use the double-shear value of the rivet in your calculations. Remember, the result represents the number of rivets to be used in each of the splice plates.

Make a layout of the rivet pattern on paper, using a rivet patch similar to that used in attaching the bulkhead to the skin. Allow an edge distance of $2^1/_2$ rivet diameters. If the damage is near a stringer and the distance E is equal to or greater than the length of the rivet layout, use a splice plate at each end with an insert piece.

Form the insert piece from material of the same type and thickness as that used in the original member; make this piece of the proper length to have $^1/_{32}$ inch clearance on each end. Form the splice plates so they match the contour of that section of the bulkhead. Apply zinc chromate to all contacting surfaces and rivet the pieces together, using 2117 alloy universal head rivets.

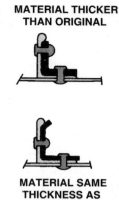

MATERIAL THICKER THAN ORIGINAL

MATERIAL SAME THICKNESS AS ORIGINAL

Figure 8-4-10. Determining the thickness of splice pieces

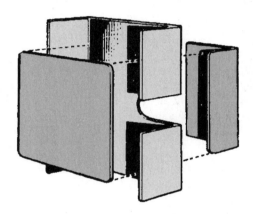

Figure 8-4-11. Bulkhead repair if not more than $^1/_3$ of cross-sectional area is damaged

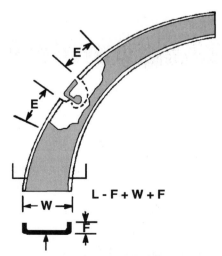

L - F + W + F

CROSS SECTION OF STRINGER

Figure 8-4-12. Determining length of break in a former

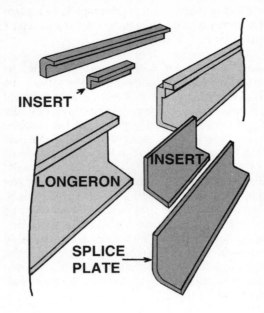

Figure 8-4-13. Formed longeron repair

Longeron Repair

The longeron, in many instances, is a comparatively heavy member which serves approximately the same purpose as the stringer. Consequently, the repair of these members is similar. However, in order to reduce the number of large diameter rivets of 2024–T alloy which must be used, you may substitute bolts on the larger type members. This use of bolts eliminates the necessity of heat treating the rivets. However, due to the greater accuracy required, bolts take more time for installation.

If the longeron consists of a formed section and an extruded angle section, consider each section separately (Figure 8-4-13). Repair the former section according to procedures previously described for flat and formed sections, but reduce the rivet pitch so as not to exceed 4 to 6 rivet diameters. Repair the extruded section with bolts or Hi-shear rivets. Determine the required number by applying the rivet formula, using the shear and of bolts (Table 8-3-2). Ream the bolt holes for a light drive fit. Make

the legs of the splice plate long enough to line up with the edges of both the original piece, and the insert. In selecting material for the filler plate, remember that it must be the same thickness as the original longeron section.

In a longeron repair made with bolts only, determine the required number of bolts by use of the rivet formula using the double shear values of bolts. See MIL Handbook-5 for the double shear values. For ease of forming and fitting, make the splice plates in two parts of material of the same thickness as that in the original longeron. Form the insert either from sheet stock or a section of similar extrusion.

Spar Repair

The spar structure carries the loads of the other components of the wing. It is therefore important that you exercise particular care when making repairs to this member so that the original strength of the structure is not diminished. The spar is so constructed that two general classes of repairs—web repairs and cap strip repairs—are usually necessary. The repairs discussed here are typical of the numerous types made on these parts.

For a spar web butt splice, first clean out the damage, then measure the full width of the web section. Determine the number of rivets to be placed in each side of the splice plate by substituting this value for length of break in the rivet formula. Prepare an insert section of the same type of material and thickness as that used in the original web.

Make a paper pattern of the rivet layout for the splice plate, using the same pitch as that employed in the attachment of the web to the cap strip. Cut the splice plates from sheet stock having the same weight as that in the web, or one thickness heavier, and transfer the rivet layout from the paper pattern to the splice plates.

Give all contacting surfaces a corrosion-resistance treatment and rivet the component parts of the repair into place. The rivets used in attaching the insert section to the cap strips

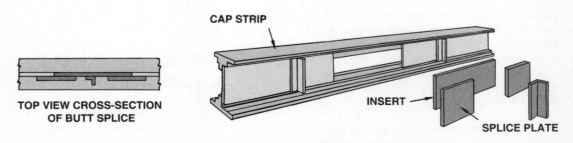

Figure 8-4-14. Exploded view of a spar web butt splice

are in addition to those calculated for attaching the splice plates. Replace all web stiffeners removed during the repair. Figure 8-4-14 shows an exploded view of a splice.

In a spar web joggle splice, no splice plates are utilized. Instead, you form the web repair section in such a way that it overlaps the original web sufficiently to accommodate the required number of rivets. Make a joggle in each end of the repair section so that the repair piece contacts the cap strips to which it is riveted. Rivet calculation for this repair is similar to that described for butt splicing.

Many forms of cap strips are used in aircraft manufacture. Each requires a distinct type of repair. In calculating the number of rivets required in an extruded T cap strip repair, take the width of the base of the T, plus the length of the leg, as the length of the break and use double-shear values. Figure 8-4-15 shows an exploded view of a cap strip repair.

Place one-fourth of the required number of rivets in each row of original rivets in the base of the T-section. Locate them midway between each pair of the original rivets. Locate the balance of the rivets along the leg of the T-section in two rows. Consider all original rivet locations within the area of the splice as part of the required rivets.

Make the filler piece of a similar piece of T-section extrusion, or of two pieces of flat stock. You may make the splice pieces of extruded angle material or form it from sheet stock—in either case, it must be of the same thickness as the cap strip. The rivets used in the leg of the cap strip may be either of the round-, flat- or universal-head type, but the rivets used in the base must be of the same type as those employed in the skin.

Repair of milled cap strips is limited to damages occurring to the flanges. Damage beyond these areas requires replacement of the entire cap strip. To make a typical flange repair, substitute the depth of the trimmed-out area as the length of the break in the rivet formula and calculate the number of rivets required. Form a splice plate of the required length and drill it to match the original rivet layout. Cut an insert piece to fit the trimmed-out area and rivet the repair in place. If the trimmed-out area is more than four inches in length, use an angle splice plate to provide added strength.

Truss Repair

Truss type construction is employed very seldom, the most common application being in the construction of ribs and spars. The best method of handling truss damage is to replace the damaged part. Sometimes, however, repair is necessary.

In making a truss tubing repair, take the circumference of the tube as the length of the damage, substitute that value in the rivet formula, and calculate the number of bolts required to make the repair, Use the double-shear value of bolts as given in Table 8-3-2 and MIL Handbook-5. Make a filler insert of hard wood to fit the inside of the tubing very closely. This hardwood filler prevents crushing of the tubing as the bolts are drawn up. Also make two U-shaped splice plates and a filler plate of aluminum alloy of the same thickness as that in the tubing walls. An alternate method of truss tubing repair is to cut away part of the damaged truss tubing, form two splice plates and rivet them into place without using a hardwood filler insert.

When making a truss chord member repair follow a procedure similar to that for truss tubing repair, but use a tubular insert in place of the U-shaped splice plates. If it is necessary to remove any rivets from nearby structures when making either repair, replace the rivets with bolts. All bolts should have a light-drive fit.

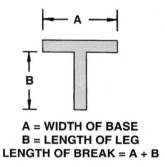

A = WIDTH OF BASE
B = LENGTH OF LEG
LENGTH OF BREAK = A + B

DETERMINING LENGTH OF BREAK OF A T-SPAR

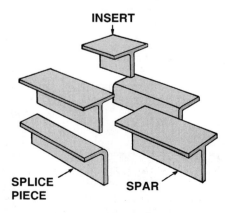

T-SPAR CAP STRIP REPAIR

Figure 8-4-15. Exploded view of a cap strip repair

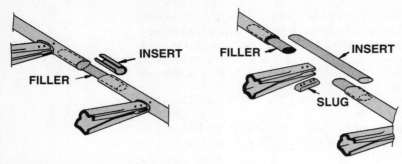

Figure 8-4-16. Trailing edge repair between ribs

Trailing Edge Repair

In most cases, trailing edges are made of 2024–T aluminum alloy. Some, however, are of stainless steel. Permanent repairs to stainless steel members must be made with stainless steel stock. The trailing edge is considered a noncritical area of the airplane and repairs need only restore the member to its original shape and rigidity. Check with an FAA Designated Engineering Representative before continuing.

Damage occurring in the trailing edge section between ribs is repaired as shown in Figure 8-4-16. Cut the damaged area away and make a filler of either hardwood, fiber, or cast aluminum alloy to fit snugly inside the trailing edge tubing. The filler should be long enough to accommodate three rivets spaced at 6 to 8 diameters. You may arrange two rows of two rivets each provided the trailing edge has sufficient width to maintain proper edge distance and a pitch of not less than four diameters.

Make an insert piece of aluminum alloy sheet of the same thickness as the original stock and shape it to match the trailing edge member. Assemble the pieces as shown in Figure 8-4-16 and rivet into place, using countersunk rivets and forming countersunk shop heads so as to provide a smooth contour. This is called NASA flush riveting.

Note the repair procedure for damage occurring at or near a rib. In this case, first remove sufficient trailing edge material to allow the complete splice to fall between the ribs. This usually requires the use of two splices joined by an insert piece made of similar trailing edge material or of formed sheet stock. The remainder of the procedure is similar to that for damage between ribs.

Web Repair

Web repairs may be classified generally into two types—those made to web sections considered critical, such as those in wing ribs (Figure 8-4-17); and those considered noncritical, such as those in elevators, rudders, flaps, and the like. In the latter type of repair, only original form and rigidity need be considered. Repairs to critical web sections, however, must be made in such a way that the original strength of the member is restored.

In repairing a critically stressed web, first clean out the damage, then calculate the number of rivets required for the repair. If the cutout line passes through a lightening hole, the length of the break is equivalent to the total length of the material remaining above and below the hole plus the length of the flanges— otherwise, the length of the break is simply the depth of the rib plus the length of the flanges.

Substitute the appropriate value in the rivet formula and determine the number of rivets to be used on each side of the break. Lay out a row of rivets along each edge of the web, leaving an edge distance of 3 diameters and a spacing of 6 to 8 diameters. Make the patch plate from sheet stock of the same thickness or one thickness heavier than that of the original web.

The length of the patch plate should be equal to the width of the break plus the rivet layout space plus an edge distance of 2-1/2 rivet diameters plus the width of a flange on each end equal to the width of the flange on the original web member. Make horizontal angle stiffeners to fit on the underside of the repair—make them the same length as the patch plate. Make two angle inserts to fill the gap in the web section and to provide a continuous riveting area. Assemble the parts and rivet in place.

To complete the repair, rivet a vertical angle stiffener, made from the same thickness and type of material as the original web, across the patch plate midway between the edges of the damage cutout.

LENGTH OF BRAKE EQUALS
X + Y + 2 FLANGES

LENGTH OF BRAKE EQUALS
Z + 2 FLANGES

Figure 8-4-17. Typical repair to rib web

In repairing a noncritical web, form an insert and patch plate of the same type of material and thickness as that in the original web. Use a minimum of four rivets in two rows on each side of the break. Maximum rivet spacing may be equivalent to 12 rivet diameters.

Section 5

FAA Approved Repair Procedures

Anytime a repair is contemplated, first you have to figure out how it should be repaired, then you must make sure that the repair is, or can be, FAA approved. No matter the type of aircraft, the process is the same.

The repair must return the original strength to the part being repaired. It must also allow for the stress carried by the part to flow through the original structure as the airplanes designers intended. If not, then the design strength will be upset and additional failures are apt to occur as a result of the repair.

While this may sound like a daunting task, in reality it is not. The methods and procedures you use in all repairs will be determined by a process called acceptable methods.

AC43.13-1B - Acceptable Methods, Techniques, and Practices

Often called the bible of aircraft repair, AC43.13 has been one of the most misused Advisory Circulars in history. Developed from the old Civil Aeronautics Manual 18, AC43.13 was designed to provide repair information for older aircraft for which no repair manual was available.

Manufacturers of light, non-pressurized, general aviation aircraft started using the manual as a reference for their repair procedures. Most FAA Form 337's used AC43.13 as a reference for approving various repair methods. The trouble was that AC43.13 was only advisory in nature, and not approved data.

That problem has been fixed in the current version of the FAA manual. Obtain a copy, read the preamble, and then put the book in your working library. You will use it forever.

Figures 8-5-1 through 8-5-9 are reproductions of figures found in AC43.13-1B. Even though these figures have been used for many years, they can sometimes be confusing. The reproductions shown here have been altered in only one respect; the repair parts have been shaded. This allows the illustration to be understood more easily.

Manufacturers Repair and Structural Repair Manuals

All aircraft manufacturers are required to publish repair manuals for their products as part of an FAA requirement. The content of these manuals varies considerably, depending on the specific manufacturer and the complexity and use of the final product.

Small general aviation aircraft generally defer to FAA published repair instructions as contained in Advisory Circular AC43.13-1B for day to day repair procedures. Typically, this class of airplane will not have a structural repair manual. The airplanes are not complex, parts are readily available, and parts replacement can be accomplished with little, or fairly simple, fixtures.

Larger aircraft, particularly turbine, turbojet, and airline equipment, typically do not rely on outside documents for repair procedures.

Large general aviation aircraft normally have very complete repair instructions. In general, the instructions cover all like models of that aircraft, varying principally in avionics and electronics installations. In other words, an ABC airplane structural repair manual can be used for all ABC airplanes. These manuals are developed according to a format developed by the Airline transport Association (ATA) specification. The specification is known as ATA Spec. 100.

In the case of airline equipment, the structural repair manuals are part of the airlines approved maintenance program. They will vary somewhat by different airlines, just as each airlines equipment and internal procedures vary. One manual does not cover all like models of the same airplane as used by different airlines. In all cases the aircraft manufacturer provides the basic information, gearing the content towards the specific airlines program.

Structural repair manuals are very complete. They not only cover the methods and practices that are approved for that airplane, they also cover the required jigs and fixtures that may be necessary to maintain alignment during repair. Additionally, the manuals allow for very little variance from the previously approved procedures.

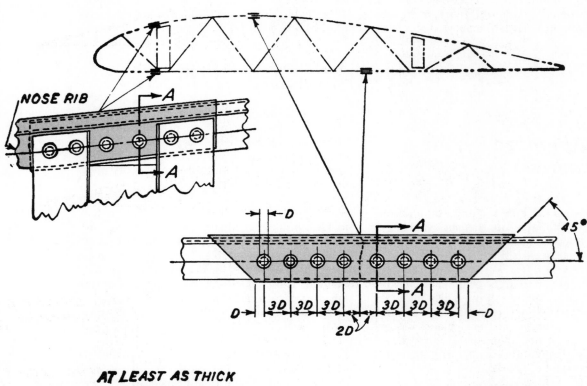

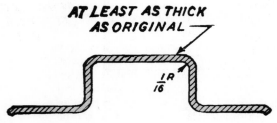

AT LEAST AS THICK
AS ORIGINAL

$\frac{1R}{16}$

MATERIAL—DURAL
OR AL. ALLOY USED IN
ORIGINAL CONSTRUCTION
SCALE = TWICE SIZE

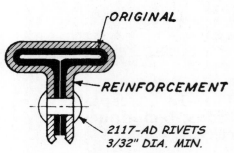

ORIGINAL

REINFORCEMENT

2117-AD RIVETS
3/32" DIA. MIN.

SECTION A-A
SCALE = TWICE SIZE

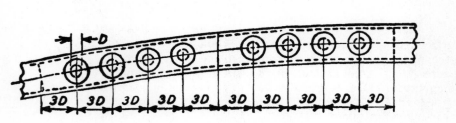

2017-T3
SQ. ROD

2117-AD RIVETS
1/8" DIA. MIN.

Figure 8-5-1. Typical repair for buckled or cracked metal wing rib capstrips

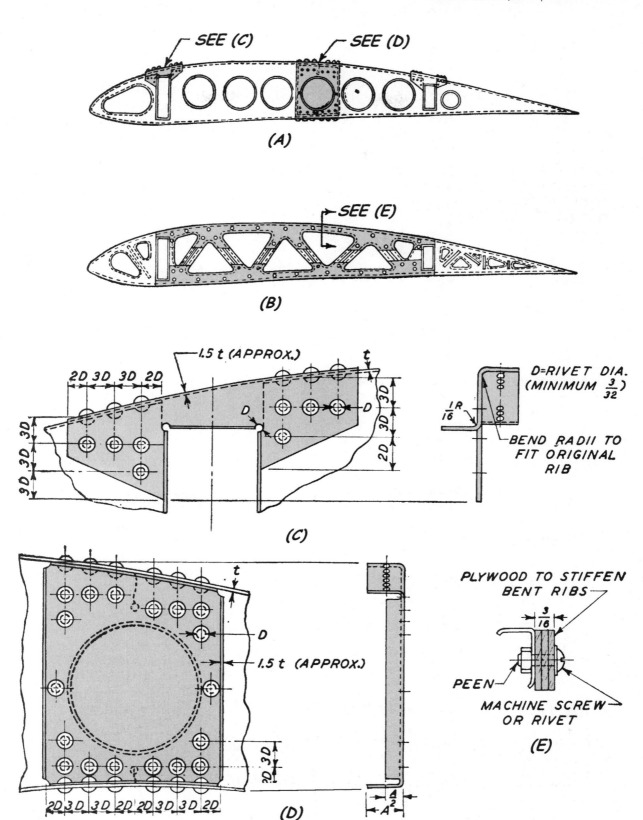

NOTE: FOR MINIMUM NUMBER OF RIVETS REQUIRED, SEE AC 43.13-1B PARAGRAPH 4-58g AND SUBSEQUENT.

Figure 8-5-2. Typical metal rib repairs (usually found on small and medium-sized aircraft).

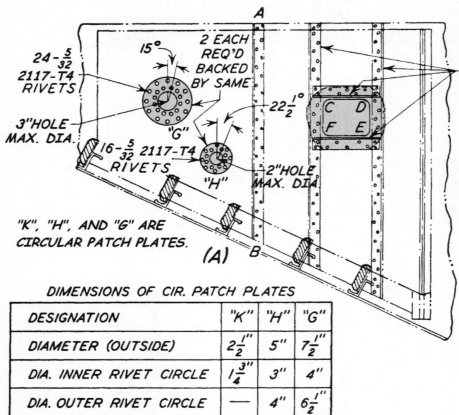

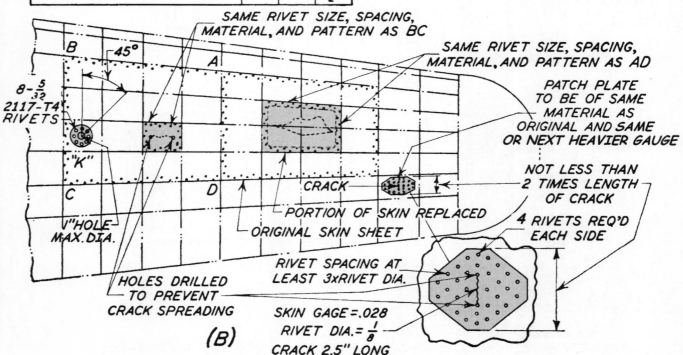

Figure 8-5-3. Typical repairs of stressed sheet metal coverings

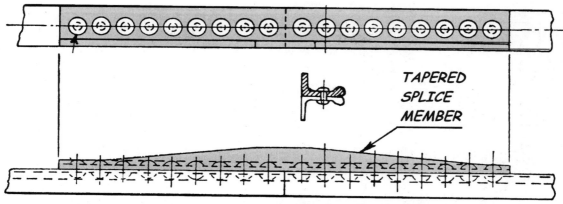

NOTE: UNSHADED SECTIONS ARE ORIGINAL AND/OR
REPLACEMENT SECTIONS. SHADED SECTIONS
ARE CONNECTING OR REINFORCING SECTIONS.

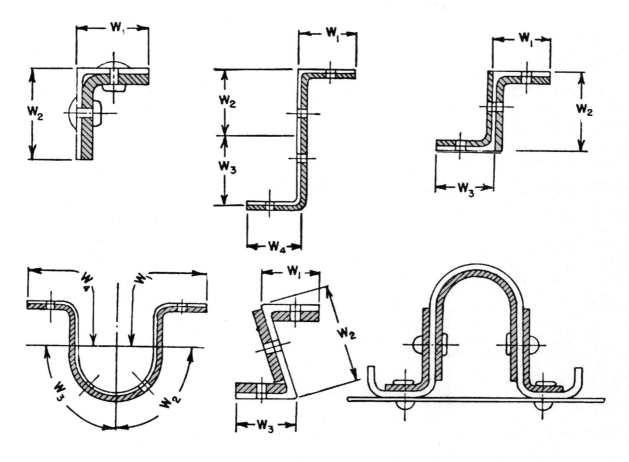

NOTE: FOR MINIMUM NUMBER OF RIVETS REQUIRED, SEE AC43.13-1B
PARAGRAPH 4-58g AND SUBSEQUENT.

Figure 8-5-4. Typical stringer and flange splices

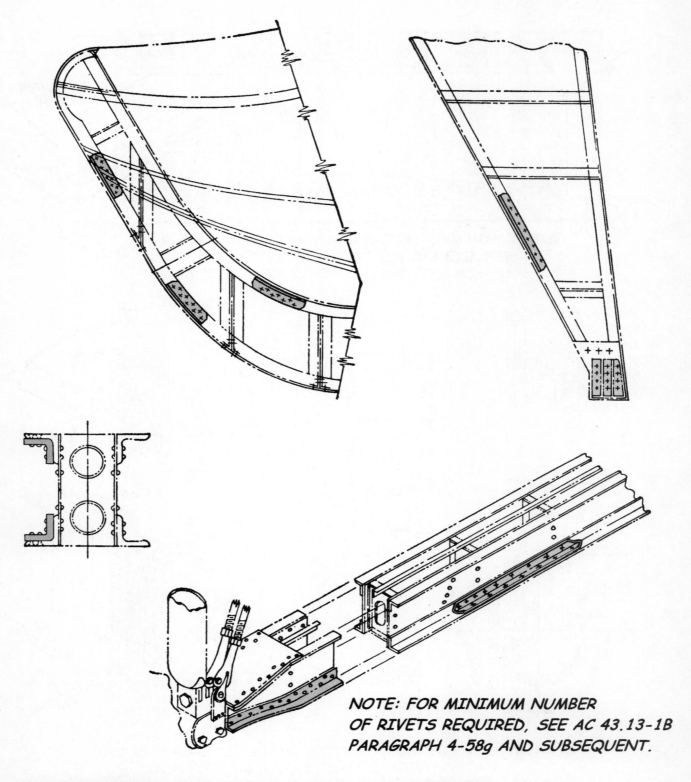

NOTE: FOR MINIMUM NUMBER
OF RIVETS REQUIRED, SEE AC 43.13-1B
PARAGRAPH 4-58g AND SUBSEQUENT.

NOTE: STRENGTH INVESTIGATION IS USUALLY REQUIRED
FOR THIS TYPR OF REPAIR.

Figure 8-5-5. Application of typical flange splices and reinforcement

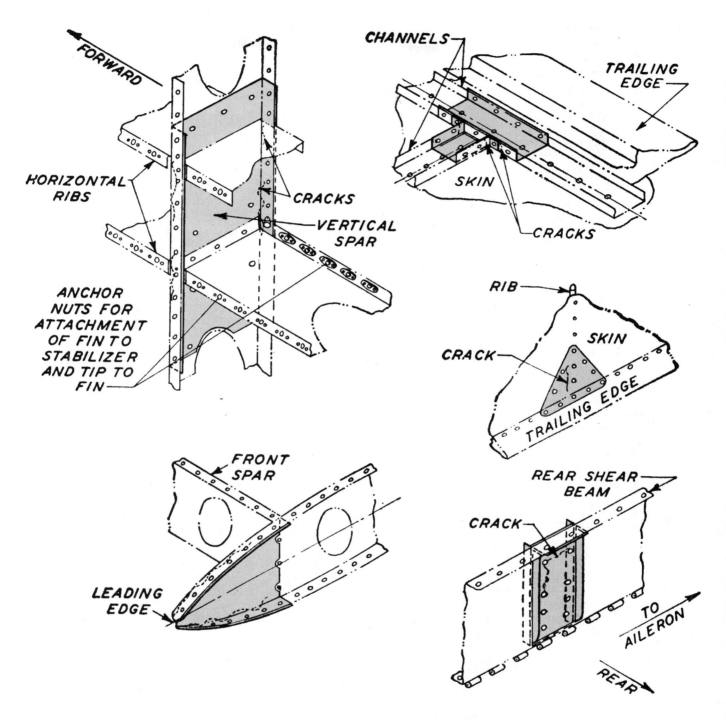

FORWARD

CHANNELS

TRAILING EDGE

HORIZONTAL RIBS

CRACKS

VERTICAL SPAR

SKIN

CRACKS

ANCHOR NUTS FOR ATTACHMENT OF FIN TO STABILIZER AND TIP TO FIN

RIB

SKIN

CRACK

TRAILING EDGE

FRONT SPAR

LEADING EDGE

REAR SHEAR BEAM

CRACK

TO AILERON

REAR

NOTE: ALL REINFORCING PLATES TO BE OF SAME ALLOY AND APPROX. 1.5 THICKNESS OF ORIGINAL

Figure 8-5-6. Typical methods of repairing cracked leading and trailing edges and rib intersections

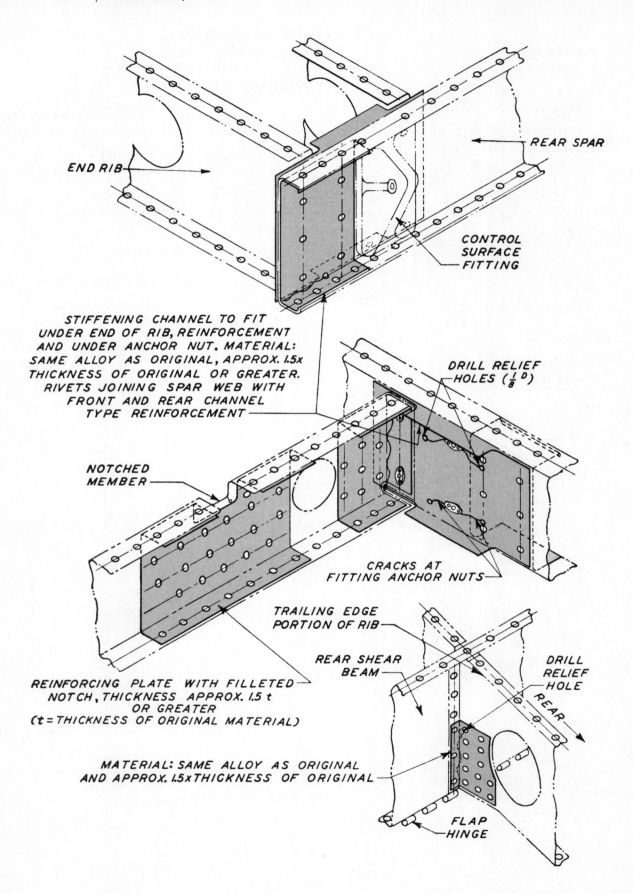

REAR SPAR

END RIB

CONTROL
SURFACE
FITTING

STIFFENING CHANNEL TO FIT
UNDER END OF RIB, REINFORCEMENT
AND UNDER ANCHOR NUT. MATERIAL:
SAME ALLOY AS ORIGINAL, APPROX. 1.5x
THICKNESS OF ORIGINAL OR GREATER.
RIVETS JOINING SPAR WEB WITH
FRONT AND REAR CHANNEL
TYPE REINFORCEMENT

DRILL RELIEF
HOLES ($\frac{1}{8}$ D)

NOTCHED
MEMBER

CRACKS AT
FITTING ANCHOR NUTS

TRAILING EDGE
PORTION OF RIB

REAR SHEAR
BEAM

DRILL
RELIEF
HOLE

REAR

REINFORCING PLATE WITH FILLETED
NOTCH, THICKNESS APPROX. 1.5 t
OR GREATER
(t = THICKNESS OF ORIGINAL MATERIAL)

MATERIAL: SAME ALLOY AS ORIGINAL
AND APPROX. 1.5x THICKNESS OF ORIGINAL

FLAP
HINGE

Figure 8-5-7. Typical methods of replacing cracked members at fittings

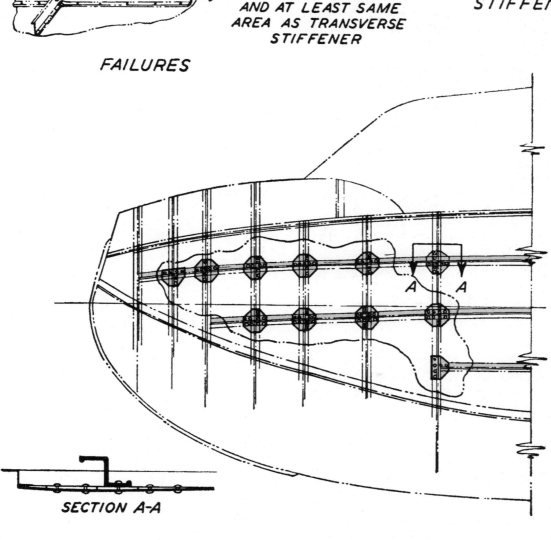

TRANSVERSE STIFF.

CRACKS IN WING SKIN AND TRANS. STIFFENER AT DRAG RIB JUNCTION
REPAIR BY OUTSIDE GUSSETS

DRAG RIB

LONG. STIFF.

CRACK IN TRANS. STIFFENER DUE TO FATIGUE FAILURE

DRAG RIB

REINFORCEMENT TO BE SAME MATERIAL AND AT LEAST SAME AREA AS TRANSVERSE STIFFENER

SPAN

FAILURES

REPAIR OF CRACKED STIFFENER

SECTION A-A

Figure 8-5-8. Typical methods of repairing cracked frame and stiffener combinations

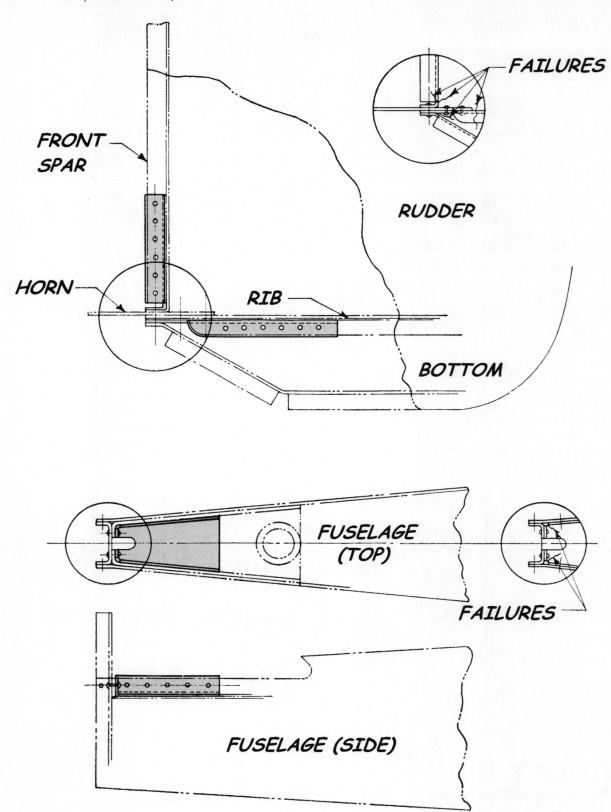

FRONT SPAR

FAILURES

RUDDER

HORN

RIB

BOTTOM

FUSELAGE (TOP)

FAILURES

FUSELAGE (SIDE)

NOTE: USE SAME MATERIAL, NEXT HEAVIER GAUGE FOR REPLACEMENT.

Figure 8-5-9. Typical repairs to rudder and to fuselage at tail post

ATA Specification 100

Manuals for transport category airplanes quickly became very large and unwieldy. Finding a specific item was difficult, to say the least. With different manufacturers arranging the in different order, any attempt at automation became impossible. With the advent of microfilm readers, a system was needed to allow for automated lookups. The Airline Transport Association, with the input of aircraft manufacturers, operators, the FAA, and certified repair facilities, developed specification ATA 100.

The established ATA 100 Chapters are shown in Table 8-5-1. These major chapters are further broken down into sections/sub-sections (Table 8-5-2).

Designated Engineering Representatives (DER)

In the real world not all items requiring repairs will fall into nice neat categories with specific directions for each repair. Nevertheless, each repair method must still be approved. A sheet metal technician is not allowed to determine what will work and what will not. In most cases it will require the advice of a certified aircraft engineer to design a repair process. This person is called a Designated Engineering Representative, or DER for short.

DER's are certified by the FAA to design and approve non-standard repairs that are not covered by the maintenance or structural repair manuals. They also design and approve aircraft modifications. The services of a DER can be the best, and frequently the only, method of approving non-standard repairs. Your local FAA inspector should be able to advise you when DER services must be obtained.

Because outside DER services can be very expensive, and because time can be of the essence, most airlines have an engineering office at their main maintenance base. These in-house engineering departments are generally staffed by factory representatives from the aircraft and engine manufacturers.

Type Certificates

As part of the design and approval process each airplane has a document called a type certificate. This document contains all the standards to which the aircraft was designed and approved. It also includes all original and optional equipment for that design. Each subsequent aircraft manufactured must conform to the type certificate, including all equipment installed on the original approved design.

SYSTEM/CHAPTER	TITLE
5	TIME LIMITS/MAINTENANCE CHECKS
6	DIMENSIONS & AREAS
7	LIFTING & SHORING
8	LEVELING & WEIGHING
9	TOWING & TAXIING
10	PARKING & MOORING
11	PLACARDS & MARKINGS
12	SERVICING
20	STANDARD PRACTICES-AIRFRAME
21	AIR CONDITIONING
22	AUTO FLIGHT
23	COMMUNICATIONS
24	ELECTRICAL POWER
25	EQUIPMENT/FURNISHINGS
26	FIRE PROTECTION
27	FLIGHT CONTROLS
28	FUEL
29	HYDRAULIC POWER
30	ICE AND RAIN PROTECTION
31	INDICATING/RECORDING SYSTEMS
32	LANDING GEAR
33	LIGHTS
34	NAVIGATION
35	OXYGEN
36	PNEUMATIC
37	VACUUM
38	WATER/WASTE
39	ELECTRICAL/ELECTRONIC PANELS & MULTIPURPOSE PARTS
49	AIRBORNE AUXILIARY POWER
51	STRUCTURES
52	DOORS
53	FUSELAGE
54	NACELLES/PYLONS
55	STABILIZERS
56	WINDOWS
57	WINGS
71	POWER PLANT
72	ENGINE TURBINE/TURBO-PROP
73	ENGINE FUEL & CONTROL
74	IGNITION
75	AIR
76	ENGINE CONTROLS
77	ENGINE INDICATING
78	EXHAUST
79	OIL
80	STARTING
81	TURBINES
82	WATER INJECTION
83	ACCESSORY GEAR-BOXES
91	CHARTS

Table 8-5-1. ATA 100 chapter listings

SYS/CHAP	SUBSYS/SECTION	TITLE
05		TIME LIMITS/MAINTENANCE CHECKS
	-00	General
	-10	Time Limits
	-20	Scheduled Maintenance Checks
	-50	Unscheduled Maintenance Checks
06		DIMENSIONS AND AREAS
07		LIFTING AND SHORING
	-00	General
	-10	Jacking
	-20	Shoring
08		LEVELING AND WEIGHING
	-00	General
	-10	Weighing & Balancing
	-20	Leveling
09		TOWING AND TAXIING
	-00	General
	-10	Towing
	-20	Taxiing
10		PARKING AND MOORING
	-00	General
	-10	Parking
	-20	Mooring
11		PLACARDS AND MARKINGS
	-00	General
	-10	Exterior Color Schemes and Markings
	-20	Exterior Placards and Markings
	-30	Interior Placards and Markings
12		SERVICING
	-00	General
	-10	Replenishing
	-20	Scheduled Servicing

SYS/CHAP	SUBSYS/SECTION	TITLE
	-30	Unscheduled Servicing
20		STANDARD PRACTICES - AIRFRAME
21		AIR CONDITIONING
	-00	General
	-10	Compression
	-20	Distribution
	-30	Pressurization Control
	-40	Heating
	-50	Cooling
	-60	Temperature Control
	-70	Moisture or Air Contaminant Control
22		AUTO FLIGHT
	-00	General
	-10	Autopilot
	-20	Speed - Attitude Correction
	-30	Auto Throttle
	-40	System Monitor
23		COMMUNICATIONS
	-00	General
	-10	Speech Communications
	-20	Data Transmission and Automatic Calling
	-30	Passenger Address and Entertainment
	-40	Interphone
	-50	Audio Integrating
	-60	Static Discharging
	-70	Audio and Video Monitoring
24		ELECTRICAL POWER
	-00	General
	-10	Generator Drive
	-20	AC Generation
	-30	DC Generation

Table 8-5-2A. ATA Specification 100 Systems and sub-systems

SYS/ CHAP	SUBSYS/ SECTION	TITLE
	-40	External Power
	-50	Electrical Load Distribution
25		**EQUIPMENT AND FURNISHINGS**
	-00	General
	-10	Flight Compartment
	-20	Passenger Compartment
	-30	Buffet/Galley
	-40	Lavatories
	-50	Cargo Compartments
	-60	Emergency
	-70	Accessory Compartments
26		**FIRE PROTECTION**
	-00	General
	-10	Detection
	-20	Extinguishing
	-30	Explosion Suppression
27		**FLIGHT CONTROLS**
	-00	General
	-10	Aileron and Tab
	-20	Rudder and Tab
	-30	Elevator and Tab
	-40	Horizontal Stabilizer or Stabilator
	-50	Flaps
	-60	Spoiler, Drag Devices and Variable Aerodynamic Fairings
	-70	Gust Lock and Damper
	-80	Lift Augmenting
28		**FUEL**
	-00	General
	-10	Storage
	-20	Distribution
	-30	Dump

SYS/ CHAP	SUBSYS/ SECTION	TITLE
	-40	Indicating
29		**HYDRAULIC POWER**
	-00	General
	-10	Main
	-20	Auxiliary
	-30	Indicating
30		**ICE AND RAIN PROTECTION**
	-00	General
	-10	Airfoil
	-20	Air Intakes
	-30	Pitot and Static
	-40	Windows, Windshields and Doors
	-50	Antennas and Radomes
	-60	Propellers/Rotors
	-70	Water Lines
	-80	Detection
31		**INDICATING AND RECORDING SYSTEMS**
	-00	General
	-30	Recorders
	-40	Central Computers
	-50	Central Warning Systems
32		**LANDING GEAR**
	-00	General
	-10	Main Gear and Doors
	-20	Nose Gear and Doors
	-30	Extension and Retraction
	-40	Wheels and Brakes
	-50	Steering
	-60	Position and Warning
	-70	Supplementary Gear
33		**LIGHTS**

Table 8-5-2B. ATA Specification 100 Systems and sub-systems

SYS/ CHAP	SUBSYS/ SECTION	TITLE
	-00	General
	-10	Flight Compartment
	-20	Passenger Compartment
	-30	Cargo and Service Compartments
	-40	Exterior Lighting
	-50	Emergency Lighting
34		**NAVIGATION**
	-00	General
	-10	Flight Environment Data
	-20	Attitude and Direction
	-30	Landing and Taxiing Aids
	-40	Independent Position Determining
	-50	Dependent Position Determining
	-60	Position Computing
35		**OXYGEN**
	-00	General
	-10	Crew
	-20	Passenger
	-30	Portable
36		**PNEUMATIC**
	-00	General
	-10	Distribution
	-20	Indicating
37		**VACUUM**
	-00	General
	-10	Distribution
	-20	Indicating
38		**WATER OR WASTE**
	-00	General
	-10	Potable
	-20	Wash

SYS/ CHAP	SUBSYS/ SECTION	TITLE
	-30	Waste Disposal
	-40	Air Supply
39		**ELECTRICAL/ELECTRONIC PANELS AND MULTIPURPOSE PARTS**
	-00	General
	-10	Instrument and Control Panels
	-20	Electrical and Electronic Equipment Racks
	-30	Electrical and Electronic Junction Boxes
	-40	Multipurpose Electrical and Electronic Parts
	-50	Integrated Circuits
	-60	Printed Circuit Card Assemblies
49		**AIRBORNE AUXILIARY POWER**
	-00	General
	-10	Power Plant
	-20	Engine
	-30	Engine Fuel and Control
	-40	Ignition/Starting
	-50	Air
	-60	Engine Controls
	-70	Indicating
	-80	Exhaust
	-90	Oil
51		**STRUCTURES**
	-00	General
52		**DOORS**
	-00	General
	-10	Passenger/Crew
	-20	Emergency Exit
	-30	Cargo
	-40	Service
	-50	Fixed Interior
	-60	Entrance Stairs

Table 8-5-2C. ATA Specification 100 Systems and sub-systems

SYS/CHAP	SUBSYS/SECTION	TITLE
	-70	Door Warning
	-80	Landing Gear
53		FUSELAGE
	-00	General
	-10	Main Frame
	-20	Auxiliary Structure
	-30	Plates/Skin
	-40	Attach Fittings
	-50	Aerodynamic Fairings
54		NACELLES / PYLONS
	-00	General
	-10	Main Frame
	-20	Auxiliary Structure
	-30	Plates/Skin
	-40	Attach Fittings
	-50	Fillets/Fairings
55		STABILIZERS
	-00	General
	-10	Horizontal Stabilizer / Stabilator Or Canard
	-20	Elevator
	-30	Vertical Stabilizer
	-40	Rudder
56		WINDOWS
	-00	General
	-10	Flight Compartment
	-20	Cabin
	-30	Door
	-40	Inspection and Observation
57		WINGS
	-00	General
	-10	Main Frame

SYS/CHAP	SUBSYS/SECTION	TITLE
	-20	Auxiliary Structure
	-30	Plates/Skin
	-40	Attach Fittings
	-50	Flight Surfaces
71		POWER PLANT GENERAL
	-00	General
	-10	Cowling
	-20	Mounts
	-30	Fireseals
	-40	Attach Fittings
	-50	Electrical Harness
	-60	Air Intakes
	-70	Engine Drains
72		ENGINE TURBINE/TURBOPROP
	-00	General
	-10	Reduction Gear and Shaft Section (Turboprop)
	-20	Air Inlet Section
	-30	Compressor Section
	-40	Combustion Section
	-50	Turbine Section
	-60	Accessory Drives
	-70	By-Pass Section
72		ENGINE RECIPROCATING
	-00	General
	-10	Front Section
	-20	Power Section
	-30	Cylinder Section
	-40	Supercharger Section
	-50	Lubrication
73		ENGINE FUEL AND CONTROL
	-00	General

Table 8-5-2D. ATA Specification 100 Systems and sub-systems

SYS/ CHAP	SUBSYS/ SECTION	TITLE
	-10	Distribution
	-20	Controlling
	-30	Indicating
74		IGNITION
	-00	General
	-10	Electrical Power Supply
	-20	Distribution
	-30	Switching
75		AIR
	-00	General
	-10	Engine Anti-Icing
	-20	Accessory Cooling
	-30	Compressor Control
	-40	Indicating
76		ENGINE CONTROLS
	-00	General
	-10	Power Control
	-20	Emergency Shutdown
77		ENGINE INDICATING
	-00	General
	-10	Power
	-20	Temperature
	-30	Analyzers
78		EXHAUST
	-00	General
	-10	Collector/Nozzle

SYS/ CHAP	SUBSYS/ SECTION	TITLE
	-20	Noise Suppressor
	-30	Thrust Reverser
	-40	Supplementary Air
79		OIL
	-00	General
	-10	Storage
	-20	Distribution
	-30	Indicating
80		STARTING
	-00	General
	-10	Cranking
81		TURBINES
	-00	General
	-10	Power Recovery
	-20	Turbo-Supercharger
82		WATER INJECTION
	-00	General
	-10	Storage
	-20	Distribution
	-30	Dumping and Purging
	-40	Indicating
83		ACCESSORY GEAR BOXES
	-00	General
	-10	Drive Shaft Section
	-20	Gear Box Section
91		CHARTS

Table 8-5-2E. ATA Specification 100 Systems and sub-systems

Supplemental Type Certificates

However, changes and improvements to equipment and materials do occur as time progresses. These items can not simply be used because we believe them to be better. There is, however, a process whereby their use can be approved. The process of approval is called a Supplemental Type Certificate (STC). It is a modification of the original type certificate for the installation or revision of the original equipment, or installation of additional items not included in the original equipment list. There are STCs for items such as additional avionics, different engines, modified interiors, different wing tips, modified exhaust systems, and many others.

There are a couple of things to remember about STCs. To begin, they are the property of the person(s) that initially obtained their approval. The STC can be bought by others for use on other airplanes. Sometimes an STC is nothing more than the approval paperwork for a modification. In other cases they are extensive kits that comprise many specially fabricated parts and assemblies that must be used to accomplish the modification. Some STCs can be expensive, both in purchase price and installation labor.

No STC can be installed without purchasing the rights to do so. The rights to its use belong to the developer and may not simply be copied.

If you or a customer are considering a change that would require an STC that needs to be approved, contact the local FAA office. If an identical modification has already been approved, it is almost always less expensive not to develop an STC from scratch.

The FAA maintains a list of STCs in a document called a Summary Of Supplemental type Certificates. It can be obtained from the FAA or from a government book store.

Maintenance and Repair Records

Although maintenance records may be the responsibility of an A&P technician or, in the case of a certified repair station, the head inspector, you still need to understand them. The best way is to obtain and study the following FAA Advisory Circulars:

- **AC43.9-1F** - Instructions For Completion of FAA Form 337, Major Repair And Alteration
- **AC43-9B** - Maintenance Records

- **AC20-109A** - Service Difficulty Program (General Aviation)

Each employer may operate under a different approval process, and record keeping may be different from one to the next. Never the less, you will be required to keep extensive records on your work activities. It's best to become familiar with the process.

Approved Parts

A fairly blanket statement can be made that will cover most aircraft parts. If they are not obtained from the aircraft manufacturer or one of his agents, or from the holder of an STC, or from someone who has a PMA, they are counterfeit. This does not cover the parts that you are allowed to fabricate in the process of a repair.

This statement does not cover the small standard parts like nuts, bolts, rivets, etc. Approval of standard parts is covered in that section.

Unapproved Parts

The problem of unapproved parts in aircraft maintenance is a serious one. The problem can show up any time a part must be replaced. It is beyond the scope of this text to address the range of problems brought up by this subject. As a sheet metal technician, your contact with un-approved parts will be less than that of an A&P technician. Nevertheless, you still must be aware of the problem and act accordingly.

In order to prevent yourself from contributing to the problem, obtain a copy of Advisory Circular AC21-109A - Detecting And Reporting Suspected Unapproved Parts from the FAA.

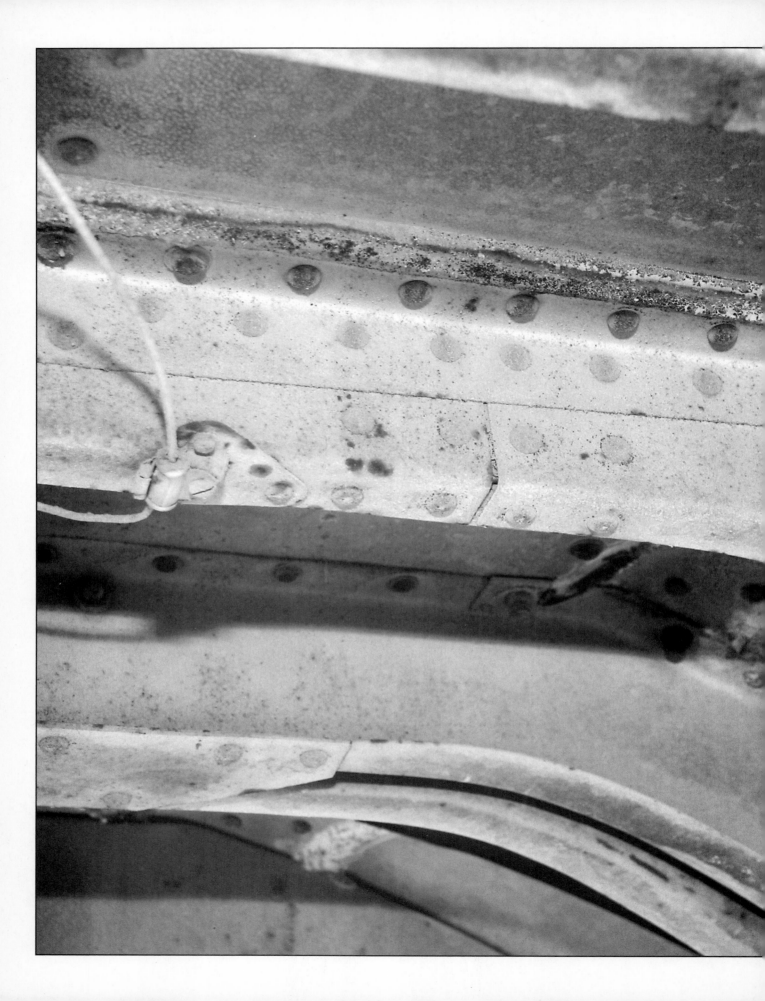

Corrosion Control

Corrosion and its control are of primary importance to all operators. Corrosion weakens primary structural members, which if allowed to continue must be replaced or reinforced in order to sustain loads to which they may be subjected. Such replacements or reinforcements are costly and time-consuming, resulting in unscheduled delays and frequently in keeping the airplane out of service for a considerable time. Preventive maintenance of the aircraft on a regular schedule, as with any valuable equipment, is the only sound practice. It minimizes the cost of total labor expended and productive time lost. It puts both of these costs on a predictable basis and removes uncertainty and guesswork on the actual condition of the equipment.

Section 1

Definition of Corrosion

Corrosion is a natural phenomenon which destroys metal by chemical or electrochemical action and converts it into a metallic compound such as an oxide, hydroxide, or sulfate (Figure 9-1-1). The tendency of most metals to corrode creates one of the major problems in the maintenance of aircraft, particularly in areas where adverse atmospheric or weather conditions exist.

Metal corrosion is the deterioration of the metal by chemical or electrochemical attack and can take place internally as well as on the surface. As in the rotting of wood, this deterioration may change the smooth surface, weaken the interior, or damage or loosen adjacent parts.

Learning Objective

DESCRIBE
- methods of corrosion inspection
- types of corrosion
- radiographic analysis
- methods of corrosion prevention

EXPLAIN
- causes of corrosion
- how certain agents lead to corrosion
- why certain areas of an aircraft are corrosion-prone
- how corrosion treatments differ depending on metal type

APPLY
- perform dye-penetrant inspections
- perform ultrasonic testing
- remove corrosion

Left. Corrosion removal is often part of the repair process when working with metallic structures.

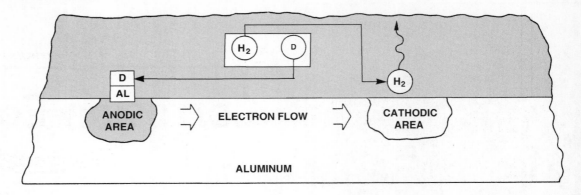

BASIC REQUIREMENTS FOR CORROSION:
(1) POTENTIAL DIFFERENCE WITHIN MATERIAL
(2) CONDUCTIVE PATH BETWEEN AREAS
(3) ELECTROLYTE COVERING BOTH AREAS

Figure 9-1-1. An electrochemical action

Corrosion Detection

Corrosion can cause eventual structural failure if left unchecked. The appearance of the corrosion varies with the metal. On aluminum alloys and magnesium, it appears as surface pitting and etching, often combined with a gray or white powdery deposit. On copper and copper alloys, the corrosion forms a greenish film; on steel, a reddish rust. When the gray, white, green, or reddish deposits are removed, each of the surfaces may appear etched and pitted, depending upon the length of exposure and severity of attack. If these surface pits are not too deep, they may not significantly alter the strength of the metal; however, the pits may become sites for crack development. Some types of corrosion can travel beneath surface coatings and can spread until the part fails.

Section 2

Inspection Methods

Visual Inspection

The primary method of corrosion detection is visual. Visual inspection must be relied upon to find corrosive attack during its incipient stage. However, many situations exist where visual inspection is not feasible, and therefore other detection techniques must be used. These other techniques consist of liquid dye penetrants, magnetic particle, X-ray, and ultrasonic devices, all of which have achieved success in the detection of corrosion.

Visual inspections of metal surfaces can reveal several signs of corrosive attack.

The most visible sign of corrosive attack is corrosion deposits. Corrosion deposits of aluminum or magnesium compounds are generally a white or grayish-white powder, while the color of ferrous compounds varies from red to dark reddish-brown.

Other indications of corrosive attack are small localized discolorations on the surface of the metal. Surfaces protected by paint or plating may only give indications of more advanced forms of corrosive attack by the presence of blisters in the protective film, indicating that the corrosion product has a greater volume than that of the consumed metal. Bulges in lap joints may be indicative of a buildup of corrosion products, although the corrosive attack is well advanced.

Often inspection areas are obscured by structural members, equipment installations, or for some other reason are awkward to check visually. Magnifying glasses, mirrors, borescopes, and fiberscopes like that seen in Figure 9-2-1, can provide the means to check obscured or difficult to reach areas. Ingenuity is encouraged as long as the improvised inspection methods are thorough and safe.

Dye-Penetrant Inspection

Dye-penetrant inspection is a nondestructive test for defects open to the surface in parts made of any nonporous material. It is used with equal success on such metals as aluminum, magnesium, brass, copper, cast iron, stainless steel, and titanium. It may also be used on ceramics, plastics, molded rubber, and glass.

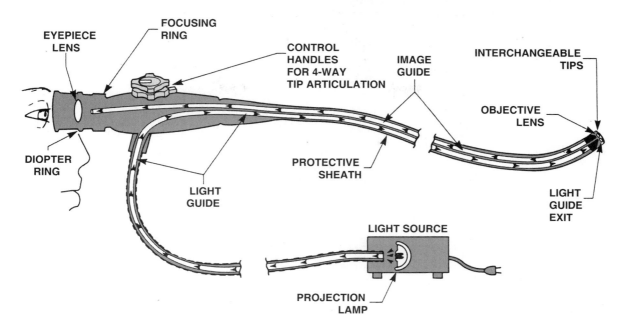

Figure 9-2-1. A typical fiber-optic borescope

Defects such as surface cracks or unwanted porosity can be detected using the dye-penetrant inspection method. These defects may be caused by fatigue cracks, shrinkage cracks, shrinkage porosity, cold shunts, grinding and heat-treat cracks, seams, forging laps, and bursts. Penetrant inspection will also indicate a lack of bond between joined metals. However, the main disadvantage of the dye-penetrant inspection is that the defect must be open to the surface in order to let the penetrant get into the defect.

The success of the dye-penetrant inspection depends upon a penetrating liquid entering the surface opening and remaining in that opening, Figure 9-2-2, making it clearly visible to the operator. It calls for visual examination of the part after it has been processed, but the visibility of the defect is increased so that it can be detected. Visibility of the penetrating material is increased by the addition of a dye, which may be either of two types: visible or fluorescent.

The Dye-Penetrant Process

The visible penetrant consists of dye penetrant, dye remover-emulsifier and developer.

The fluorescent penetrant inspection consists of a black light assembly as well as spray cans of penetrant, cleaner, and developer. The light assembly consists of a power transformer, a flexible power cable, and a hand-held lamp. Due to its size, the lamp may be used in almost any position or location. An example of a fluo-

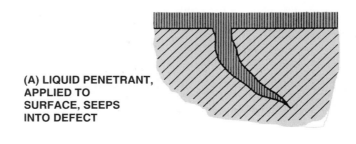

(A) LIQUID PENETRANT, APPLIED TO SURFACE, SEEPS INTO DEFECT

(B) PENETRANT REMOVED FROM SURFACE, BUT DEFECT REMAINS FULL

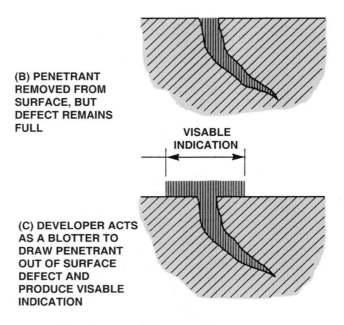

VISABLE INDICATION

(C) DEVELOPER ACTS AS A BLOTTER TO DRAW PENETRANT OUT OF SURFACE DEFECT AND PRODUCE VISABLE INDICATION

Figure 9-2-2. Penetrant and developer action

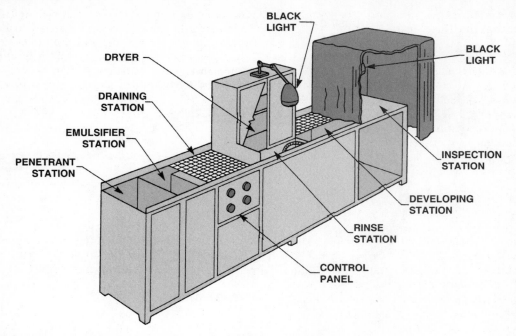

Figure 9-2-3. A typical fluorescent penetrant inspection work station

rescent penetrant work station can be seen in Figure 9-2-3.

The steps to be taken when performing a penetrant inspection are:

1. Thoroughly clean the metal surface
2. Apply penetrant
3. Remove penetrant with remover-emulsifier or cleaner
4. Dry the part
5. Apply the developer
6. Inspect and interpret the results

Interpretation of Results

The success and reliability of a penetrant inspection depends upon the thoroughness with which the part was prepared. Several basic principles applying to penetrant inspection are:

- The penetrant must enter the defect in order to form an indication. It is important to allow sufficient time so the penetrant can fill the defect. The defect must be clean and free of contaminating materials so that the penetrant is free to enter.

- If all penetrant is washed out of a defect, an indication cannot be formed. During the washing or rinsing operation, prior to development, it is possible that the penetrant will be removed from within the defect, as well as from the surface.

- Clean cracks are usually easy to detect. Surface openings that are uncontaminated, regardless of how fine, are seldom difficult to detect with the penetrant inspection.

- The smaller the defect, the longer the penetrating time. Fine crack-like apertures require a longer penetrating time than defects such as pores.

- Visible penetrant-type developer, when applied to the surface of a part, will dry to a smooth, even, white coating. As this developer dries, bright red indications will appear where there are surface defects. If no red indications appear, there are no surface defects.

- When conducting the fluorescent penetrant-type inspection, the defects will show up (under black light) as a brilliant yellow-green color and the sound areas will appear deep blue-violet.

- It is possible to examine an indication of a defect and to determine its cause as well as its extent. Such an appraisal can be made if something is known about the manufacturing processes to which the part has been subjected.

Size of the Indication

The size of the indication or accumulation of penetrant will show the extent of the defect, and the brilliance will be a measure of its depth. Deep cracks will hold more penetrant and, therefore, will be broader and more brilliant. Very fine openings can hold only small amounts of penetrants and, therefore, will appear as fine lines.

False Indications

False indications do not occur with the dye-penetrant inspection method. There are, however, two conditions which may create accumulations of penetrant that are sometimes confused with true surface cracks and discontinuities.

Poor washing. Poor washing is the major cause of false indications. If all the surface penetrant is not removed in the washing or rinsing operation following the penetrant dwell time, the unremoved penetrant will be visible. Evidences of incomplete washing are usually easy to identify since the penetrant is in broad areas, rather than in the sharp patterns found with true indications. When accumulations of unwashed penetrant are found on a part, the part should be completely reprocessed. Degreasing is recommended for removal of all traces of the penetrant.

Press fit parts. Press-fit parts may create a false indication. If a wheel is press-fit onto a shaft, penetrant will show an indication at the fit line. This is perfectly normal since the two parts are not meant to be welded together. Indications of this type are easy to identify since they are so regular in form and shape.

Ultrasonic Testing

Ultrasonic testing, through the use of ultrasonic detection equipment has made it possible to locate defects in all types of materials without damaging the material being inspected. Minute cracks, checks, and voids, too small to be seen by X-ray, are located by ultrasonic inspection. An ultrasonic test instrument requires access to only one surface of the material to be inspected and can be utilized with either straight line or angle beam testing techniques.

Methods of Ultrasonic Testing

Two basic methods are used for ultrasonic inspection: immersion testing and contact testing.

Immersion testing. In this method of inspection, the part under examination and the search unit are totally immersed in a liquid coolant, which may be water or any other suitable fluid.

Contact testing. Contact testing is readily adapted to field use, and is the method discussed in this chapter. In this method the part under examination and the search unit are coupled with a viscous material, liquid or a paste, which wets both the face of the search unit and the material under examination.

Ultrasonic Systems

There are two basic ultrasonic systems: pulsed and resonance. The pulsed system may be either echo or through-transmission. The echo is the most versatile of the two pulse systems. An example of a pulse-echo unit can be seen in Figure 9-2-4.

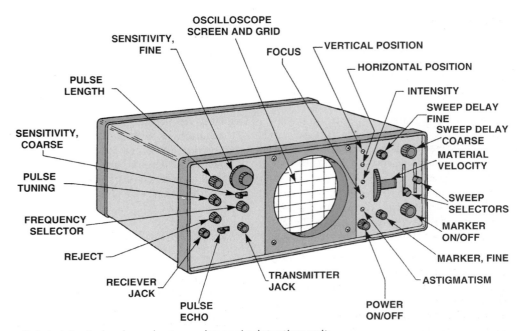

Figure 9-2-4. A typical pulse-echo type ultrasonic detection unit

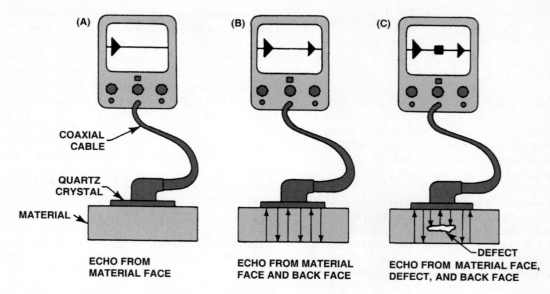

COAXIAL CABLE

QUARTZ CRYSTAL

MATERIAL

ECHO FROM MATERIAL FACE

ECHO FROM MATERIAL FACE AND BACK FACE

DEFECT

ECHO FROM MATERIAL FACE, DEFECT, AND BACK FACE

Figure 9-2-5. Operation principles of ultrasonic testing

Pulse Echo System

With the pulse-echo system, flaws are detected by measuring the amplitude of signals reflected, and the time required for these signals to travel between specific surfaces and the discontinuity.

Time base system. The time base, which is triggered simultaneously with each transmission pulse, causes a spot to sweep across the screen of the cathode-ray tube (CRT). The spot sweeps from left to right across the face of the scope 50 to 5,000 times per second, or higher if required for high-speed automated scanning. Due to the speed of the cycle of transmitting and receiving, the picture on the oscilloscope appears to be stationary.

A few microseconds after the sweep is initiated, the rate generator electrically excites the pulser and the pulser in turn emits an electrical pulse. The transducer converts this pulse into a short train of ultrasonic sound waves. If the interfaces of the transducer and the specimen are properly orientated, the ultrasound will be reflected back to the transducer when it reaches the internal flaw and the opposite surface of the specimen.

The time interval between the transmission of the initial impulse and the reception of the signals from within the specimen is measured by the timing circuits. The reflected pulse received by the transducer is amplified, then transmitted to the oscilloscope, where the pulse received from the flaw is displayed on the CRT screen. The pulse is displayed in the same relationship to the front and back pulses

as the flaw is in relation to the front and back surfaces of the specimen.

The principle of operation is pictured in Figure 9-2-5, where electrical pulses are transformed by the crystal into ultrasonic vibrations which are transmitted into the material. The portion of the electrical pulse delivered to the CRT causes an initial pulse indication, as shown in Figure 9-2-5A. The back reflection has formed Figure 9-2-5B, the vibrations having traveled to the bottom of the part and reflected back to the searching unit, which transforms them back into electrical pulses.

The screen's vertical indication of their return is known as the first back-reflection indication. If a defect is present (Figure 9-2-5C), a portion of the vibrations traveling through the material is reflected from the defect, causing an additional indication on the screen. The horizontal-sweep travel indicates the time elapsed since the vibrations left the crystal.

Referred to as straight-beam testing, this type of operation is suitable for the detection of flaws whose faces are parallel to the plane of the part. By means of angle-beam testing, also referred to as shear-wave testing, the usefulness of the reflectoscope (Figure 9-2-5) includes the following:

1. Flaws whose planes lie at an angle to the plane of the part

2. Discontinuities in areas that cannot be reached with the standard straight-beam technique

3. Some internal defects in plate and sheet stock

4. Some types of internal defects in tubing, pipe or bar stock, such as inclusions and small cracks near the surface

5. Cracks in parent metal resulting from welding

6. Some defects in welds

Angle-beam testing differs from straight-beam testing only in the manner in which the ultrasonic waves pass through the material being tested. As shown in Figure 9-2-6, the beam is projected into the material at an acute angle to the surface by means of a crystal cut at an angle and mounted in plastic. The beam or a portion thereof reflects successively from the surfaces of the material or any other discontinuity, including the edge of the piece. In straight-beam testing, the horizontal distance on the screen between the initial pulse and the first back reflection represents the thickness of the piece; while in angle-beam testing, this distance represents the width of the material between the searching unit and the opposite edge of the piece.

Resonance System

This system differs from the pulse method in that the frequency of transmission is, or can be, continuously varied. The resonance method is principally used for thickness measurements when the two sides of the material being tested are smooth and parallel. The point at which the frequency matches the resonance point of the material being tested is the thickness-determining factor. It is necessary that the frequency of the ultrasonic waves, corresponding to a particular dial setting, be accurately known. Checks should be made with standard test blocks to guard against possible drift of frequency.

Theory behind the resonance system. If the frequency of an ultrasonic wave is such that its wavelength is twice the thickness of a specimen (fundamental frequency), then the reflected wave will arrive back at the transducer in the same phase as the original transmission so that strengthening of the signal, or a resonance, will occur. If the frequency is increased so that three times the wavelength equals four times the thickness, then the reflected signal will return completely out of phase with the transmitted signal and cancellation will occur. Further increase of the frequency, so that the wavelength is equal to the thickness again, gives a reflected signal in phase with the transmitted signal and resonance occurs once more.

By starting at the fundamental frequency and gradually increasing the frequency, the successive cancellations and resonances can be noted and the readings used to check the fundamental frequency reading (Figure 9-2-7).

In some instruments, the oscillator circuit contains a motor-driven capacitor which changes the frequency of the oscillator. In other instruments, the frequency is changed by electronic means.

The change in frequency is synchronized with the horizontal sweep of a CRT. The horizontal axis thus represents a frequency range. If the frequency range contains resonances, the circuitry is arranged to present these vertically. Calibrated transparent scales are placed in front of the tube, and the thickness can be read directly. The instruments normally operate between 0.25 MHz and 10 MHz, and in four or five bands.

Types of materials that can be tested. The ultrasonic resonance system can be used to test the thickness of such metals as steel, cast iron, brass, nickel, copper, silver, lead, aluminum, and magnesium. In addition, areas of corrosion or wear on tanks, tubing, airplane wing skins, and other structures or products can be located and evaluated.

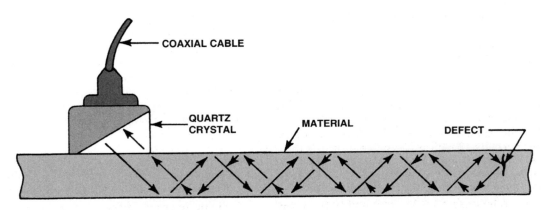

Figure 9-2-6. Angle-beam testing

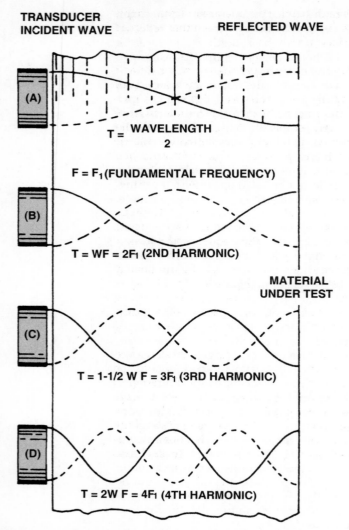

TRANSDUCER INCIDENT WAVE   **REFLECTED WAVE**

(A)

$$T = \frac{\text{WAVELENGTH}}{2}$$

$F = F_1$ (FUNDAMENTAL FREQUENCY)

(B)

$T = WF = 2F_1$ (2ND HARMONIC)

MATERIAL UNDER TEST

(C)

$T = 1\text{-}1/2\ W\ F = 3F_1$ (3RD HARMONIC)

(D)

$T = 2W\ F = 4F_1$ (4TH HARMONIC)

Figure 9-2-7. Fundamental and harmonic frequencies as used in ultrasonic testing

Direct-reading, dial-operated ultrasonic resonance instruments are available that measure thickness between 0.025 inch and 3 inches with an accuracy of better than 1 percent.

Ultrasonic inspection requires a skilled operator who is familiar with the equipment being used as well as the inspection method to be used for the many different parts being tested.

Radiological Inspection

X-rays and gamma radiations, because of their unique ability to penetrate material and disclose discontinuities, have been applied to the radiological (X-ray) inspection of metal fabrications and nonmetallic products.

The radiation is projected through the part to be inspected, penetrating the part and producing an invisible or latent image in the film as shown in Figure 9-2-8. When processed, the film becomes a radiograph, or shadow picture of the object. This inspection medium, in a portable unit, provides a fast and reliable means for checking the integrity of airframe structures and engines.

Radiological inspection techniques are used to locate defects or flaws in airframe structures or engines with little or no disassembly. This is in marked contrast to other types of nondestructive testing, which usually require removal, disassembly, and stripping of paint from the suspected part before it can be inspected. Due to the nature of X-ray, extensive training is required to become a qualified radiographer, and only qualified radiographers are allowed to operate the X-ray units.

The X-ray Process

Three major steps in the X-ray process discussed in subsequent paragraphs are:

1. Exposure to radiation
2. Processing of film
3. Interpretation of the radiograph

Preparation and Exposure

The factors of radiological exposure are so interdependent that it is necessary to consider all factors for any particular radiologic exposure. These factors include, but are not limited to:

1. Thickness and density of material
2. Shape and size of the object
3. Type of defect to be detected
4. Characteristics of X-ray machine used
5. Exposure distance
6. Exposure angle
7. Characteristics of film
8. Types of intensifying screen, if used

Knowledge of the X-ray unit's capabilities should form a background for the other exposure factors. In addition to the unit rating in kilovoltage, the size, portability, ease of manipulation, and exposure particulars of the available equipment should be thoroughly understood.

Previous experience on similar objects is also very helpful in the determination of the overall exposure techniques. A log or record of previous exposures will provide specific data as a guide for future radiographs.

Film Processing

After exposure to X-rays, the latent image on the film is made permanently visible by processing it successively through a developer chemical solution, an acid bath, and a fixing bath, followed by a clear water wash.

The film consists of a radiation-sensitive silver salt suspended in gelatin to form an emulsion. The developer solution converts radiation-affected elements in the emulsion to black metallic silver. These black metallic particles form the image. The longer the film remains in the developer, the more metallic silver is formed, causing the image to become progressively darker. Excessive time in the developer solution results in overdevelopment.

An acid rinse bath, sometimes referred to as a stop bath, instantly neutralizes the action of the developer and stops further development. Due to the soft emulsion and the nonabsorbent quality of the base of most negative materials, only a very weak acid bath is required. The purpose of the fixing bath is to arrest the image at the desired state of development.

When a radiation-sensitive material is removed from the developing solution, the emulsion still contains a considerable amount of silver salts which have not been affected by the developing agents. These salts are still sensitive, and if they are allowed to remain in the emulsion, ordinary light will ultimately darken them and obscure the image. Obviously, if this occurs, the film will be useless.

The fixing bath prevents this discoloration by dissolving the salts of silver from the developed free-silver image. Therefore, to make an image permanent, it is necessary to fix the radiation-sensitive material by removing all of the unaffected silver salt from the emulsion.

After fixing, a thorough water rinse is necessary to remove the fixing agent which, if allowed to remain, will slowly combine with the silver image to produce brownish-yellow stains of silver sulfide, causing the image to fade.

NOTE: *All processing is conducted under a subdued light of a color (normally red) to which the film is not readily sensitive.*

Radiological Interpretation

From the standpoint of quality assurance, radiological interpretation is the most important phase of radiography. It is during this phase that an error in judgment can produce disastrous consequences. The efforts of the whole radiographic process are centered in this phase; the part or structure is either accepted or rejected.

Conditions of unsoundness or other defects which are overlooked, not understood, or improperly interpreted can destroy the purpose and efforts of radiography and can jeopardize the structural integrity of an entire aircraft. A particular danger is the false sense of security imparted by the acceptance of a part or structure based on improper interpretation.

As a first impression, radiological interpretation may seem simple, but a closer analysis of the problem soon dispels this impression. The subject of interpretation is so varied and complex that it cannot be covered adequately in this type of document. Instead, this chapter will give only a brief review of basic requirements for radiological interpretation, including some descriptions of common defects.

Experience has shown that, whenever possible, radiological interpretation should be conducted close to the radiologic operation. It is helpful, when viewing radiographs, to have access to the material being tested. The radiograph can thus be compared directly with the material being tested, and indications due to such things as surface condition or thickness variations can be immediately determined.

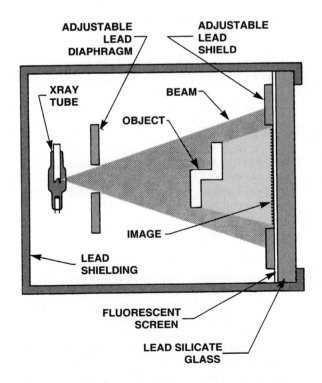

Figure 9-2-8. Producing a radiographic image on film

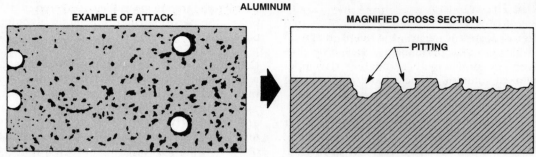

Figure 9-3-1. Pitting as seen on the surface, and in a magnified cross-section

Analyzing a Radiograph

The following paragraphs present several factors which must be considered when analyzing a radiograph.

There are three basic categories of flaws: voids, inclusions, and dimensional irregularities. The last category, dimensional irregularities, is not pertinent to these discussions because its prime factor is one of degree, and radiography is not that exacting. Voids and inclusions may appear on the radiograph in a variety of forms ranging from a two-dimensional plane to a three-dimensional sphere.

A crack, tear, or cold shut will most nearly resemble a two-dimensional plane, whereas a cavity will look like a three-dimensional sphere. Other types of flaws, such as shrink, oxide inclusions, porosity, etc., will fall somewhere between these two extremes of form

It is important to analyze the geometry of a flaw, especially for such things as the sharpness of terminal points. For example, in a crack-like flaw the terminal points will appear much sharper than they will for a sphere-like flaw, such as a gas cavity. Also, material strength may be adversely affected by flaw shape.

A flaw having sharp points could establish a source of localized stress concentration. Spherical flaws affect material strength to a far lesser degree than do sharp. pointed flaws. Specifications and reference standards usually stipulate that sharp-pointed flaws, such as cracks, cold shunts, etc., are cause for rejection.

Material strength is also affected by flaw size. A metallic component of a given area is designed to carry a certain load plus a safety factor. Reducing this area by including a large flaw weakens the part and reduces the safety factor. Some flaws are often permitted in components because of these safety factors; in this case, the interpreter must determine the degree of tolerance or imperfection specified by the design engineer.

Both flaw size and flaw shape should be considered carefully, since small flaws with sharp points can be just as bad as large flaws with no sharp points.

Another important consideration in flaw analysis is flaw location. Metallic components are subjected to numerous and varied forces during their effective service life. Generally, the distribution of these forces is not equal in the component or part, and certain critical areas may be rather highly stressed.

The interpreter must pay special attention to these areas. Another aspect of flaw location is that certain types of discontinuities close to one another may potentially serve as a source of stress concentrations; therefore, this type of situation should be closely scrutinized.

An inclusion is a type of flaw which contains entrapped material. Such flaws may be either of greater or lesser density than the item being radiographed. The foregoing discussions on flaw shape, size, and location apply equally to inclusions and to voids. In addition, a flaw containing foreign material could become a source of corrosion.

Radiation Hazards

Radiation from X-ray units and radioisotope sources produces changes in all matter through which it passes, including living tissue. When the radiation strikes the molecules living tissue, the effect may be no more than to dislodge a few electrons; but an excess of these changes could cause irreparable harm.

Penetrating radiation is likely to be most harmful in the center of the body where the vital organs are located. The skin usually absorbs most of the radiation and, therefore, reacts earliest to radiation.

If the whole body is exposed to a very large dose of radiation, it could result in death. In general, the type and severity of the pathological effects of radiation depend on the amount of radiation received at one time and the percentage of the total body exposed. The smaller doses of radiation may cause blood and intestinal disorders in a short period of time. Delayed effects include leukemia and cancer, skin damage and loss of hair.

Prior to working in a radiation hazard environment, become familiar with all of the applicable Occupational Safety and Health Administration (OSHA) and Nuclear Regulatory Commission (NRC) standards, and apply them. Mark radiation areas with OSHA standard signs and placards, and keep unauthorized personnel out of the area. Wear, and ensure that others in the radiation area wear and monitor radiation detectors.

Section 3

Types of Corrosion

Different Forms of Corrosion

There are many forms of corrosion. The form of corrosion depends on the metal involved and the corrosion-producing agents present. Those described in this section are the more common forms found on airframe structures.

Oxidation

One of the most simple forms of corrosion, and perhaps the one with which we are most familiar, is dry corrosion, or, as it is most generally known, oxidation.

When a metal such as aluminum is exposed to a gas containing oxygen, a chemical reaction takes place at the surface between the metal and the gas. In this case, two aluminum atoms join three oxygen atoms to form aluminum oxide: Al_2O_3

If the metal is iron or steel (ferrous metal), two atoms of iron will join three atoms of oxygen and form iron oxide or rust: Fe_2O_3

There is one big difference between iron oxide and aluminum oxide. The film of aluminum oxide is unbroken, and once it is formed, further reaction with the oxygen continues at a greatly reduced rate; almost stops. Iron oxide, on the other hand, forms a porous or interrupted film, and the metal will continue to react with the oxygen in the air until the metal is completely eaten away.

Protection From Oxidation

In order to protect iron from dry corrosion or rusting, the best procedure is to prevent oxygen from coming into contact with the surface. This may be done temporarily by covering the surface with oil or grease, or for more permanent protection, with a coat of paint.

Aluminum alloy may be protected from oxidation by the formation of an oxide film on its surface. This film insulated the aluminum from any electrolyte (gas or liquid), and will not, itself, further react with the oxygen. The formation of this film is discussed in detail in methods of corrosion treatment under the headings of anodizing and alodining.

Types of Corrosion

Uniform Surface Corrosion

Surface corrosion appears as a general roughening, etching, or pitting of the surface of a metal, frequently accompanied by a powdery deposit of corrosion products. Surface corrosion may be caused by either direct chemical or electrochemical attack.

Occasionally corrosion will spread under the surface coating and cannot be recognized by either the roughening of the surface or the powdery deposit. Instead, the paint or plating will be lifted off the surface in small blisters which result from the pressure of the underlying accumulation of corrosion products.

A common type of uniform surface corrosion is caused by the reaction of metallic surfaces with airborne chlorine or sulfur compounds, oxygen, or moisture in the atmosphere, and often combinations of these agents may attack a surface simultaneously. Reactive compounds from exhaust gases, as well as fumes from storage batteries, frequently cause uniform surface corrosion.

The amount of damage caused by uniform surface corrosion is ordinarily determined by comparing the thickness of the corroded metal with that of an undamaged specimen.

Pitting Corrosion

Pitting corrosion is confined to very small areas of the metal surface, while the remainder of the surface is unaffected. The corrosion pits are often randomly located over the surface, however, some preferential attack may occur at the grain boundaries of the metal. A surface and cross-sectional example are seen in Figure 9-3-1.

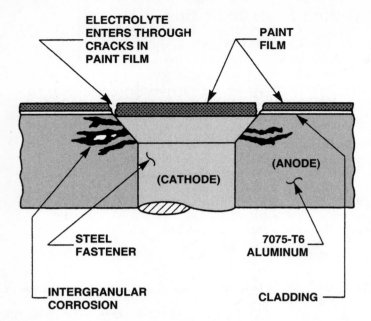

Figure 9-3-2. Intergranular corrosion of 7075-T6 aluminum adjacent to a steel fastener

Pitting results from the chemical action of moisture, acid, alkali, or saline solutions on the metal after the paint surface oxide or other protective film has either been removed or penetrated. Once pitting has begun, it is propagated by means of concentration cells or galvanic action.

The pits found in pitting types of corrosion usually have a rather short, well-defined edge with walls that run almost perpendicular to the surface of the metal.

All forms of pits have one thing in common regardless of their shape. They penetrate deeply into the metal and cause damage completely out of proportion to the amount of metal consumed.

Intergranular Corrosion

Intergranular corrosion concentrates on the boundaries of the metal grains, first consuming the material between the grain boundaries, and then attacking the grains themselves.

The damage from intergranular corrosion, like pitting corrosion, causes a loss of strength and

ductility that is out of proportion to the amount of the metal destroyed. An example of intergranular corrosion is shown in Figure 9-3-2.

Aluminum alloys and some stainless steels are particularly susceptible to intergranular corrosion. A lack of uniformity in the grain of these metals is caused by changes that occur in the alloy during heating and cooling.

Intergranular corrosion may exist without visible surface evidence, and is difficult to detect in its original stage. Ultrasonic and eddy current inspection methods provide the best success in detecting this particular form of corrosion.

Exfoliation. Exfoliation is a severely destructive form of intergranular corrosion characterized by the actual leafing-out of corroded sections of metal away from the rest of the part (Figure 9-3-3).

Exfoliation corrosion is found most often on extruded parts. This is because the extrusion process elongates the grains of the metal. The corrosive attack on the grain boundary material produces corrosion products which take up more volume than that originally occupied by the unaffected grain boundaries, causing the part to swell.

By the time exfoliation corrosion is detected, the intergranular attack usually is so advanced that the static strength of the part is impaired because of the reduction of its effective cross-sectional area.

Section 4

Galvanic Cells

Galvanic cells may originate from localized differences of materials in the surface of an alloy, because the dissimilar metals in alloys provide a basis for galvanic action within the alloys themselves (Figure 9-4-1).

Galvanic Cell Corrosion

If an electrolytic medium is provided (like the condensation from a salt-air atmosphere), the metal can literally destroy itself.

The degree of attack depends on the relative activity of the two surfaces; the greater the difference in activity, the more severe the attack.

The materials listed in group I of Table 9-4-1, are quite active and corrode easily. They

Figure 9-3-3. Exfoliation as seen in a magnified cross-section

require maximum protection. Group IV materials are the least active and therefore require minimum protection.

Concentration Cell Corrosion

Concentration cell corrosion occurs when two or more areas of metal surface are in contact with different concentrations of the same solution (Figure 9-4-2). There are two basic types of concentration cell corrosion: oxygen, and metal ion concentration cells.

Oxygen Cell Concentration

In the case of oxygen concentration cell corrosion, the solution in contact with the metal surface will normally contain dissolved oxygen. An oxygen cell can develop at any point where the oxygen in the air is not allowed to diffuse into the solution, thereby creating a difference in oxygen concentration between two points. Typical locations of oxygen concentration cells are under either metallic or nonmetallic deposits, such as dirt, on the metal surface and under faying surfaces, such as riveted lap joints. Oxygen cells can also develop under gaskets, wood, rubber, plastic tape, or other materials in contact with the metal surface.

Metal Ion Cell Concentration

With metal ion concentration cell corrosion, the solution may consist of water and ions of the

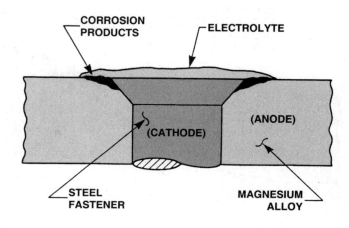

Figure 9-4-1. Galvanic cells corrosion

GROUP I	Magnesium and its alloys: aluminum alloys 5052, 5056, 6061 and 6063
GROUP II	Cadmium, zinc, aluminum and their alloys, except the aluminum alloys in Group I
GROUP III	Iron, lead and tin and their alloys except stainless steel
GROUP IV	Copper, chromium, nickel, silver, gold, platinum, titanium, cobalt and rhodium and their alloys, stainless steel and graphite

Table 9-4-1. Galvanic grouping of metals

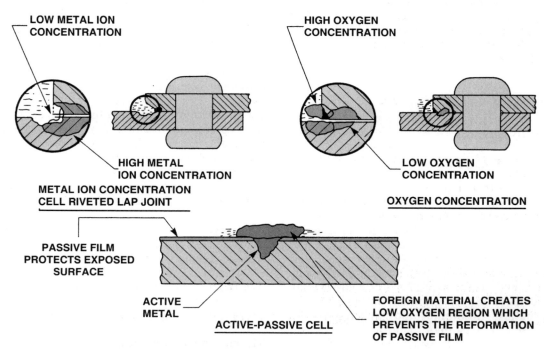

Figure 9-4-2. Concentration cell corrosion

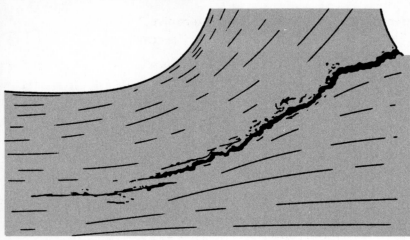

Figure 9-5-1. Stress corrosion cracking

metal which is in contact with the water. A high concentration of the metal ions will normally exist under faying surfaces where the solution is stagnant, and a low concentration of metal ions will exist adjacent to the crevice which is created by the faying surface. An electrical potential will exist between the two points; the area of the metal in contact with the high metal ion concentration will be anodic and will be corroded.

> **CAUTION:** *If water is allowed to stagnate in a metallic structure, either an oxygen or metal ion concentration cell can develop. Small deposits of corrosion products may give an indication of the damage that has been sustained.*

Measures should be taken to remove corrosion upon its first appearance rather than wait until it becomes large enough to bother with. Waiting can result in expensive repairs while corrective action at the first sign of corrosion is very inexpensive

Section 5

Stress Corrosion

Stress corrosion occurs as the result of the combined effect of sustained tensile stresses and a corrosive environment. While stress corrosion cracking is found in most metal systems, it is particularly characteristic of aluminum, copper, certain stainless steels, and high-strength alloy steels (over 240,000 p.s.i.). It usually occurs along lines of cold-working and may be transgranular or intergranular in nature. Aluminum alloy bellcranks with pressed-in bushings, landing gear shock struts with pipe-thread type grease fittings, clevis pin joints, shrink fits, and overstressed

tubing B-nuts are examples of parts which are susceptible to stress corrosion cracking (Figure 9-5-1).

Crack initiation generally results from a physical breakdown of protective surface films and the subsequent corrosive attack on the part in conjunction with the application of stress forces.

Several elements determine crack propagation. Factors such as the alloy type, changes in the composition of the alloy or its environment, the type of heat treatment, and the method of metal forming all contribute to the direction and length of the crack. Finally, for each type alloy, specific environmental conditions must exist before stress-corrosion can occur.

Section 6

Fretting Corrosion

Fretting corrosion is a particularly damaging form of corrosive attack which occurs when two mating surfaces, normally at rest with respect to one another, are subject to slight relative motion. While the fit between two surfaces may be very tight, it is rarely tight enough to prevent oxygen or other corrosive agents from entering and attacking unprotected surfaces (Figure 9-6-1).

Mechanical fretting and chemical corrosion in combined action is referred to as fretting corrosion. It is characterized by pitting of the surfaces, and the generation of considerable quantities of finely divided debris. Since the restricted movements of the two surfaces prevent the debris from escaping very easily, an extremely localized abrasion occurs.

The presence of water vapor greatly increases this type of deterioration. If the contact areas are small and sharp, deep grooves resembling Brinell markings or pressure indentations may be worn in the rubbing surface. As a result, this type of corrosion (on bearing surfaces) has also been called false brinelling.

Section 7

Filiform Corrosion

Metals coated with organic coatings tend to undergo a type of corrosion resulting in numerous threadlike filaments of corrosion products under the coating. It is caused by the diffusing of oxygen and water through the coating and is considered a special type of oxygen concentration cell corrosion.

The effects of filiform corrosion can be prevented by storing the aircraft in a low-humidity environment (below 65 percent relative humidity). The progress of filiform corrosion can be markedly decreased by the use of coatings which have a high resistance to diffusion by water.

Section 8

Corrosive Agents

Substances that are capable of causing a corrosive reaction sometimes are called corrosive agents. The most common corrosive agents are acids, alkalis, and salts. The atmosphere and water, the two most common media for these agents, may sometime tend to act as corrosive agents too.

Acids and Alkalis

Acids

In general, moderately strong acids will corrode most of the alloys used in airframes. The most destructive are sulfuric acid (battery acid), halogen acids (hydrochloric, hydrofluoric, and hydrobromic), and organic acids found in the wastes of humans and animals.

Alkalis

Although alkalis as a group are generally not as corrosive as acids, aluminum and magnesium alloys are exceedingly prone to corrosive attack by many alkaline solutions, unless the solutions contain a corrosion inhibitor.

Particularly corrosive to aluminum are washing soda, potash (wood ashes), and lime (cement dust). One alkali, ammonia, is an exception because aluminum alloys are highly resistant to it. Magnesium alloys are also resistant to alkaline corrosive attack. In fact they develop a protective film when exposed to caustic alkaline solutions.

Salts

While it may be difficult to generalize about salts as corrosive agents, most salt solutions are good electrolytes and can promote corrosive attack.

Some stainless steel alloys are resistant to attack by salt solutions but aluminum alloys, magnesium alloys and other steels are extremely vulnerable to solutions containing salts. Exposure of airframe materials to salts or their solutions is extremely undesirable.

Mercury Spills/Corrosion Damage

Once started, the corrosive action of mercury is rapid in both pitting and intergranular attack and is very difficult to control.

The presence of mercury and mercury salts in air cargo is a definite possibility. Loading, unloading, and general shifting of such cargo can and does result occasionally in damaged containers, cartons, electronic tubes, etc., with subsequent leakage of mercury on aircraft surfaces and structures.

Spillage of mercury or mercury compounds within an airplane requires immediate action to isolate and recover the substance to prevent possible corrosion damage and embrittlement of aluminum alloy structural components, stainless steels (300 and 400 series), and unplated brass components such as cable turnbuckle barrels. By a process known as amalgamation, mercury can penetrate any break in the finish (anodize/alodine), paint, or seal coating of a metal structural component. Bright, polished, shining, or scratched surfaces, as well as moisture, will hasten the process.

Mercury and mercury compounds attack the metal grain boundaries and seriously embrittles and reduces the strength of parts.

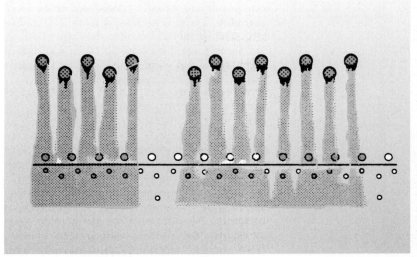

Figure 9-6-1. Fretting corrosion

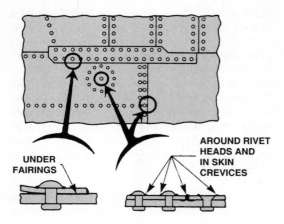

Figure 9-9-1. Exhaust trail areas corrosion points

Corrosive attack of freshly scratched aluminum alloy is very rapid, and complete penetration of sheet material is known to occur within 3 or 4 minutes.

Water

The corrosivity of water will depend on the type and quantity of dissolved mineral and organic impurities and dissolved gases (particularly oxygen) in the water. Physical factors such as water temperature and velocity also have a direct bearing on the corrosivity.

The most corrosive of natural waters (sea and fresh waters) are those that contain salts. Water in the open sea is extremely corrosive, but waters in harbors are often even more so because they are contaminated by industrial waste and are diluted by fresh water.

The corrosivity of fresh water varies from locality to locality due to the wide variety of dissolved impurities that may be present in any particular area. However, soft water and rain water are usually considered to be very corrosive. Hard waters tend to be less corrosive to most metals because they are alkaline, but some metals such as alloys of aluminum and magnesium seem to be reactive to alkaline waters and corrode readily.

Air

The major atmospheric corrosive agents are oxygen and airborne moisture, both of which are in abundant supply. Corrosion often results from the direct action of atmospheric oxygen and moisture on metal, and the presence of additional moisture often accelerates corrosive attack, particularly on ferrous alloys. However, the air in the atmosphere is also cluttered with many other corrosive gases and contaminants.

Two specific types, industrial and marine atmospheres, are unusually corrosive.

The air in industrial atmospheres contain many contaminants, the most common of which are partially oxidized sulfur compounds. When these sulfur compounds combine with moisture, they form sulfur based acids that are highly corrosive to most metals. In areas where there are chemical industrial plants, other corrosive atmospheric contaminants may be present in large quantities, but such conditions are usually confined to a specific locality.

A marine atmosphere (an airmass over oceans, seas, or other large bodies of salt water) contains chlorides in the form of salt particles or droplets of salt-saturated water. Since saline moisture is an electrolyte, it provides an excellent medium for corrosive attack on aluminum and magnesium alloys which are vulnerable to this type of environment.

Organic Growths

Microorganisms live in jet fuels which are contaminated with water and iron oxides or mineral salts. Slime is formed by these fungoid creatures which often serve as excellent electrolytes and promote corrosion.

From the standpoint of corrosion prevention, it is necessary to keep aircraft fuel tanks clean and use only clean, water-free fuel. Water condensate must be drained from the fuel tank frequently. Further, fuel storage facilities should be monitored to ensure that the fuel is clean.

Biocide treatment may be used for control of microorganisms in jet fuel tanks. Although not feasible, complete elimination of water and contaminants from the fuel reduces tank corrosion. Experience with fuel containing biocide has shown that when used in the correct proportions, it is effective in eliminating many types of microbial growth, thus reducing tank corrosion.

Section 9

Corrosion-Prone Areas

Engine Exhaust and Exhaust Trail Areas

Both jet and reciprocating engine exhaust deposits are very corrosive and give particular trouble where gaps, seams, hinges, and fairings are located down the exhaust path and where deposits may be trapped and not reached by normal cleaning methods.

Special attention should be paid to areas around rivet heads and in skin crevices, as shown in Figure 9-9-1. Fairings and access plates in the exhaust areas should be removed for inspection.

Exhaust deposit buildup in remote areas such as the empennage surfaces should not be overlooked. Buildup in these areas will usually be slower and sometimes completely absent; it can be a problem on some aircraft.

Battery Compartments and Battery Vent Openings

Despite improvements in protective paint finishes and in methods of sealing and venting, battery compartments continue to be corrosion problem areas. Fumes from overheated electrolyte are difficult to contain and will spread to adjacent cavities and cause a rapid, corrosive attack on all unprotected metal surfaces.

Battery vent openings on the aircraft skin should be included in the battery compartment inspection and maintenance procedure. Regular cleaning and neutralization of acid deposits will minimize corrosion from this cause.

Lavatories and Food Service Areas

Deck areas behind lavatories, sinks, and ranges where spilled food and waste products may collect, if not kept clean, are potential trouble spots. Even if some contaminants are not corrosive in themselves, they will attract and retain moisture and in turn cause corrosive attack. Carefully inspect bilge areas located under galleys and lavatories, clean these areas frequently, and keep paint touched up.

Particular attention must be paid to areas around human waste disposal openings on the aircraft exteriors. Human waste products and the chemicals used in lavatories are very corrosive to the common aircraft metals. Clean these areas frequently and keep the paint touched up.

Wheel Well and Landing Gear

This area probably receives more punishment than any other area on the aircraft because of mud, water, salt, gravel, and other flying debris that is picked up from ramps, taxiways, and runways and thrown by the tires.

Because of the many complicated shapes, assemblies, and fittings found in the wheel well and landing gear areas, complete area paint film coverage is difficult to attain.

A partially applied preservative tends to mask corrosion rather than prevent it. Due to heat generated by braking action, preservatives cannot be used on some main landing gear wheels. During inspection of this area, pay particular attention to the following trouble spots, as illustrated in Figure 9-9-2:

1. Magnesium wheels, especially around bolt heads, lugs, and wheel-web areas, particularly for the presence of entrapped water or its effects.

2. Exposed rigid tubing, especially at B-nuts and ferrules, under clamps and tubing identification tapes.

3. Exposed position indicator switches and other electrical equipment.

4. Crevices between stiffeners, ribs, and lower skin surfaces, which are typical water and debris traps.

External Skin Areas

External aircraft surfaces are readily visible and accessible for inspection and maintenance. Even here, certain types of configurations or combinations of materials become troublesome under certain operating conditions and require special attention.

Relatively little corrosion trouble is experienced with magnesium skins if the original surface finish and insulation are adequately maintained.

Trimming, drilling, or riveting destroy some of the original surface treatment which is never completely restored by touchup procedures. Any inspection for corrosion should include all magnesium skin surfaces with special attention to edges, areas around fasteners, and cracked, chipped, or missing paint.

Corrosion of metal skin joined by spot welding is the result of the entrance and entrapment of corrosive agents between the layers of metal. This type of corrosion is evidenced by corrosion products appearing at the crevices through which the corrosive agents enter.

More advanced corrosive attack causes skin buckling and eventual spot-weld fracture. Skin buckling in its early stages may be detected by sighting along spot-welded seams or by using a straightedge. The only technique

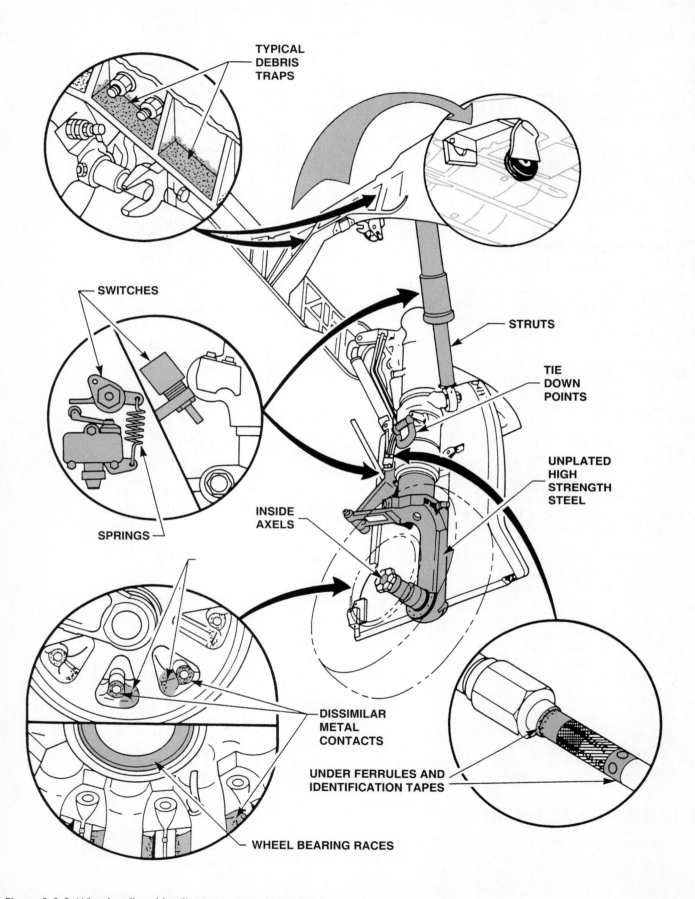

Figure 9-9-2. Wheel well and landing gear corrosion points

for preventing this condition is to keep potential moisture entry points, including seams and holes created by broken spot welds, filled with a sealant or a suitable preservative compound.

Engine Frontal Areas and Cooling Air Vents

These areas are being constantly abraded with airborne dirt and dust, bits of gravel from runways, and rain erosion which tend to remove the protective finish. Inspection of these areas, shown in Figures 9-9-3 and 9-9-4, should include all sections in the cooling air path, with special attention to places where salt deposits may be built up during marine operations.

It is imperative that incipient corrosion be inhibited and that paint touchup and hard film preservative coatings be maintained intact on seaplane and amphibian engine surfaces at all times.

Inaccessible Areas

Fuel Tanks

Because fuel tanks are usually located inside wing and fuselage structures, it is often difficult to gain access to inspect fittings and other hardware on the outside of the tank for corrosion. In addition, as was previously mentioned in this chapter, fuel tanks are targets for bacterial growth; particularly in tanks used for turbine fuels. While inspection inside the tank may be extremely difficult or impossible, bacterial growth can be controlled with the use of growth-inhibiting additives added to the fuel when refueling.

Piano Hinges

As can be seen in Figure 9-9-5, piano-type hinges are prime spots for corrosion due to the dissimilar metal contact between the steel pin and aluminum hinge. They are also natural traps for dirt, salt, or moisture. Inspection of hinges should include lubrication and actuation through several cycles to ensure complete lubricant penetration.

Wing Flap and Spoiler Recesses

Dirt and water may collect in flap and spoiler recesses and go unnoticed because they are normally retracted. For this reason these recesses are potential corrosion problem areas.

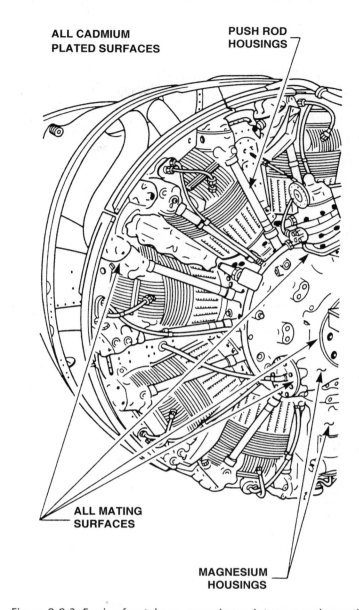

ALL CADMIUM PLATED SURFACES

PUSH ROD HOUSINGS

ALL MATING SURFACES

MAGNESIUM HOUSINGS

Figure 9-9-3. Engine frontal area corrosion points on a reciprocating engine

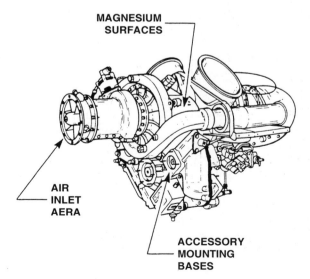

MAGNESIUM SURFACES

AIR INLET AERA

ACCESSORY MOUNTING BASES

Figure 9-9-4. Turbine engine frontal area corrosion points

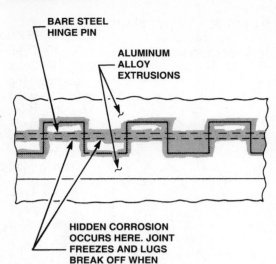

Figure 9-9-5. Piano hinge corrosion points

Bilge Areas

These are natural sumps for waste hydraulic fluids, water, dirt, and odds and ends of debris. Residual oil quite often masks small quantities of water which settle to the bottom and set up a hidden chemical cell.

Seaplane and amphibian aircraft bilge areas are protected by small bags of potassium dichromate inhibitor suspended near the low point in each bilge compartment. These crystals dissolve in any waste water and tend to inhibit the attack on exposed metal surfaces.

Inspection procedures should include replacement of these bags when most of the chemical has been dissolved.

Water Entrapment Areas

Corrosion will result from entrapped water. With the exception of sandwich structures,

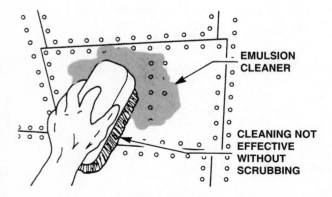

Figure 9-10-1. Remove oil and surface dirt

design specifications usually require that the aircraft have drains installed in all areas where water collects. In many cases, these drains are ineffective either due to improper location or because they are plugged by sealants, extraneous fasteners, dirt, grease, or debris. Potential entrapment areas are not a problem when all drains are functioning, and the aircraft is maintained in a normal ground attitude. However, the plugging of a single drain hole or the altering of the level of the aircraft can result in a corrosion problem if water becomes entrapped in one of these bathtub areas. Daily inspection of low point drains would be practical.

Engine-Mount Structures

Because of their purpose and location, engine-mount structures are subjected to extremes of heat, vibration, and torque from the engine and its accessories. To withstand the tortures placed on mount structures, most engine mounts are manufactured from welded tubular steel. Therefore, engine-mount structures are inspected for corrosion, and corrosion treated, in much the same manner as other tubular steel airframe components, such as push/pull tubes, airframe structural tubing, tubular landing gear, etc. Particular attention must be paid to areas where moisture or other contaminants could possibly get inside the tubing, such as threaded, riveted, or welded areas.

Where economically feasible, corroded tubing should be cleaned, the structural integrity of the material tested (through the use of magnaflux, radiography, or other suitable test procedure) and treated to prevent a recurrence of the same or similar corrosion. Where the cost is prohibitive, the alternative is replacement of the part. In some cases parts of the engine-mount structure can be individually replaced. In other cases the entire mount assembly must be replaced.

Control Cables

All control cables, whether plain carbon steel or corrosion-resistant steel, should be inspected to determine their condition at each inspection period. Cables should be inspected for corrosion by random cleaning of short sections with solvent-soaked cloths. If external corrosion is evident, tension should be relieved and the cable checked for internal corrosion. Cables with internal corrosion should be replaced. Light external corrosion should be removed with a stainless steel wire brush. When corrosion products have been removed, recoat the cable with preservative.

Welded Areas

Many types of fluxes used in brazing, soldering, and welding are corrosive and they chemically attack the metals or alloys with which they are used. Therefore, it is important that residual flux be removed from the metal surface immediately after the joining operation. Flux residues are hygroscopic in nature; that is, they are capable of absorbing moisture, and unless carefully removed, tend to cause severe pitting.

Weld decay is another form of intergranular corrosion. It occurs because the process of welding often produces an undesirable heat treatment adjacent to the welded area, in turn producing separate phases of the metal, one of which may be preferentially attacked under adverse environmental conditions.

Electronic Equipment

Electronic and electrical package compartments cooled by ram air or compressor bleed air are subjected to the same conditions common to engine and accessory cooling vents and engine frontal areas. While the degree of exposure is less because of a lower volume of air passing through and special design features incorporated to prevent water formation in the enclosed spaces, this is still a trouble area that requires special attention.

Circuit breakers, contact points, and switches are extremely sensitive to moisture and corrosive attack and should be inspected for these conditions as thoroughly as design permits. If design features hinder examination of these items while in the installed condition, advantage should be taken of component removals for other reasons with careful inspection for corrosion required before reinstallation.

Section 10

Removal and Treatment of Corrosion

In general, any complete corrosion treatment involves cleaning and stripping of the corroded area, removing as much of the corrosion products as practicable, neutralizing any residual materials remaining in pits and crevices, restoring protective surface films, and applying temporary or permanent coatings or paint finishes.

Surface Preparation

Surface cleaning and paint removal. The removal of corrosion necessarily includes removal of surface finishes covering the attacked or suspected area. In order to assure maximum efficiency of the stripping compound, the area must be cleaned of grease, oil, dirt, or preservatives. This preliminary cleaning operation is also an aid in determining the extent of corrosion spread, since the stripping operation will be held to the minimum consistent with full exposure of the corrosion damage. Extensive corrosion spread on any panel should be corrected by fully treating the entire section (Figure 9-10-1).

Material Selection

The selection of the type of materials to be used in cleaning will depend on the nature of the matter to be removed. Dry-cleaning solvent may be used for removing oil, grease, or soft preservative compounds. For heavy-duty removal of thick or dried preservatives, other compounds of the solvent-emulsion type are available for abrasives that may be used for corrosion removal (Table 9-10-1).

The use of a general-purpose, water-rinsable stripper is recommended for most applications. Wherever practicable, paint removal from any large area should be accomplished outside (in open air) and preferably in shaded areas. If inside removal is necessary, adequate ventilation must be assured. Synthetic rubber surfaces, including aircraft tires, fabric, and acrylics, must be thoroughly protected against possible contact with paint remover. Care must also be exercised in using paint remover around gas or watertight seam sealants, since this material will tend to soften and destroy the integrity of these sealants.

Masking

Mask off any opening that would permit the stripping compound to get into aircraft interiors or critical cavities. Paint stripper is toxic and contains ingredients harmful to both skin and eyes. Rubber gloves, aprons of acid-repellent material, and goggle-type eyeglasses should be worn if any extensive paint removal is to be accomplished. The following is a general stripping procedure:

Application of Stripper

Brush the entire area to be stripped with a cover of stripper to a depth of $1/32$ to $1/16$ inch. Any paintbrush makes a satisfactory appli-

Metals or Materials to Be Processed	Restrictions	Operation	Aluminum Oxide	Silicon Carbide	Garnet	Abrasive Fabric or Pad	Aluminum	Stainless Steel	Pumice 350 Mesh or Finer	Abrasive Wheel
Ferrous Alloys	Does not apply to steel heat treated to strengths 220,000 p.s.i. and above	Corrosion removal or fairing	150 Grit or finer	180 Grit or finer	–	Fine to ultra fine	X	X	X	X
		Finishing	400	–	–	–	X	X	X	–
Aluminum Alloys (Except Clad Aluminum)	Do not use silicon carbide	Corrosion removal or fairing	150 Grit or finer		–	7/0 Grit or finer	Very fine and ultra fine	–	–	X	–
		Finishing	400	–	–	–	X	–	X	–
Clad Aluminum	Sanding limited to the removal of minor scratches	Corrosion removal or fairing	240 Grit or finer	–	7/0 Grit or finer	Very fine and ultra fine	–	–	X	X
		Finishing	400	–	–	–	–	–	X	–
Magnesium Alloys	–	Corrosion removal or fairing	240 Grit or finer	–	–	Very fine and ultra fine	X	–	X	X
		Finishing	400	–	–	–	X	–	X	–
Titanium	–	Cleaning and finishing	150 Grit or finer	180 Grit or finer	–	–	–	X	X	X

Table 9-10-1. Abrasives for corrosion removal

cator, except that the bristles will be loosened by the effect of paint remover on the binder, and the brush should not be used for other purposes after being exposed to paint remover.

Allow the stripper to remain on the surface for a sufficient length of time to wrinkle and lift

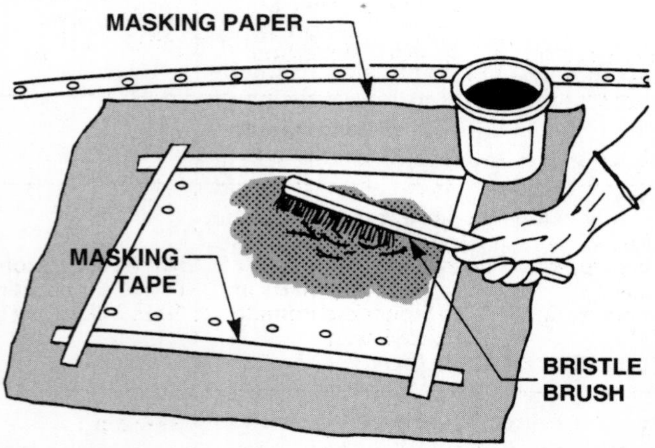

Figure 9-10-2. Cleaning and paint stripping

the paint. This may be from 10 minutes to several hours, depending on both the temperature and humidity, and the condition of the paint coat being removed. Scrub the surface with a bristle brush saturated with paint remover to further loosen finish that may still be adhering to the metal.

Reapply the stripper as necessary in areas that remain tight or where the material has dried, and repeat the above process. Only nonmetallic scrapers may be used to assist in removing persistent paint finishes.

Removal of Residue

Remove the loosened paint and residual stripper by washing and scrubbing the surface with water and a broom or brush. If water spray is available, use a low-to-medium pressure stream of water directly on the scrubbing broom or brush. If steam cleaning equipment is available and the area is sufficiently large, cleaning may be accomplished using this equipment together with a solution of steam cleaning compound. On small areas, any method may be used that will assure complete rinsing of the cleaned area (Figure 9-10-2).

Corrosion of Aluminum and Aluminum Alloys

Corrosion attack on aluminum surfaces is usually quite obvious, since the products of corrosion are white and generally more voluminous than the original base metal. Even in its early stages, aluminum corrosion is evident as general etching, pitting, or roughness of the aluminum surfaces.

> **NOTE:** *Aluminum alloys commonly form a smooth surface oxidation which is from 0.001 to 0.0025 inch thick. This is not considered detrimental as such a coating provides a hard shell barrier to the introduction of corrosive elements. Such oxidation is not to be confused with the severe corrosion discussed in this paragraph.*

General surface attack of aluminum penetrates relatively slowly, but is speeded up in the presence of dissolved salts. Considerable attack can usually take place before serious loss of structural strength develops. However, at least three forms of attack on aluminum alloys are particularly serious:

1. The penetrating pit-type corrosion through the walls of aluminum tubing.

2. Stress-corrosion cracking of materials under sustained stress.

3. The intergranular attack which is characteristic of certain improperly heat-treated aluminum alloys.

Corrosion of aluminum, in general, can be more effectively treated in place than corrosion occurring on other structural materials used in aircraft. Treatment includes the mechanical removal of as much of the corrosion products as practicable, and the inhibition of residual materials by chemical means, followed by the restoration of permanent surface coatings. Table 9-10-2 shows typical corrosion removal and treatment procedures for aluminum alloys.

Section 11
Treatment of Aluminum Alloys

Treatment of Unpainted Aluminum Surfaces

Relatively pure aluminum has considerably more corrosion resistance compared with the stronger aluminum alloys. Advantage is taken of this by laminating a thin sheet of relatively pure aluminum over the base aluminum alloy. This is called cladding and the resultant alloy is alclad. The protection obtained is good, and the alclad surface can be maintained in a polished condition. In cleaning such surfaces, however, care must be taken to prevent staining and marring of the exposed aluminum and, more important from a protection standpoint, to avoid unnecessary mechanical removal of the protective alclad layer and the exposure of the more susceptible aluminum alloy base mate-

TYPES OF CORROSION	STEP 1 CLEANING TO REMOVE FOREIGN MATTER	STEP 2 PAINT STRIPPING (WHEN APPLICABLE)	STEP 3 CORROSION REMOVAL	STEP 4 SURFACE TREATMENT (WHEN APPLICABLE)
Light or heavy pitting or etching of aluminum (clad)	Remove foreign matter with cleaner, Spec MIL-C-25769	Readily accessible areas: strip with stripper, MIL-R-25134 Confined areas: strip with solvent	Remove corrosion with brightener, Spec MIL-25378 or remove by mechanical method	Chromate conversion coating, Spec MIL-C-5541
Intergranular or exfoliation corrosion of aluminum	As above	As above	Remove corrosion by mechanical methods	As above
Light or heavy corrosion on small aluminum parts which can be removed for treatment	Painted parts: clean and strip in solution of paint and varnish remover, Spec MIL-R-7751. Unpainted parts: clean with compound, Spec MIL-C-5543 or vapor degrease	Not required. If cleaning accomplished with paint and varnish remover, Spec MIL-R-7751	Remove corrosion and oxide film by immersion of parts in phosphoric-chromate acid solution	Immersion chromate conversion coating, Spec MIL-C-5541
Stress corrosion cracking of aluminum	Not applicable	See step 1	See step 1	See step 1

Table 9-10-2. Typical corrosion removal and treatment procedures for aluminum alloys

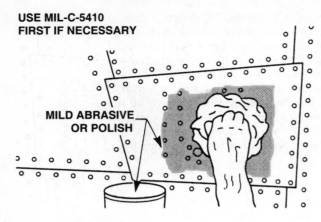

**USE MIL-C-5410
FIRST IF NECESSARY**

**MILD ABRASIVE
OR POLISH**

Figure 9-11-1. Hand polish alclad surfaces

rial. A typical aluminum corrosion treatment sequence follows:

Remove oil and surface dirt with any suitable mild cleaner prior to abrasive cleaning of aluminum surfaces.

Hand polish the corroded areas with fine abrasives or with metal polish. Metal polish intended for use on clad aluminum aircraft surfaces must not be used on treated aluminum since it is abrasive enough to actually remove the protective film. It effectively removes stains and produces a high, lasting polish on unpainted alclad. If a surface is particularly difficult to clean, a cleaner and brightener compound for aluminum can be used before polishing to shorten the time and lessen the effort necessary to get a clean surface (Figure 9-11-1).

Treat any superficial corrosion present, using an inhibitive wipe-down material. An alternate treatment is processing with a solution of sodium dichromate and chromium trioxide. Allow these solutions to remain on the corroded area for 5 to 20 minutes, and then remove the excess by rinsing and wiping the surface dry with a clean cloth.

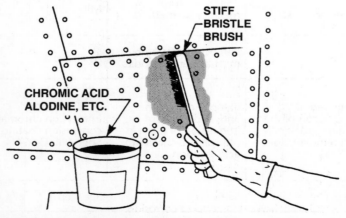

**STIFF
BRISTLE
BRUSH**

**CHROMIC ACID
ALODINE, ETC.**

Figure 9-11-2. Treating corroded aluminum surfaces

Overcoat the polished surfaces with waterproof wax.

Aluminum surfaces that are to be subsequently painted can be exposed to more severe cleaning procedures and can also be given more thorough corrective treatment prior to painting. The following sequence is generally used:

1. Thoroughly clean the affected surfaces of all soil and grease residues prior to processing. Any general aircraft cleaning procedure may be used.

2. If residual paint films remain, strip the area to be treated. Procedures for the use of paint removers, and the precautions to observe, were previously mentioned in this chapter under Surface Cleaning and Paint Removal.

Superficial Corrosion Treatment

Treat superficially corroded areas with a 10 percent solution of chromic acid and sulfuric acid. Apply the solution by swab or brush. Scrub the corroded area with the brush while it is still damp (Figure 9-11-2). While chromic acid is a good inhibitor for aluminum alloys, even when corrosion products have not been completely removed, it is important that the solution penetrate to the bottom of all pits and underneath any corrosion that may be present.

Thorough brushing with a stiff fiber brush should loosen or remove most existing corrosion and assure complete penetration of the inhibitor into crevices and pits. Allow the chromic acid to remain in place for at least 5 minutes, then remove the excess by flushing with water or wiping with a wet cloth. There are several commercial chemical surface treatment compounds, similar to the type described above, which may also be used.

Dry the treated surface and restore recommended permanent protective coatings as required in accordance with the aircraft manufacturer's procedures (Figure 9-11-3). Restoration of paint coatings should immediately follow any surface treatment performed. In any case, make sure that corrosion treatment is accomplished or is reapplied on the same day that paint refinishing is scheduled.

Treatment of Anodized Surfaces

Anodizing is a common surface treatment of aluminum alloys. When this coating is damaged in service, it can be only partially restored by chemical surface treatment. Therefore, any corrosion correction of anodized surfaces should avoid destruction of the oxide film in the unaffected area. Avoid the use of steel wool, steel wire brushes, or severe abrasive materials.

Aluminum wool, aluminum wire brushes, or fiber bristle brushes are the approved tools for cleaning corroded anodized surfaces. Care must be exercised in any cleaning process to avoid unnecessary breaking of the adjacent protective film.

Take every precaution to maintain as much of the protective coating as practicable. Otherwise, treat anodized surfaces in the same manner as other aluminum finishes. Chromic acid and other inhibitive treatments tend to restore the oxide film.

Treatment of Intergranular Corrosion in Heat-Treated Aluminum Alloy Surfaces

Intergranular corrosion is an attack along grain boundaries of improperly or inadequately heat-treated alloys, resulting from precipitation of dissimilar constituents following heat treatment. In its most severe form, actual lifting of metal layers (exfoliation) occurs. More severe cleaning is a must when intergranular corrosion is present. The mechanical removal of all corrosion products and visible delaminated metal layers must be accomplished to determine the extent of the destruction and to evaluate the remaining structural strength of the component. The following processes can be used as a means of repairing this type of corrosion:

- Use metal scrapers, rotary files, or abrasive steels to assure that all corrosion products are removed and that only structurally sound aluminum remains.

- Rotary files must be sharp to insure that they cut the metal without excessive smearing. A dull cutting tool will smear the metal over corrosion cracks or fissures and give the appearance that corrosion has been removed.

- Carbide tip rotary files or metal scrapers should be utilized since they stay sharp longer. Blasting is not a satisfactory method to remove intergranular corrosion.

- Inspection with a 5- to 10-power magnifying glass or the use of dye penetrant will assist in determining if all unsound metal and corrosion products have been removed.

- When complete removal has been attained, blend or fair out the edges of the damaged areas. Blending, where required, can

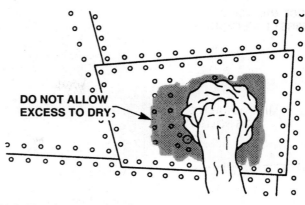

DO NOT ALLOW EXCESS TO DRY

Figure 9-11-3. Dry the treated surface

best be accomplished by using aluminum oxide impregnated, rubber-base wheels.

- Chemically inhibit the exposed surfaces completely and restore paint coatings in the same manner as on any other aluminum surface.

- Any loss of structural strength in critical areas should be evaluated by engineers. Further, if damage exceeds the permissible limit chart in the handbook of structural repair for the aircraft model involved, the manufacturer should be contacted.

Section 12

Treatment of Ferrous Metals

Mechanical Removal of Iron Rust

The most practicable means of controlling the corrosion of steel is the complete removal of

Figure 9-12-1. Mechanical removal of corrosion from steel surfaces

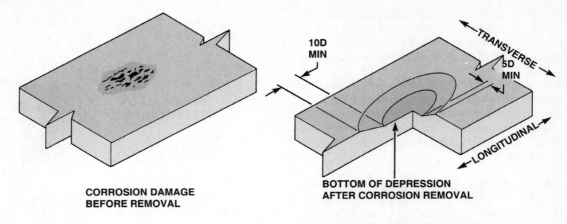

CORROSION DAMAGE
BEFORE REMOVAL

BOTTOM OF DEPRESSION
AFTER CORROSION REMOVAL

DAMAGE REMOVED AND SURFACE
SMOOTHED WITH SHALLOW
ELLIPTICAL DISH-OUT

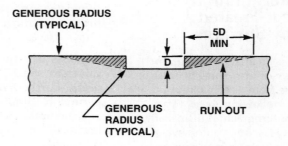

GENEROUS RADIUS
(TYPICAL)

GENEROUS
RADIUS
(TYPICAL)

RUN-OUT

EXAMPLE OF 1:5 BLENDING RATIO
DETAIL 1

NOTE:

● DEPTH = DEPTH OF DEPRESSION

● REFER TO SPECIFIC ALLOWABLE DAMAGE
LIMITS FOR MAXIMUM ALLOWABLE DEPTH.

● SINCE MAXIMUM DEPTH VARIES AT DIFFERENT
LOCATIONS, MAXIMUM SIZE OF DISH-OUT WILL
ALSO VARY.

● THE BLENDING RATIO SHALL BE MAINTAINED
AT ALL TIMES UNLESS OTHERWISE SPECIFIED
IN A SPECIFIC REPAIR.

● SEE DETAIL 2 FOR EXAMPLES OF BLENDING.

Figure 9-12-2. Blendout of pits in the corroded area

corrosion products by mechanical means and restoring corrosion-preventive coatings. Except on highly stressed steel surfaces, the use of abrasive papers and compounds, small power buffers and buffing compounds, hand wire brushing, or steel wool are all acceptable cleanup procedures (Figure 9-12-1). However, it should be recognized that in any such use of abrasives, residual rust usually remains in the bottom of small pits and other crevices. It is practically impossible to remove all corrosion products by abrasive or polishing methods alone. As a result, once a part has rusted it usually corrodes again more easily than it did the first time.

Chemical Surface Treatment of Steel

There are approved methods for converting active rust to phosphates and other protective coatings. The use of phosphoric acid proprietary chemicals are examples of such treatments. However, these processes require shop-installed equipment and are impracticable for field use. Other commercial preparations are effective rust converters where tolerances are not critical and where thorough rinsing and neutralizing of residual acid is possible. These situations are generally not applicable to assembled aircraft,

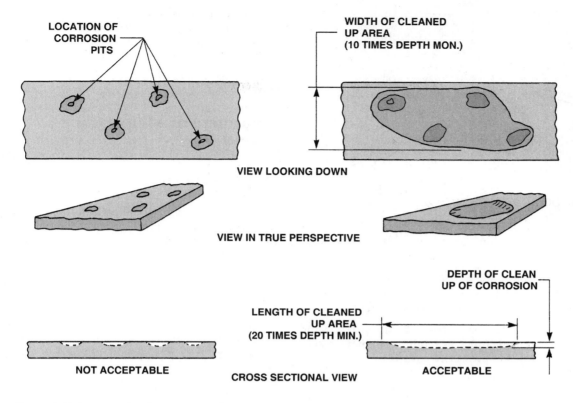

LOCATION OF
CORROSION
PITS

WIDTH OF CLEANED
UP AREA
(10 TIMES DEPTH MON.)

VIEW LOOKING DOWN

VIEW IN TRUE PERSPECTIVE

DEPTH OF CLEAN
UP OF CORROSION

LENGTH OF CLEANED
UP AREA
(20 TIMES DEPTH MIN.)

NOT ACCEPTABLE

CROSS SECTIONAL VIEW

ACCEPTABLE

Figure 9-12-3. Example of acceptable cleanup of corrosion pits

and the use of chemical inhibitors on installed steel parts is not only undesirable but very dangerous. The danger of entrapment of corrosive solutions and the resulting uncontrolled attack, which could occur when such materials are used under field conditions, outweigh any advantages to be gained from their use.

Example of Corrosion Removal From Steel Parts

If possible, corroded steel parts should be removed from the aircraft. When it is impossible to remove the part, observe the aircraft preventative preparations and safety precautions. No chemical removal or chemical conversion coatings are allowed on steel parts. An example of corrosion removal techniques for steel is as follows:

1. Positively identify the metal as steel and establish its heat value.

2. Clean the area to be reworked.

3. Strip the paint in the area, if needed.

4. Remove all degrees of corrosion damage from steel which has been heat-treated at a low level of hardness. Corrosion removal on steel treated to a high level of hardness should be accomplished only by dry abrasive blasting which is described later.

5. Mechanically remove all degrees of corrosion from steel parts heat treated at a low level of hardness as follows:

   a. Use goggles or a face shield to preclude injury from flying particles. Protect adjacent areas to prevent additional damage from corrosion products removed by this mechanical process.

   b. Remove heavy deposits of corrosion products by alternating between a stainless steel hand brush and dry abrasive blasting. Exercise extreme care to prevent overheating the surfaces when using power tools on high-stress steels.

   c. Remove residual corrosion by hand sanding or with approved hand operated power tools. Select appropriate abrasive from Table 9-10-1.

6. The surface is highly reactive immediately following corrosion removal; consequently, primer coats should be applied within 1 hour after sanding.

7. Blend depressions resulting from rework as covered in Figures 9-12-2 and 9-12-3. Then surface finish with 400-grit abrasive paper.

8. Clean the reworked area being careful never to use kerosene or petroleum base solvents.

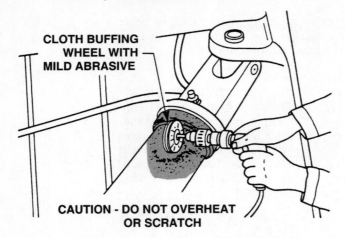

CLOTH BUFFING
WHEEL WITH
MILD ABRASIVE

CAUTION - DO NOT OVERHEAT
OR SCRATCH

Figure 9-12-4. Careful removal of corrosion from a highly stressed steel part

9. Determine the depth of the faired depressions, as required, to ensure that rework limits have not been exceeded.

10. Apply protective finish or specific organic finish as required. Remove masking and protective covering.

Removal of Corrosion From Highly Stressed Steel Parts

Any corrosion on the surface of a highly stressed steel part is potentially dangerous, and the careful removal of corrosion products is required. Surface scratches or changes in surface structure from overheating can also cause sudden failure of these parts. Corrosion products must be removed by careful processing, using mild abrasive papers such as rouge or fine grit aluminum oxide, or fine buffing compounds on cloth buffing wheels.

It is essential that steel surfaces not be overheated during buffing (Figure 9-12-4). After careful removal of surface corrosion, protective paint finishes should be reapplied immediately.

Special treatment of stainless steel alloys. Do not use chemical cleaners on stainless steels. Stainless steels are of two general types: magnetic and nonmagnetic. Magnetic steels are of the ferritic or martensitic types and are identified by numbers in the 400 series.

Corrosion often occurs on 400 series stainless steels. Nonmagnetic steels are of the austenitic type and are identified by numbers in the 300 series. They are much more corrosion resistant than the 400 series steels, particularly in a marine environment.

Austenitic steels develop corrosion resistance by an oxide film which should not be removed even though the surface is discolored. The original oxide film is normally formed at time of fabrication. If any deterioration or corrosion does occur on austenitic steels and the structural integrity or serviceability of the part is affected, it will be necessary to remove and replace the part.

Treatment of Magnesium Alloys

Corrosion of Magnesium Alloys

Magnesium is the most chemically active of the metals used in aircraft construction and is, therefore, the most difficult to protect. When a failure in the protective coating does occur, the prompt and complete correction of the coating failure is imperative if serious structural damage is to be avoided.

Magnesium attack is probably the easiest type of corrosion to detect in its early stages, since magnesium corrosion products occupy several times the volume of the original magnesium metal destroyed. The beginning of attack shows as a lifting of the paint films and white spots on the magnesium surface. These rapidly develop into snow-like mounds or even white whiskers. Re-protection involves the removal of corrosion products, the partial restoration of surface coatings by chemical treatment, and a reapplication of protective coatings.

Treatment of Wrought Magnesium Sheet and Forgings

Magnesium skin attack will usually occur around edges of skin panels, underneath hold-down washers, or in areas physically damaged by shearing, drilling, abrasion, or impact. If the skin section can be removed easily, this should be done to assure complete inhibition and treatment. If insulating washers are involved, screws should be loosened, at least sufficiently to permit brush treatment of the magnesium under the insulating washer. Complete mechanical removal of corrosion products should be practiced insofar as practicable. Such mechanical cleaning should be limited to the use of stiff, hog-bristle brushes and similar nonmetallic cleaning tools, particularly if treatment is to be performed under field conditions. Any entrapment of steel particles from steel-wire brushes or steel tools, or contamination of treated surfaces by dirty abrasives, can cause more trouble than the initial corrosive attack. Corroded magnesium may generally be treated as follows:

1. Clean and strip the paint from the area to be treated. (Paint stripping procedures were discussed earlier in this chapter.)

2. Using a stiff, hog-bristle brush, break loose and remove as much of the corrosion products as practicable. Steel-wire brushes, carborundum abrasives, or steel cutting tools should not be used.

3. Treat the corroded area liberally with a chromic acid solution, to which has been added sulfuric acid, and work into pits and crevices by brushing the area while still wet with chromic acid, again using a nonmetallic brush.

4. Allow the chromic acid to remain in place for 5 to 20 minutes before wiping up the excess with a clean, damp cloth. Do not allow the excess solution to dry and remain on the surface, as paint lifting will be caused by such deposits.

5. As soon as the surfaces are dry, restore the original protective paint.

Treatment Of Installed Magnesium Castings

Magnesium castings, in general, are more porous and more prone to penetrating attack than wrought magnesium skins. However, treatment is, for all practical purposes, the same for all magnesium areas. Engine cases, bellcranks, fittings, numerous covers, plates, and handles are the most common magnesium castings.

When attack occurs on a casting, the earliest practicable treatment is required if dangerous corrosive penetration is to be avoided. In fact, engine cases submerged in salt water overnight can be completely penetrated. If it is at all practicable, parting surfaces should be separated to effectively treat the existing attack and prevent its further progress. The same general treatment sequence for magnesium skin should be followed.

If extensive removal of corrosion products from a structural casting is involved, a decision from the manufacturer may be necessary to evaluate the adequacy of structural strength remaining. Specific structural repair manuals usually include dimensional tolerance limits for critical structural members and should be referred to, if any question of safety is involved.

Section 13

Corrosion Prevention

It is important that aircraft be kept thoroughly clean of deposits containing contaminating substances such as oil, grease, dirt, or other foreign materials.

Cleanliness

Avoid damage to aircraft by not using harmful cleaning, polishing, brightening, or paint-removing materials. Use only those compounds which conform to existing government or established industry specifications, or products that have been specifically recommended by the aircraft manufacturer as being satisfactory for the intended application. Observe the product manufacturer's recommendations concerning use of their agent.

Chemical cleaners must be used with great care in cleaning assembled aircraft. The danger of entrapping corrosive materials in faying surfaces and crevices counteracts any advantages in their speed and effectiveness. Use materials which are relatively neutral and easy to remove.

Battery Acid

Spilled battery acid is removed by using sodium bicarbonate (baking soda), or sodium borate (borax) 20 percent by weight dissolved in water. After the acid is neutralized, remove alkali salts completely by flushing the area with large quantities of water to prevent corrosion. An application of acid-proof paint to the structure surrounding the battery may be an effective control for this type of corrosion.

Corrosion-Inhibiting Film

By covering materials with protective coatings of corrosion-inhibiting film, corrosion is often prevented. Care must be taken when handling materials coated with a protective film to prevent penetration or breaking of the film covering.

Anodizing and Related Processes

In anodizing, aluminum alloys are placed in an electrolytic bath causing a thin film of aluminum oxide to form on the surface of the aluminum. This is resistant to corrosion and affords a good paint base. Other processes which do not provide as good a corrosive protection as anodizing are, however, good paint bases. These processes are:

- Alkaline cleaning followed by chromic acid dip
- Alcoholic phosphoric acid cleaner
- Alkaline dichromate treatment

Contacting Metals	Aluminum Alloy	Cadmium Plate	Zinc Plate	Carbon and Alloy Steels	Lead	Tin Coating	Copper and Alloys	Nickel and Alloys	Titanium Alloys	Chromium Plate	Corrosion Resisting Steel	Magnesium Alloys
Aluminum Alloy				■	■	■	■	■	■	■	■	■
Cadmium Plate				■	■	■	■	■	■	■	■	■
Zinc Plate				■	■	■	■	■	■	■	■	■
Carbon and Alloy Steels	■	■	■				■	■	■	■	■	■
Lead	■	■	■				■	■	■	■	■	■
Tin Coating	■	■	■				■	■	■	■	■	■
Copper and Alloys	■	■	■	■	■	■						■
Titanium and Alloys	■	■	■	■	■	■						■
Chromium Plate	■	■	■	■	■	■						■
Corrosion Resisting Steel	■	■	■	■	■	■						■
Magnesium Alloys	■	■	■	■	■	■	■	■	■	■	■	

NOTE: Dark shaded areas indicate dissimilar metal contact

Table 9-14-1. Dissimilar metal contacts that will result in electrolytic corrosion

Plating

Steels are commonly plated with other metals to prevent corrosion. Plating is accomplished by placing the material in an electrolytic bath where metal from the plating solution is deposited on it. The various metals used in plating vary in the corrosion protection that they afford steel. For instance cadmium and zinc corrode before the steel; hence, slight breaks or cracks through the plating of these metals will not result in rusting of the exposed steel since the surface metal is corroded and protects the steel. Chromium does not protect steel by this method, because steel will corrode before the chromium and thus depends on the tightness of the plating for its protection.

Phosphate Rust Proofing

This process is commercially known as Parkerizing, Bonderizing, Granodizing. The coating placed on the part is used to protect steel parts after machining and before painting.

Chrome-Pickle Treatment

Magnesium parts which have been immersed or brushed with a solution of nitric acid and sodium dichromate will be protected for temporary storage. The coating also serves as a bond for subsequent organic finishes. Sealed chrome-pickle treatment is used on magnesium parts for long term protection. Diluted chromic acid is a touch-up treatment. It is less critical to apply and can be applied over previously applied thin chromate films.

Dichromate Treatment

The dichromate treatment consists of boiling magnesium parts in a solution of sodium dichromate. This treatment provides a good paint base and protective qualities on all standard wrought magnesium alloys except the magnesium-thorium alloys HK 31A, HM 21A, and HM 31A. No coating forms on these alloys. Acid pickling of the magnesium surface prior to application of the dichromate treatment is required if maximum corrosion resistance of the finish is expected.

Stannate Immersion Treatment

This treatment deposits a layer of tin, as a protective paint base, on magnesium parts which contain inserts and fasteners of a dissimilar metal such as brass, copper, or steel. This treatment cannot be used with parts containing aluminum inserts or fasteners because the high alkalinity of the bath attacks the aluminum.

Galvanic Anodizing Treatment

This is an electrolytic process used to provide a paint base and corrosion preventive film on magnesium alloys containing manganese.

Cladding

Aluminum alloys which are susceptible to corrosion are frequently clad with pure aluminum. Slight pits, scratches, or other defects through the cladding material will not result in corrosion of the core, since the pure aluminum on the edges of the defect will be preferentially corroded, protecting the core.

Metal Spraying

Metal is melted and sprayed on the surface to be protected, providing a sealing film. Extra care must be taken to properly prepare the surface to prevent peeling of the sprayed coating.

Organic Coatings

Zinc chromate primer, enamels, chlorinated rubber compounds, etc., are organic coatings commonly used to protect metals.

Dope-proofing

When doped fabrics are applied over an organic finished metal structure, the dope will have a tendency to loosen the finish on the metal. For this reason, organic coatings on the metal are usually covered with a dope-proof paint, metal foil, or with cellulose tape to prevent the dope from striking through.

Section 14

Dissimilar Metal Insulation

Certain metals are subject to corrosion when placed in contact with other metals. This is commonly referred to as electrolytic or dissimilar metals corrosion.

Protection of Dissimilar Metal Contacts

Contact of different bare metals creates an electrolytic action when moisture is present. If this moisture is salt water, the electrolytic action is accelerated. The result of dissimilar-metal contact is oxidation (decomposition) of one or both metals. The chart shown in Table 9-14-1 lists the metal combinations requiring a protective separator. The separating materials may be metal primer, aluminum tape, washers, grease, or sealant, depending on the metals involved.

Contacts Not Involving Magnesium

All dissimilar joints not involving magnesium are protected by the application of a minimum of two coats of zinc chromate primer in addition to normal primer requirements. Primer is applied by brush or spray and allowed to air-dry 6 hours between coats.

Contacts Involving Magnesium

To prevent corrosion between dissimilar-metal joints in which magnesium alloy is involved, each surface is insulated as follows:

1. At least two coats of zinc chromate are applied to each surface. Next, a layer of pressure-sensitive vinyl tape 0.003 inch thick is applied smoothly and firmly enough to prevent air bubbles and wrinkles. To avoid creep-back, the tape is not stretched during application. When the thickness of the tape interferes with the assembly of parts, where relative motion exists between parts, or when service temperatures above 250°F are anticipated, the use of tape is eliminated and extra coats (minimum of three) of primer are applied.

2. Mechanical corrosion removal by blasting. Abrasive blasting is a process for cleaning or finishing metals, plastics, or other materials by directing a stream of abrasive particles against the surface of the parts. Abrasive blasting is used for the removal of rust and corrosion and for cleaning prior to further processing such as painting or plating.

10
Shop Safety

Safety is a major concern for everyone involved in aviation. The entire system is structured on a "zero error" philosophy. Shop safety must be viewed in the same manner. As you gain experience in aviation, you will recognize that there are very few "accidents". Almost everything had a "cause" and produced an "effect". By being observant, following the manufacturers guidelines for the equipment you are working on, or operating, you will not become part of the problem, but part of the excellent safety record most of aviation enjoys.

Aviation not only needs you to think, it needs you to think ahead. Done correctly, you will never get a surprise, because you looked ahead and saw it coming.

Section 1

Occupational Safety & Health Administration (OSHA)

OSHA is the Federal program that oversees basic safety programs for all occupations. As a result, the rules can seem overwhelming; maybe even nonsensical at times. While it is not the intent of this chapter to be an authority on OSHA, it should make you aware of a couple of points that seem to be overlooked from time to time.

Material Safety Data Sheets (MSDS)

Almost every chemical used in aircraft maintenance is toxic to some degree. Take the time to read the directions and warnings on the con-

Left. There are many potential hazards around aircraft that the technician must be aware of.

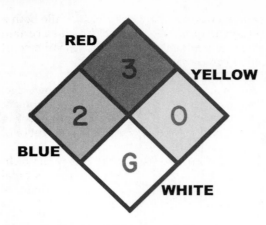

Figure 10-1-1. The MSDS data on the colored tags makes instant recognition possible

tainers. Expansion of this information, including special instructions to medical personnel, won't all fit on the container label. This information is contained in an MSDS sheet. Every commercial product has an MSDS sheet. MSDS sheets for every material used in your facility are required by law to be available to you and to all emergency response and medical people.

Most facilities will keep all MSDS sheets in a binder. If an emergency arises the information is required to be available. In this way, if an accident happens, the MSDS sheet can accompany the injured party to a medical facility. They will then know how to treat the emergency.

OSHA Warning Labels

There is a simple to understand system that rates all commercial chemicals and areas in which chemicals are used and stored. At a glance everyone concerned knows what chemicals are at hand. It consists of a sign divided into four different colored parts. Each color covers an aspect of the contents behavior or effects. A number or letter in each colored area coincides with a specific rating contained in an MSDS sheet. The higher the number, the higher the risk.

Blue

Blue represents the general health hazard of a material. In Figure 10-1-1, the two indicates a moderate health hazard.

Red

Flammable hazards are indicated by the red square. The three in the figure means the material is a serious flammable hazard.

Yellow

In this case, the zero indicates a minimum stability hazard. An example of a maximum stability hazard would be rocket fuel.

White

The 'G' in the white area means the material will require the use of goggles, respirator, and gloves to be safely handled.

Employee Training

Each employer is required to make sure each employee has received training in MSDS responsibilities and can read the warning signs. If an employer fails to provide the required training, it could seriously affect his insurance coverage. Therefore, after attending a class, your employer may want you to sign a statement that you attended the class.

Lockout/Tagout Program

All equipment requires maintenance or repair. This includes the shop equipment that you operate every day. Should you have to turn off the main switch at the power panel in order to perform maintenance, you want it to stay off until you are finished. Should someone come along and turn it back on while you are working on it, you could be seriously injured; maybe fatally.

There are fixtures for each switch and cord used in any commercial shop. These fixtures include provision for two padlocks. You should have one key, and your supervisor should have the other one. In addition, the switch should have a warning tag, as shown in Figure 10-1-2, attached in an obvious location.

By adhering to lockout/tagout rules, no one can ever be seriously injured during machine or electrical maintenance.

Failure will result in someone, sooner or later, being injured by inadvertent activation of the machine during maintenance.

Section 2

Shop Safety

Good housekeeping in hangars, shops, and on the flightline is essential to safety and efficient maintenance. The highest standards of orderly work arrangements and cleanliness should be observed during the maintenance of aircraft.

Where continuous work shifts are established, the outgoing shift should remove and properly store personal tools, rollaway boxes, all workstands, maintenance stands, hoses, electrical cords, hoists, crates, and boxes that are superfluous to the work to be accomplished.

Signs should be posted to indicate dangerous equipment or hazardous conditions. Also signs provide information on the location of first-aid and fire equipment, exits, and other information.

Safety lanes, pedestrian walkways, or fire lanes should be painted around the perimeter inside the hangars. This should be done as a safety measure to prevent accidents and to keep pedestrian traffic out of work areas.

Safety is everyone's business, and communication is key to ensuring everyone's safety. Technicians and supervisors should watch for their own safety and for the safety of others working around them. If someone else is conducting their actions in an unsafe manner, communicate with them, reminding them of their safety and that of others around them.

Electrical Safety

Working on or with electrical equipment poses certain physiological safety hazards. It is known that when electricity is applied to the human body, it can create severe burns in the area of entrance to, and at the point of exit from the body. In addition, the nervous system is affected, and can be damaged or destroyed.

Physiological Safety

To safely deal with electricity, the technician must have a knowledge of the principles of electricity, and a healthy respect for its capability to do both work and damage.

Wearing or use of proper safety equipment can give a psychological assurance at the same time it physically protects the user. Rubber gloves, safety glasses, rubber or grounded safety mats, and other safety equipment all can be used to contribute to the physiological safety of the technician working on or with electrical equipment.

Two factors that affect safety when working with or around electricity are fear and overconfidence. These two factors are major causes of accidents involving electricity. While both a certain amount of fear is healthy, and a certain level of confidence is necessary, extremes of either can be deadly.

Fear is often born of a lack of knowledge. People that try to work on electrical equipment with no knowledge of its principles, or a lack of confidence in their work, are often fearful of it.

Overconfidence leads to risk taking. The technician who does not respect electricity's capabilities will, sooner or later, become a victim of electricity's awesome power.

Fire Safety

Anytime current flows, whether during generation or transmission, a by-product of that flow is heat. The greater the current flow, the greater the amount of heat created. When this heat becomes too great, protective coatings on wiring and other electrical devices can melt, causing shorting, which leads to more current

Figure 10-1-2. The lockout/tagout program prevents inadvertent operation of machines during repairs/maintenance

flow and greater heat. This heat can become so great that metals can melt, liquids vaporize, and flammable substances ignite.

The single most important factor in preventing electrical fires is to keep the area around electrical work or electrical equipment clean, uncluttered, and free of all unnecessary flammable substances.

Ensure that all power cords, wires, and lines are free of kinks and bends which can damage the wire. When several wires inside a power cord are broken, the current passing through the remaining wires is caused to increase. This generates more heat than the insulation coatings on the wire are designed to withstand and can lead to a fire.

Closely monitor all current flow. Control it through the use of variable resistors or variable voltage controls. When current flow exceeds the prescribed limits of the work being done, remove the power source, find the cause, and correct it.

Section 3

Safety Around Compressed Gases

Compressed air, like electricity, is an excellent tool as long as it is under control.

The following "do's and don'ts" apply when working with or around compressed gases:

- Air hoses should be inspected frequently for breaks and worn spots. Unsafe hose should be replaced immediately.

- All connections should be kept in a no-leak condition.

- In-line oilers, if installed, should be maintained in operating condition.

- The system should have water sumps installed and should be drained at regular intervals.

- Air used for paint spraying should be filtered to remove oil and water.

- Never use compressed air to clean hands or clothing. Pressure can force debris into the flesh leading to infection.

- Never "horseplay" with compressed air.

- Air hoses should be straightened, coiled, and properly stored when not in use.

Many accidents involving compressed gases occur during aircraft tire mounting. To prevent possible personal injury, tire dollies and other appropriate lifting and mounting devices should be used in mounting or removing heavy aircraft tires.

When inflating tires on any type of aircraft wheels, tire cage guards should always be used. Because of possible personal injury, extreme caution is required to avoid over inflation of high-pressure tires. Pressure regulators should be used on high-pressure air bottles to eliminate the possibility of over-inflation of tires.

Tire cages need not be used when adjusting pressure in tires installed on aircraft. Clip-on tire chucks and remote pressure gauges will reduce the chances of personal injury.

Section 4

Safety Around Machine Tools

Hazards in a shop's operation increase when the operation of lathes, drill presses, grinders, and other types of machines are used. Each machine has its own set of safety practices.

Drill Presses

The drill press can be used to bore and ream holes, to do facing, milling, and other similar types of operations. Following a few precautions can reduce the chance of injury.

- Wear eye protection.

- Clamp the work securely.

- Set the proper r.p.m. for the material used.

- Do not allow the spindle to feed beyond its limit of travel while drilling.

- Stop the machine before adjusting work or attempting to remove jammed work.

- Clean the area when finished.

Lathes

Lathes are used in turning work of a cylindrical nature. This work may be performed on the inside or outside of the cylinder. The work is secured in the chuck to provide the rotary motion, and the forming is done by contact with a securely mounted tool. Following the precautions listed below will reduce the chance of injury.

- Wear eye protection.
- Use sharp cutting tools.
- Allow the chuck to stop on its own. Do not attempt to stop the chuck by hand pressure.
- Examine tools and work for cracks or defects before starting the work.
- Do not set tools on the lathe. Tools may be caught by the work and thrown.
- Stop the lathe before measuring the work.

Milling Machines

Milling machines are used to shape or dress, cut gear teeth, slots or key ways, and similar work. The following precautions can reduce the chance of injury:

- Wear eye protection.
- Clean the work bed prior to work.
- Secure the work to the bed to prevent movement during milling.
- Select the proper tools for the job.
- Do not change the feed speed while working.
- Lower the table before moving under or away from the work.
- Make sure all clamps and bolts will pass under the arbor.

Grinders

Grinders are used to sharpen tools, dress metal, and perform other operations involving the removal of small amounts of metal. The following precautions will reduce the chance of injury:

- Wear eye protection even if the grinder has a shield.
- Inspect the grinding wheel for defects prior to use.
- Do not force grinding wheels onto the spindle. They fit snugly, but do not require force to install them. Also, do not put any side pressure on a wheel or it can explode!
- Check the wheel flanges and compression washer. They should be one-third the diameter of the wheel.
- Do not stand in the arc of the grinding wheel while operating, in case the wheel explodes.

Welding

Welding should not be performed except in designated areas. Any part to be welded should be removed from the aircraft, if possible. Repair would then be accomplished in the welding shop under a controlled environment.

A welding shop should be equipped with proper tables, ventilation, tool storage, and fire prevention and extinguishing equipment.

Welding on an aircraft should be performed outside, if possible. If welding in the hangar is necessary, these precautions should be observed:

1. During welding operations there should be no open fuel tanks, and no work on fuel systems should be in progress.
2. No painting in progress.
3. No aircraft within 35 feet of the welding operation.
4. Immaculate housekeeping should prevail around the welding area.
5. Only qualified welders should be permitted to do the work.
6. The welding area should be roped off and placarded. Suitable portable flash guards should be used in order to reduce the possibility of eye damage.
7. Fire extinguishing equipment of a minimum rating of 20B should be in the immediate area with 80B rated equipment as a backup. These ratings will be explained later in this chapter.
8. There should be trained fire watches in the area around the welding operation.
9. Aircraft being welded should be in towable condition, with a tug attached, and the aircraft parking brakes released. A qualified operator should be on the tug, and mechanics available to assist in the towing operation should it become necessary to tow the aircraft. If the aircraft is in the hangar, the hangar doors should be opened.

Section 5

Fire Safety

Work on and around aircraft and their components requires the use of electrical tools and equipment, spark-producing tools and equipment, heat-producing tools and equipment, flammable and explosive liquids, and gases. As a result, a high potential exists for fire to occur, and measures must be taken to prevent; should one occur, extinguish it.

The key to fire safety is a knowledge of what causes fire, how to prevent it, and how to put it out. This knowledge must be instilled in each technician, emphasized by their supervisors through sound safety programs, and occasionally practiced. Airport or other local fire departments can normally be called upon to assist in training personnel and helping to establish fire safety programs for the hangar, shops, and flightline.

Fire Protection

Requirement for a Fire

Three things are required for a fire: Fuel, heat, and oxygen. Fuel is something that in the presence of heat will combine with oxygen, thereby releasing more heat and as a result reduces itself to other chemical compounds. Heat can be considered the catalyst which accelerates the combining of oxygen with fuel, in turn releasing more heat. Oxygen is the element which combines chemically with another substance through the process of oxidation. Rapid oxidation accompanied

by a noticeable release of heat and light is called combustion or burning (Figure 10-1-1). Remove any one of these things and the fire goes out.

Classification of Fires

The National Fire Protection Association (NFPA), for commercial purposes, has classified fires into three basic types: Class A, Class B, and Class C.

Class A fires are fires in ordinary combustible materials such as wood, cloth, paper, upholstery materials, etc.

Class B fires are fires in flammable petroleum products or other flammable or combustible liquids, greases, solvents, paints, etc.

Class C fires are fires involving energized electrical wiring and equipment.

A fourth class of fire, with which the technician should be familiar, the Class D fire, is defined as fire in flammable metal. Class D fires are not commercially considered by the National Fire Protection Association to be a basic type or category of fire. Usually Class D fires involve magnesium in the shop or in aircraft wheels and brakes, or are the result of improper or poorly conducted welding operations.

EXTINGUISHING MATERIALS	CLASSES OF FIRE				SELF-EXTINGUISHING	SELF-EXPELLING	CARTRIDGE OF N_2 GAS	STORED PRESSURE	PUMP	HAND
	A	B	C	D						
Water and Antifreeze	X						X	X	X	X
Soda-Acid Water	X				X					
Wetting Agent	X						X			
Foam	X	X			X					
Loaded Stream	X	X+					X	X		
Multipurpose Dry Chemical	X+	X	X				X	X		
Carbon Dioxide		X+	X			X				
Dry Chemical		X	X				X	X		
Bromotrifluoromethane (Halon 1301)		X	X			X				
Bromochlorodifluoromethane (Halon 1211)		X	X					X		
Dry Powder (Metal Fires)				X			X			X

NOTE:
+ Smaller sizes of these extinguishers are not recognized for use on these classes of fires

Table 10-5-1. Extinguisher operations and methods of expelling agent

Any one of these types of fires can occur during maintenance on or around, or operations involving aircraft. There is a particular type extinguisher which is most effective for each type of fire.

Types of Fire Extinguishers

Water extinguishers are the best type to use on Class A fires. The water has two effects on the fire, in that it can deprive the fire of oxygen, and at the same time cool the temperature of the material being burned (Table 10-5-1).

Since most petroleum products float on water, water-type fire extinguishers are not recommended for Class B fires.

Extreme caution must be used when fighting electrical fires with water-type extinguishers. Not only must all electrical power be removed or shut off to the burning area, but residual electricity in capacitors, coils, etc. must be considered to prevent severe injury, and possibly death from electrical shock.

Water Type

Never use water-type fire extinguishers on Class D fires. Because metals burn at extremely high temperatures, the cooling effect of water causes an explosive expansion of the metal.

Water fire extinguishers are operated in a variety of ways. Some are hand pumped, while some are pressurized. The pressurized types of extinguishers may have a gas charge stored in the container with the water, or it may contain a soda-acid container where acid is spilled into a container of soda inside the extinguisher. The chemical reaction of the soda and the acid causes pressure to build inside the fire extinguisher, forcing the water out.

The soda-acid water fire extinguisher has been obsolete for some time. Nevertheless, there are several hundred thousand units still in the field. They will continue to be around for some time (Figure 10-5-1).

Carbon Dioxide (CO$_2$)

Carbon dioxide (CO$_2$) extinguishers are used for Class B and C fires, extinguishing the fire by depriving it of oxygen (Table 10-5-2). Additionally, like water-type extinguishers, CO$_2$ cools the burning material. Following are some general rules for CO$_2$ extinguishers:

1. Never use CO$_2$ on Class D fires. As with water extinguishers, the cooling effect of CO$_2$ on the hot metal can cause explosive expansion of the metal.

2. When using CO$_2$ fire extinguishers, all parts of the extinguisher can become

GROUP	DEFINITION	EXAMPLES
6 (LEAST TOXIC)	Gases or vapors which in concentrations up to at least 20% by volume for durations of exposure of the order of 2 hours do not appear to produce injury	Bromotrifluoromethane (Halen 1301)
5	Gases or vapors much less toxic than Group 4 but more toxic than Group 6	Carbon Dioxide
4	Gases or vapors which in concentrations of the order of 2 to 2.5% for durations of exposure of the order of 1 hour are lethal or produce serious injury	Dibromodifluoromethane (Halen 1202)
3	Gases or vapors which in concentrations of the order of 2 to 2.5% for durations of exposure of the order of 1 hour are lethal or produce serious injury	Bromochloromethane (Halen 1011) Carbon Tetrachloride (Halen 104)
2	Gases or vapors which in concentrations of the order of 0.5 to 1% for durations of exposure of the order of 1/2 hour are lethal or produce serious injury	Methyl Bromide (Halen 1001)

Table 10-5-2. Toxicity table

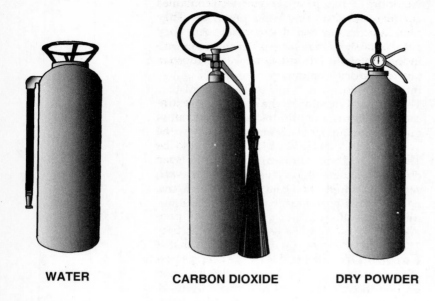

WATER **CARBON DIOXIDE** **DRY POWDER**

Figure 10-5-1. Fire extinguisher visual identification

extremely cold, and remain so for a short time after operation. Wear protective equipment or take other precautions to prevent cold injury (such as frostbite) from occurring.

3. Extreme caution must be used when operating CO_2 fire extinguishers in closed or confined areas. Not only can the fire be deprived of oxygen, but so too can the operator.

4. CO_2 fire extinguishers generally use the self-expelling method of operation. This means that the CO_2 has sufficient pressure at normal operating pressure to expel itself. This pressure is held inside the container by some type of seal or frangible disk, which is broken or punctured by a firing mechanism, usually a pin. This means that once the seal or disk is broken, pressure in the container is released, and the fire extinguisher is spent, requiring replacement (Table 10-5-2). A Carbon Dioxide extinguisher is shown in Figure 10-5-1.

Halogenated Hydrocarbon

Halogenated hydrocarbon extinguishers, while most effective on Class B and C fires, can be used, but are less effective on Class A and D fires. Halogenated hydrocarbon extinguishers, commonly called freon, are numbered according to chemical formulas with Halon numbers.

a. Carbon tetrachloride (Halon 104), chemical formula CCl_4, has an Underwriters

Laboratory (UL) toxicity rating of 3. As such, it is extremely toxic (Table 10-5-2).

1. Hydrochloric acid vapor, chlorine and phosgene gas are produced whenever carbon tetrachloride is used on ordinary fires. The amount of phosgene gas is increased whenever carbon tetrachloride is brought in direct contact with hot metal, certain chemicals, or continuing electrical arcs.

2. It is not approved for any fire extinguishing use. Old containers of Halon 104 found in or around shops or hangers should be disposed of in accordance with Environmental Protection Agency (EPA) regulations and local laws and ordinances.

b. Methyl bromide (Halon 1001), chemical formula CH_3Br, is a liquified gas with a UL toxicity rating of 2. Effective but very toxic, it is corrosive to aluminum alloys, magnesium, and zinc. Halon 1001 is not recommended for aircraft use.

c. Chlorobromomethane (Halon 1011), chemical formula CH_2ClBr, is a liquified gas with a UL toxicity rating of 3. Like methyl bromide, Halon 1011 is not recommended for aircraft use (Table 10-5-2).

d. Dibromodifluoromethane (Halon 1202), chemical formula CBr_2F_2, has a UL toxicity rating of 4. Halon 1202 is not recommended for aircraft use (Table 10-5-2).

e. Bromochlorodifluoromethane (Halon 1211), chemical formula $CBrClF_2$, is a liquified gas with a UL toxicity rating of 5. It is colorless, noncorrosive and evaporates rapidly leaving no residue whatever. It does not freeze or cause cold burns, and will not harm fabrics, metals, or other materials it contacts. Halon 1211 acts rapidly on fires by producing a heavy blanketing mist that eliminates oxygen from the fire source. But more importantly, it interferes chemically with the combustion process of the fire. It has outstanding properties in preventing reflash after the fire has been extinguished.

f. Bromotrifluoromethane (Halon 1301), chemical formula CF_3Br, is also a liquified gas with a UL toxicity rating of 6. It has all the characteristics of Halon 1211. The significant difference between the two is: Halon 1211 forms a spray similar to CO_2, while Halon 1301 has a vapor spray that is more difficult to direct (Table 10-5-2).

NOTE: *The Environmental Protection Agency (EPA) has restricted Halon to its 1986 production level because of its effect on the ozone layer.*

Dry Powder Extinguishers

Dry powder extinguishers, while effective on Class B and C fires, are the best for use on Class D fires (Figure 10-5-1).

The method of operation of dry powder fire extinguishers varies from gas cartridge charges, or stored pressure within the container which forces the powder charge out of the container, to tossing the powder on the fire by hand, by scooping pails or buckets of the powder from large containers or barrels.

Dry powder is not recommended for aircraft use as a fire extinguisher because chemical residues and dust left by them is often difficult to clean up, and can cause damage to electronic or other delicate equipment.

Checking Fire Extinguishers

Fire extinguishers should be checked periodically utilizing a checklist. If a checklist is unavailable, the following should be checked as a minimum:

1. Appropriate extinguisher located in the proper place
2. Safety seals unbroken
3. Remove all external dirt and rust
4. Gauge or indicator in operable range
5. Check for proper weight
6. No nozzle obstruction
7. Check for any obvious damage

Airport or other local fire departments can usually help in preparing, and often can provide fire extinguisher checklists. In addition, these fire departments can be helpful in answering questions and assisting in obtaining repairs to or replacement of fire extinguishers.

Identifying Fire Extinguishers

Fire extinguishers should be marked to indicate the suitability of the extinguisher for a particular class of fire. The markings in Figure 10-5-2 should be placed on the fire extinguisher and in a conspicuous place in the vicinity of the fire extinguisher. When the location is marked, however, extreme care must be taken to ensure that the fire extinguisher kept at that location is in fact the type depicted by the marking. In other words, if a location is marked for a Class B fire extinguisher, make sure that the fire extinguisher in that location is in fact suitable for Class B fires.

Markings should be applied by decalcomanias (decals), painting, or similar methods. They should be legible and as durable as necessary for the location. In other words, markings outside will need to be more durable than those in the hangar or office spaces.

Where markings are applied to the extinguisher, they should be located on the front of the shell (if one is installed) above or below the extinguisher nameplate. Markings should be large enough and in a form that is easily seen and identifiable by the average person with average eyesight, at a distance of at least 3 feet.

Where markings are applied to wall panels, etc., in the vicinity of extinguishers, they should be large enough and in a form that is easily seen and identifiable by the average person with average eyesight, at a distance of at least 25 feet.

ORDINARY COMBUSTIBLES

FLAMMABLE LIQUIDS

ELECTRICAL EQUIPMENT

COMBUSTIBLE METALS

Figure 10-5-2. Identification of fire extinguisher by fire type

Section 6

Safety on the Flightline

The flightline is a place of dangerous activity. Technicians who work on the flightline must constantly be aware of what is going on around them.

Hearing Protection

The noise on a flightline comes from many places. The aircraft are only one source of noise. There are auxiliary power units (APUs), fuel trucks, baggage handling equipment, etc. Each has its own frequency of sound. Combined all together, the ramp or flightline can cause hearing loss.

There are many types of hearing protection available. Hearing protection can be external or internal. The external protection is the earmuff/head phone type. The internal type fit into the auditory canal. Both types will reduce the sound level reaching the eardrum and reduce the chances of hearing loss.

Hearing protection should also be used when working with pneumatic drills, rivet guns, or other loud or noisy tools or machinery. Because of their high frequency, even short duration exposure to these sounds can cause a hearing loss and continued exposure WILL cause hearing loss.

Section 7

Foreign Object Damage (FOD)

FOD is any damage caused by any loose object to aircraft, personnel, or equipment. These loose objects can be anything from broken runway concrete to rags, safety wire, and in rare instances, mechanics.

FOD can be controlled by good housekeeping practices, a tool control program, and by providing convenient receptacles for used hardware, rags, and other consumables.

The modern jet engine can create a low pressure area in front of the engine that will cause any loose object to be drawn into the engine. On its way through the engine, FOD will do a lot of internal damage to the engine interior.

The exhaust of these engines can propel loose objects great distances with enough force to damage anything hit.

The importance of an FOD program cannot be overstressed when a technician considers the cost of engines, components, or the cost of a human life.

Section 8

Safety Around Helicopters

Every type of helicopter has its own differences. These differences must be learned to avoid damaging the helicopter or injuring the technician.

When approaching a helicopter while the blades are turning, observe the rotorhead and blades to see if they are level. This will allow the maximum clearance while you approach the helicopter.

Approach the helicopter in view of the pilot. If you can't see him, he can't see you.

Never approach a helicopter carrying anything with a vertical height that could be hit by the blades. This could cause blade damage and injury to the person.

Never approach a single rotor helicopter from the rear. The tail rotor is invisible when operating.

Never go from one side of the helicopter to the other by going around the tail. Always go around the nose of the helicopter.

When securing the rotor on some helicopters with elastomeric bearings, check the maintenance manual for the proper method. Using the wrong method could damage the bearing.

Section 9

Tiedown Procedures

Preparation of Aircraft

Aircraft should be tied down after each flight to prevent damage from sudden storms. The direction in which aircraft are to be parked and tied down should be determined by prevailing or forecast wind direction.

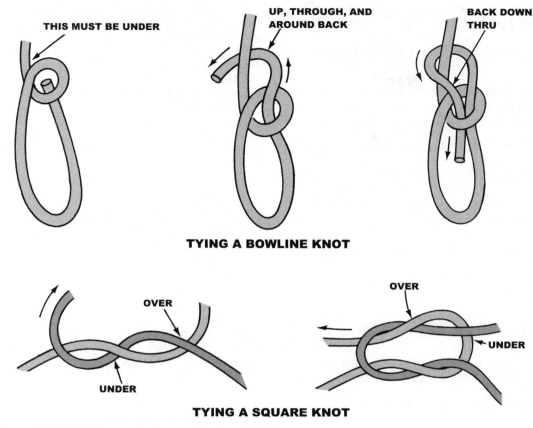

THIS MUST BE UNDER

UP, THROUGH, AND AROUND BACK

BACK DOWN THRU

TYING A BOWLINE KNOT

OVER

UNDER

OVER

UNDER

TYING A SQUARE KNOT

Figure 10-10-1. Knot commonly used for aircraft tiedown

Aircraft should be headed, as nearly as possible, into the wind, depending on the locations of the parking area's fixed tiedown points. Spacing of tiedowns should allow for ample wingtip clearance. After the aircraft is properly located, lock the nosewheel or the tailwheel in the fore-and-aft position.

Section 10

Securing Light Aircraft

Light aircraft are most often secured with ropes tied only at the aircraft tiedown rings provided for securing purposes. Rope should never be tied to a lift strut, since this practice can bend a strut if the rope slips to a point where there is no slack. Manila rope shrinks when wet; about 1 inch of slack should be provided for movement. Too much slack will allow the aircraft to jerk against the ropes. Tight tiedown ropes put inverted flight stresses on the aircraft, many of which are not designed to take such loads.

A tiedown rope holds no better than the knot. Antislip knots such as the bowline are quickly tied and are easy to untie (Figure 10-10-1).

Aircraft not equipped with tiedown fittings should be secured in accordance with the manufacturer's instructions. Ropes should be tied to outer ends of struts on high-wing monoplanes, and suitable rings should be provided where structural conditions permit, if the manufacturer has not already provided them.

The normal tiedown procedure for heavy aircraft can be accomplished with rope or cable tiedown. The number of such tiedowns should be governed by anticipated weather conditions.

Section 11

Securing Heavy Aircraft

Most heavy aircraft are equipped with surface control locks which should be engaged or installed when the aircraft is secured. Since the method of locking controls will vary on different type aircraft, check the manufacturer's instructions for proper installation or engaging procedures. If high winds are anticipated, control surface battens can also be installed to prevent damage.

The normal tiedown procedure for heavy aircraft should generally include the following:

1. Head airplane into prevailing wind whenever possible.

2. Install control locks, all covers and guards.

3. Chock all wheels fore and aft.

4. Attach tiedown reels to airplane tiedown loops and to tiedown anchors or tiedown stakes. Use tiedown stakes for temporary tiedown only. If tiedown reels are not available, $1/4$ inch wire cable or $1 1/2$ inch manila line may be used.

Section 12

Securing Seaplanes

Seaplanes can be moored to a buoy, weather permitting, or tied to a dock. Weather causes wave action and waves will cause the seaplane to bob and roll. This bobbing and rolling while tied to a dock can cause damage.

When warning of an impending storm is received and it is not possible to fly the aircraft out of the storm area, some compartments of the seaplane can be flooded, partially sinking the aircraft. In addition, the aircraft should be tied down securely to anchors. Seaplanes tied down on land have been saved from high-wind damage by filling the floats with water in addition to tying the aircraft down in the usual manner.

During heavy weather, if possible, remove the seaplane from the water and tie down in the same manner as a land plane. If this is not possible, the seaplane could be anchored in a sheltered area away from wind and waves.

Section 13

Securing Ski Planes

Ski planes are tied down, if the securing means are available, in the same manner as land planes.

Ski-equipped airplanes can be secured on ice or in snow by using a device called a deadman. A deadman is any item at hand, such as a piece of pipe, log, etc., that a rope is attached to and buried in a snow or ice trench. Keep the free end of the rope dry and unfrozen, and pack snow in the trench. If water is available, pour water into the trench; when it is frozen, tie down the aircraft with the free end of the rope.

Operators of ski-equipped aircraft sometimes pack soft snow around the skis, pour water on the snow, and permit the skis to freeze to the ice. This, in addition to the usual tiedown procedures, aids in preventing damage from windstorms.

Caution must be used when moving an aircraft that has been secured in this manner to ensure that a ski is not still frozen to the ground, otherwise damage to the aircraft or skis can occur.

Section 14

Securing Helicopters

Helicopters, like other aircraft, are secured to prevent structural damage which can occur from high-velocity surface winds.

Helicopters should be secured in hangars, when possible. If not, they should be tied down securely. Helicopters that are tied down can usually sustain winds up to approximately 65 m.p.h. If at all possible, helicopters should be evacuated to a safe area if tornadoes or hurricanes are anticipated.

For added protection, helicopters should be moved to a clear area so that they will not be damaged by flying objects or falling limbs from surrounding trees.

If high winds are anticipated with the helicopter parked in the open, the main rotor blades should be tied down. Detailed instructions for securing and mooring each type of helicopter can be found in the applicable maintenance manual. Methods of securing helicopters will vary with weather conditions, the length of time the aircraft is expected to remain on the ground, and location and characteristics of the aircraft. Wheel chocks, control locks, rope tiedowns, mooring covers, tip socks, tiedown assemblies, parking brakes, and rotor brakes are used to secure helicopters.

Typical mooring procedures are as follows:

1. Face the helicopter in the direction from which the highest forecasted wind or gusts are anticipated.

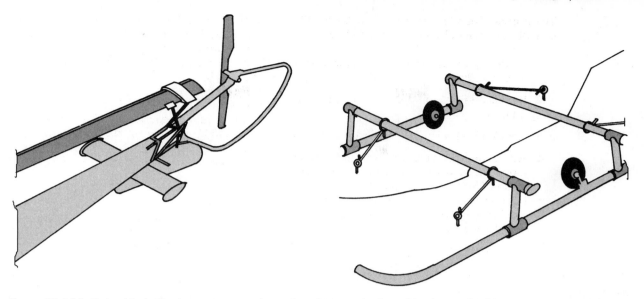

Figure 10-14-1. Rotor blade tie down straps and attach points can be found in the applicable operations handbook. Rotors must never be left unsecured.

2. Spot the helicopter slightly more than one rotor-span distance from other aircraft.

3. Place wheel chocks ahead of and behind all wheels (where applicable). On helicopters equipped with skids, retract the ground handling wheels, lower the helicopter to rest on the skids, and install wheel position lockpins or remove the ground handling wheels. Ground handling wheels should be secured inside the aircraft or inside the hangar or storage buildings. Do not leave them unsecured on the flightline.

4. Align blades and install tiedown assemblies as prescribed by the manufacturer of the helicopter. An example can be seen in Figure 10-14-1. Tie straps snugly without strain, and during wet weather, provide some slack to avoid the possibility of the straps shrinking, causing undue stresses on the aircraft and/or its rotor system(s).

5. Fasten the tiedown ropes or cables to the forward and aft landing gear cross tubes and secure to ground stakes or tiedown rings.

Section 15

Jacking and Hoisting

The aviation technician must be familiar with the jacking of aircraft in order to perform maintenance and inspection. Since jacking procedures and safety precautions vary for different types of aircraft, only general jacking procedures and precautions are discussed. Consult the applicable aircraft manufacturer's maintenance instructions for specific jacking procedures. Extensive aircraft damage and serious personal injury have resulted from careless or improper jacking or hoisting procedures. As an added safety measure, all equipment should be inspected prior to use to determine the specific lifting capacity, proper functioning of safety devices, condition of pins and locks, and general serviceability. Before hoisting or raising an aircraft on jacks, all workstands and other non-essential equipment should be removed from under or near the aircraft. No one should remain in the aircraft while it is being raised or lowered, unless required by the maintenance manual.

Glossary

Aging –

a. Generally any change in properties with time which occurs at relatively low temperature (room or elevated) after a final heat treatment of a cold marking operation. Aging is a process in which the trend is toward restoration of real equilibrium and away from an unstable condition induced by a prior operation.

b. Specifically the formation of a new phase by cooling a solid solution to super saturated state and allowing the super saturated solution to partially return to equilibrium by the formation of a less concentrated solid solution and a new phase.

Air Hardening – An alloy which does not require quenching from a high temperature to harden. Hardening of the material occurs simply by cooling in air from above critical temperature. The term refers only to the ability of the material to harden in air and does not imply any definite analysis or composition.

Air Cooling/Quenching – Cooling from an elevated temperature in air, still or forced.

Alloy – A mixture with metallic properties composed of two or more elements of which at least one is a metal. However, a metal is not designated an "alloy" based on elements incidental to its manufacture. For example; iron, carbon, manganese, silicon, phosphorus, sulphur, oxygen, nitrogen and hydrogen are incidental to the manufacture of plain carbon steel. It does not become an "alloy steel" until the elements are increased beyond regular composition or until other elements (metal) are added in significant amounts for a specific purpose.

Alloy Elements – Chemical elements comprising an alloy, usually limited to the metallic elements added to modify the basic metal properties.

Annealing – Generally it is a controlled heating procedure which leads to maximum softness, ductility and formability. The annealing procedure is utilized for the following:

a. Remove stresses.

b. Induce softness.

c. After ductility, toughness, electrical, magnetic, or physical properties.

d. Refine crystal-line structure.

e. Remove gases.

f. Produce a definite micro-structure.

Annealing Full – A controlled heating procedure which leads to maximum softness, ductility and formability.

Annealing, Isothermal – Heating of a ferritic steel to a austenitic structure (fully or partial) followed by cooling to and holding at a temperature that causes transformation of the austenite to a relatively soft ferrite and carbide structure.

Anodic Oxide Coating – A thin film of aluminum oxide formed on the surface of aluminum and aluminum alloy parts by electro-chemical means.

Austenite – A solid solution of iron carbide in gamma iron. It forms when the metal solidifies and remains a solution until it cools to about 1,350°F (732°C). Theoretically the solution would remain if the iron or steel were cooled instantaneously from a bright red heat to atmospheric temperature, but in practice, this degree of rapidity is impracticable, and only a portion of the austenite is preserved by rapid cooling. Addition of certain alloying elements such as nickel and manganese preserves austenite below 0°F (17°C).

Bark – The decarburized skin or layer just beneath the scale found after heating steel in an oxidizing atmosphere.

Base Metal – The metal to which other elements are added to form an alloy possessing specific properties.

Brittleness – Brittleness is the property of a material which permits little bending or deformation without fracture. Brittleness and hardness are closely associated.

Burning – The heating of a metal to temperatures sufficiently close to the melting point to cause permanent injury. Such injury may be caused by the melting of the more fusible constituents, by the penetration of gases such as oxygen into the metal with consequent reactions, or perhaps by the segregation of elements already present in the metal.

Carburizing (Cementation) – Adding carbon to the surface of iron-base alloys by heating the metal below its melting point in contact with carbonaceous solids, liquids, or gases.

Case – The surface layer of an iron-base alloy which has been made substantially harder than the interior by the process of case hardening.

Case Hardening – A heat treatment of a combination of heat treatments in which the surface layer of an iron-base alloy is made substantially harder than the interior by altering its composition by carburizing, cyaniding, or nitriding.

Cold Drawing – The permanent deformation of metal below its recrystallization temperature, by drawing the bay through one or more dies.

Cold Rolling – The permanent deformation of metal below its recrystallization temperature by rolling. This process is frequently applied in finishing rounds, sheets, strip, and tin plate.

Cold Working – Plastic deformation of a metal at a temperature low enough to insure strain hardening.

Conversion Coating (Chemical) – A film intentionally produced on a metal by subjection to a selected chemical solution for the purpose of providing improved corrosion resistance or to improve the adhesion of subsequently applied organic coating.

Cyaniding – Surface hardening by carbon and nitrogen absorption of an iron-base alloy article or portion of it by heating at a suitable temperature in contact with a cyanide salt, followed by quenching.

Cooling – Any decrease in temperature; however, specific term usually applies to reducing metal temperature in a gaseous environment rather than quenching in a liquid.

Decalescence – When a piece of steel is heated, the temperature rises uniformly until it reaches a point between 1,325°F (718°C) and 1,350°F (732°C). At this point the rise in temperature suddenly halts due to the fact that the metal absorbs the heat necessary for the change of state. After this halt the temperature will continue its normal rate of increase. It is the halting in the temperature range that is termed decalescence. At the point of decalescence, the carbon and iron are forming a solid solution and the steel is passing from its annealed condition into its hardened condition.

Decarburization – The removal of carbon (usually refers to the surface of solid steel) by the (normally oxidizing) action of media which reacts with carbon. The decarburized area is sometimes referred to as the bark.

Defects in Metals – Damage occurring to metal during manufacture/fabrication process. Some typical defects are as follows:

a. *Blister* - a defect in metal produced by gas bubbles either on the surface or formed beneath the surface. Very fine blisters are called pinhead or pepper blisters.

b. *Blow Hole* - a hole produced during the solidification of metal by evolved gas which in falling to escape, is held in pockets.

c. *Bursts* -ruptures made in forging or rolling.

d. *Fin (Flash)* - a thin fin of metal formed at the side of a forging or weld where a small portion of the metal is forced out between the edges of the forging or welding case.

e. *Flake* - Internal fissures (cracks or clefts) in large steel forgings or large (MASS) rolled shapes. In a fractured surface or test piece, they appear as sizable areas of silvery brightness and coarser grain size than their surroundings. Sometimes known as "chrome checks" and "hairline cracks."

f. *Ghost (Ferrite ghost)* - a faint band of ferrite.

g. *Lap* - a surface defect appearing as a seam caused from folding over hot metal, fins, or sharp corners and then rolling or forging, but not welding, them into the surface.

h. *Pipe* - a cavity formed in metal (especially ingots) during solidification of the last portion of liquid metal causes the cavity or pipe.

i. *Scab* - a rough projection on a casting caused by the mold breaking or being washed by the molten metal; or occurring where the skin from a blowhole has partly burned away and is not welded.

j. *Seam* - a crack on the surface of metal which has been closed but not welded; usually produced by blowholes which have become oxidized. If very fine, a seam may be called a hair crack or hair seam.

k. *Segregation* - a mixture of compounds and elements, which, when cooled from the molten state, solidify at different temperatures.

l. *Ductility* - the ability of a metal to withstand plastic deformation without rupture. Ductility is usually determined by tension test using a standard test (22-gauge length) specimen. The test specimen is loaded in tension to rupture. The specimen is then assembled and measured for length and diameter at the fracture. The increase in length is expressed as per cent elongation and the decrease in diameter as per cent reduction of area. The above terms measure ductility and since they are comparative, considerable experience is required for proper evaluation of material for the purpose intended.

Ductility – The property that permits permanent deformation before fracture by stress in tension.

Elastic Limit – The elastic limit of a material is the greatest load per unit area which will not produce a measurable permanent deformation after complete release of load.

Elongation – The amount of permanent extension at any stage in any process which continuously elongates a body.

Embrittlement – Loss of ductility of a metal, which may result in premature failure. (see acid brittleness).

Equalizing – Intermediate heat treatment (special) which assists in developing desired properties, primary use is for equalizing/relieving stresses resulting from cold working.

Exfoliation – The cracking or flaking off of the outer layer of an object.

Exposure – Heating to or subjecting to an elevating temperature or environment for a certain period of time.

Etching – Attack of metals structure by reagents. In metallography, the process of revealing structural details by the preferential attack of reagents on a metal surface.

a. *Micro-etching* - is for the examination of the sample under a microscope and for this purpose the sample must be very carefully polished (by an experienced person) prior to etching.

b. *Macro-etching* - is for the examination of the sample under a low power magnifying glass or by unaided eye. High polishing for this purpose is not absolutely essential; however, a good polish is necessary.

c. *Deep-etching* - is a form of macro-etching in which the sample with regular cut surface may be immersed in hot hydrocloric acid (50% acqueous solution) and then examined for major defects such as inclusions, segregations, cracks; etc.

Fatigue – The phenomenon of the progressive fracture of a metal by means of a crack which spreads under repeated cycles of stress.

Fatigue Limit – Usually used as synonymous with endurance limit.

Ferrite – A solution in which alpha iron is the solvent, and which is characterized by a body centered cubic crystal structure.

Fillet – A concave junction of two surfaces usually perpendicular.

Forming – To shape or fashion with hand/tools or by a shape or mold.

Fully Hardened – Applies generally to the maximum hardness obtainable. (In particular, applies to materials that are hardened by a strain and/or age hardening process).

Galvanic Series – A list of metals and alloys arranged in order of their relative potentials in a given environment. The galvanic series indicates the tendency of the several metals and alloys to set up galvanic corrosion. The relative position within a group sometimes changes with external conditions, but it is only rarely that changes occur from group to group.

Grains – Individual crystals in metal. When metal is in molten state, the atoms have no uniform grouping. However, upon solidification they arrange themselves in a geometric pattern.

Grain Growth – An increase in the grain size of metal.

Hardenability – The ability of an alloy to harden fully throughout the entire section thickness either by cold working or heat treatment. The maximum thickness at which this may be accomplished can be used as a measure of hardenability.

Hardening – Hardening accomplished by heating the metal to a specified temperature, then rapidly cooling by quenching in oil, water, or brine. This treatment produces a fine grain structure, extreme hardness, maximum tensile strength, and minimum ductility.

Hardness – Hardness refers to the ability of a material to resist abrasion, penetration, indentation, or cutting action. The wearing qualities of a material are in part dependent upon its hardness. Hardness and strength are properties which are closely related for wrought alloys.

Hardness Testing – Test used to determine the ability of a metal to resist penetration. The test results are usually directly related to tensile and yield strength of the metal involved. An exception would be case hardness.

Heat Treatment – An operation, or combination of operations, involving the heating and cooling of a metal or alloy in the solid state for the purpose of obtaining certain desirable conditions or properties. Heating and cooling for the sole purpose of mechanical working are excluded from the meaning of this definition.

Homogenizing – Annealing or soaking at very high temperatures in order to reduce alloy segregation by diffusion.

Inclusion – Particles of impurities, usually oxides, sulfides, silicates, and such which are mechanically held during solidification or which are formed by subsequent reaction of the solid metal.

Machinability – The cutting characteristic of metal and resulting surface finish using standard cutting tools and coolant/lubricants. There are various factors that effect the machinability of a metal such as hardness, grain size, alloy constituents, structure, inclusions; shape, type, condition of tool and coolant. The standard machinability ratings are usually based on comparison to SAE 1112/Aisi B 1112 Bessemer screw stock which is rated at 100% machinability.

Magna Flux Testing – A method of inspection used to detect/locate defects such as cavities, cracks or seams in steel parts at or very close to the surface. The test is accomplished by magnetizing the part with equipment specially designed for the purpose and applying magnetic powder, wet or dry, Flaws are then indicated by the powder clinging to them.

Malleability – Malleability is the property of a material which enables it to be hammered, rolled, or to be pressed into various shapes without fracture. Malleability refers to compression deformation as contrasted with ductility where the deformation is tensile.

Martensite – It is the decomposition product which results from very rapid cooling of austenite. The lower the carbon content of the steel, the faster it must be cooled to obtain martensite.

Mechanical Hardness – *See Hardness.*

Mechanical Properties – Those properties that reveal the reaction, elastic and inelastic, of a material to an applied force, or that involve the relationship between stress and strain; for example, tensile strength, yield strength, and fatigue limit.

Mechanical Working – Subjecting metal to pressure exerted by rolls, presses, or hammers, to change its form, or to affect the structure and therefore the mechanical and physical properties.

Modulus of Elasticity – The ratio, within the limit of elasticity, of the stress in the corresponding strain. The stress in pounds per square inch is divided by the elongation in fractions of an inch for each inch of the original gage length of the specimen.

Nitriding – Adding nitrogen to iron-base alloys by heating the metal in contact with ammonia gas or other suitable nitrogenous material. Nitriding is conducted at a temperature usually in the range 935°F – 1,000°F (502°C - 538°C) and produces surface hardening of the metal without quenching.

Normalizing – Heating iron-base alloys to approximately 100°F (550°C) above the critical temperature range, followed by cooling to below that range in still air at ordinary temperatures. This process is used to remove stresses caused by machining, forging, bending, and welding.

Physical Properties – Those properties exclusive of those described under mechanical properties; for example, density, electrical conductivity, coefficient of thermal expansion. This term has often been used to describe mechanical properties, but this usage is not recommended.

Pickling – Removing scale from steel by immersion in a diluted acid bath.

Plastic Deformation – The permanent change in size or shape of a material under stress.

Proportional Limit – The proportional limit of a material is the load per unit area beyond which the increases in strain cease to be directly proportional to the increases in stress.

Quenching – Rapid cooling by immersion in liquids or gases.

Quenching Media – Quenching media are liquids or gases in which metals are cooled by immersion. Some of the more common are brine (10 percent sodium chloride solution), water at 65°F (18°C), fish oil, paraffin base petroleum oil, machine oil, air, engine oil, and commercial quenching oil.

Recalescence – When steel is slowly cooled from a point above the critical temperature, the cooling proceeds at a uniform rate until the piece reaches a point between 1,250°F and 1,300°F (677°C and 704° C). At this time, the cooling is noticeably arrested and the metal actually rises in temperature as the change of state again takes place. This change is the opposite of decalescence and is termed recalescence.

Sensitizing – Developing a condition in stainless steels, which is susceptible to intergranular corrosion. The condition is usually formed by heating the steel above 800° F (426°C) and cooling slowly (e.g., welding).

Sheets Cold Rolled – The flat products resulting from cold rolling of sheets previously produced by hot rolling.

Sheets Hot Rolled – The flat-rolled products resulting from reducing sheet bars on a sheet mill, or slabs, blooms, and billets on a continuous stripsheet mill.

Soaking – Holding steel at an elevated temperature for the attainment of uniform temperature through-out the piece.

Solidification Range – The temperature range through which metal freezes or solidifies.

Strain – The elongation per unit length.

Stress – The internal load per unit area.

Stress-Relief – This is annealing process which removes or reduces residual stresses retained after forming, heat treating, welding or machining. The anneal is accomplished at rather low temperatures for the primary purposes of reducing residual stresses, without material affecting other properties.

Tempering (Drawing) - Reheating hardened steel to some temperature below the lower critical temperature, followed by any desired rate of cooling. Although the terms "tempering" and "drawing" are practically synonymous as used in commercial practice, the term "tempering" is preferred.

Tensile Strength – The tensile strength is the maximum load per unit area which a material is capable of withstanding before failure. It is computed from the maximum load carried during a tension test and the original cross-sectional area of the specimen.

Tension – That force tending to increase the dimension of a body in the direction of the force.

Tolerances – Slight deviations in dimensions or weight or both, allowable in the various products.

Work Hardness – Hardness developed in metal resulting from mechanical working, particularly cold working.

Yield Strength – Stress arbitrarily defined as the stress at which the material has a specified permanent set (the value of 0.2% is widely accepted).

Index

Corrections, Suggestions for Improvement, Request for Additional Information

It is Avotek's goal to provide quality aviation maintenance resources to help you succeed in your career, and we appreciate your assistance in helping.

Please complete the following information to report a correction, suggestion for improvement, or to request additional information.

REFERENCE NUMBER (*To be assigned by Avotek*)		
CONTACT INFORMATION*		
Date		
Name		
Email		
Daytime Phone		
BOOK INFORMATION		
Title		
Edition		
Page number		
Figure/Table Number		
Discrepancy/Correction (*You may also attach a copy of the discrepancy/correction*)		
Suggestion(s) for Improvement (*Attach additional documentation as needed*)		
Request for Additional Information		
FOR AVOTEK USE ONLY	Date Received	
	Reference Number Issued By	
	Receipt Notification Sent	
	Action Taken/By	
	Completed Notification Sent	

Contact information will only be used to provide updates to your submission or if there is a question regarding your submission.

Send your corrections to:

Email: comments@avotek.com
Fax: 1-540-234-9399
Mail: Corrections: Avotek Information Resources
P.O. Box 219
Weyers Cave, VA 24486 USA

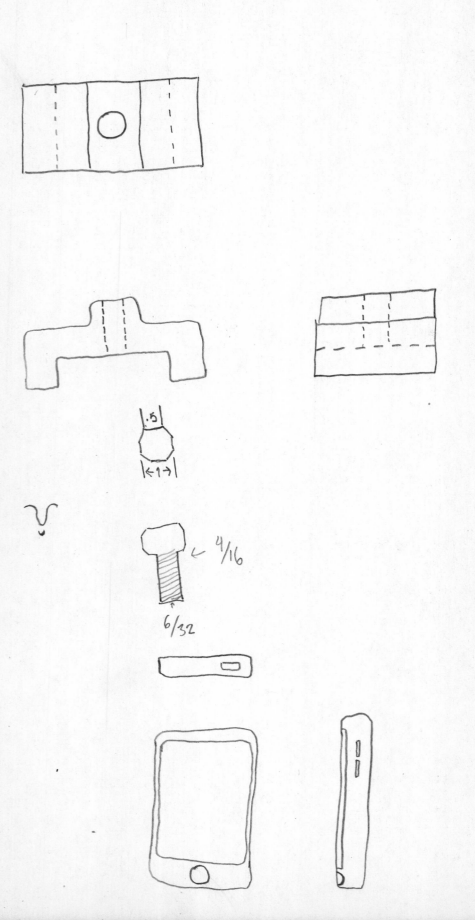

.5

|←1→|

← 4/16

6/32